Rose in Bloom

Rose in Bloom

Rose in Bloom

A Sequel to

EIGHT COUSINS

by

Louisa M. Alcott

Illustrated by

RODNEY SHACKELL

RUPERT HART-DAVIS
Upper James Street
London
1967

First published 1876
This edition first published 1967
Illustrations © Rupert Hart-Davis 1967

Printed in Great Britain by
C. Tinling & Co. Ltd.
Liverpool, London and Prescot

Contents

1	Coming Home	11
2	Old Friends with New Faces	29
3	Miss Campbell	43
4	Thorns Among the Roses	55
5	Prince Charming	62
6	Polishing Mac	74
7	Phebe	90
8	Breakers Ahead	107
9	New Year's Calls	115
10	The Sad and Sober Part	127
11	Small Temptations	135
12	At Kitty's Ball	149
13	Both Sides	163
14	Aunt Clara's Plan	174
15	Alas for Charlie!	180
16	Good Works	190
17	Among the Haycocks	199
18	Which Was It?	212
19	Behind the Fountain	227
20	What Mac Did	234
21	How Phebe Earned her Welcome	243
22	Short and Sweet	252

Illustrations

'. . . many a wistful eye followed the bright head . . .'   47

'Steve, with a red table-cloth tied round his waist,
languished upon Mac's shoulder . . .'   86

'. . . pride would not let her stay, though love
pleaded eloquently'   113

'. . . a meek little Irishwoman looking quite lost
and out of place among the luxuries . . .'   140

'Something in the mute anguish of her face seemed
to tell him what she could not speak . . .'   188

'. . . Mac read the lovely story as only one could
who entered fully into the spirit of it'   205

'. . . never did a plain gold ring slip more easily to
its place . . .'   230

'. . . she stood motionless till Phebe caught her in
her arms . . .'   250

Preface

As authors may be supposed to know better than anyone else what they intended to do when writing a book, I beg leave to say that there is no moral to this story. Rose is not designed for a model girl: and the Sequel was simply written in fulfilment of a promise; hoping to afford some amusement, and perhaps here and there a helpful hint, to other roses getting ready to bloom.

L. M. ALCOTT

September, 1876

A*

1

Coming Home

THREE YOUNG MEN stood together on a wharf one bright
October day, awaiting the arrival of an ocean steamer with an
impatience which found a vent in lively skirmishes with a small
lad, who pervaded the premises like a will-o'-the-wisp, and
afforded much amusement to the other groups assembled
there.

"They are the Campbells, waiting for their cousin, who has
been abroad several years with her uncle, the Doctor," whispered one lady to another, as the handsomest of the young men
touched his hat to her as he passed, lugging the boy, whom he
had just rescued from a little expedition down among the piles.

"Which is that?" asked the stranger.

"Prince Charlie, as he's called—a fine fellow, the most promising of the seven; but a little fast, people say," answered the
first speaker, with a shake of the head.

"Are the others his brothers?"

"No, cousins. The elder is Archie, a most exemplary young
man. He has just gone into business with the merchant uncle,
and bids fair to be an honour to his family. The other, with the
eye-glasses and no gloves, is Mac, the odd one, just out of
college."

"And the boy?"

"Oh, he is Jamie, the youngest brother of Archibald, and the
pet of the whole family. Mercy on us! he'll be in if they don't
hold on to him."

The ladies' chat came to a sudden end just there; for, by the
time Jamie had been fished out of a hogshead, the steamer hove

11

in sight and everything else was forgotten. As it swung slowly round to enter the dock, a boyish voice shouted—

"There she is! I see her and uncle and Phebe! Hooray for Cousin Rose!" and three small cheers were given with a will by Jamie, as he stood on a post waving his arms like a windmill, while his brother held on to the tail of his jacket.

Yes, there they were—Uncle Alec swinging his hat like a boy, with Phebe smiling and nodding on one side, and Rose kissing both hands delightedly on the other, as she recognized familiar faces and heard familiar voices welcoming her home.

"Bless her dear heart, she's bonnier than ever! Looks like a Madonna—doesn't she?—with that blue cloak round her, and her bright hair flying in the wind!" said Charlie excitedly, as they watched the group upon the deck with eager eyes.

"Madonnas don't wear hats like that. Rose hasn't changed much, but Phebe has. Why, she's a regular beauty!" answered Archie, staring with all his might at the dark-eyed young woman, with the brilliant colour and glossy, black braids shining in the sun.

"Dear old uncle! doesn't it seem good to have him back?" was all Mac said; but he was not looking at "dear old uncle," as he made the fervent remark, for he saw only the slender blonde girl near by, and stretched out his hands to meet hers, forgetful of the green water tumbling between them.

During the confusion that reigned for a moment as the steamer settled to her moorings, Rose looked down into the three faces upturned to hers, and seemed to read in them something that both pleased and pained her. It was only a glance, and her own eyes were full; but through the mist of happy tears she received the impression that Archie was about the same, that Mac had decidedly improved, and that something was amiss with Charlie. There was no time for observation, however; for in a moment the shoreward rush began, and, before she could grasp her travelling bag, Jamie was clinging to her like an ecstatic young bear. She was with difficulty released from his embrace, to fall into the gentler ones of the elder cousins, who took advantage of the general excitement to welcome both blooming girls with affectionate impartiality. Then the wanderers were borne ashore in a triumphal procession, while Jamie danced rapturous jigs before them even on the gangway.

Archie remained to help his uncle get the luggage through the Custom House, and the others escorted the damsels home. No sooner were they shut up in a carriage, however, than a new and curious constraint seemed to fall upon the young people; for they realized, all at once, that their former playmates were men and women now. Fortunately, Jamie was quite free from this feeling of restraint, and, sitting bodkin-wise between the ladies, took all sorts of liberties with them and their belongings.

"Well, my mannikin, what do you think of us?" asked Rose, to break an awkward pause.

"You've both grown so pretty, I can't decide which I like best. Phebe is the biggest and brightest looking, and I was always fond of Phebe; but, somehow you are so kind of sweet and precious, I really think I *must* hug you again," and the small youth did it tempestuously.

"If you love me best, I shall not mind a bit about your thinking Phebe the handsomest, because she *is*. Isn't she, boys?" asked Rose, with a mischievous look at the gentlemen opposite, whose faces expressed a respectful admiration which much amused her.

"I'm so dazzled by the brilliancy and beauty that has suddenly burst upon me, I have no words to express my emotions," answered Charlie, gallantly dodging the dangerous question.

"I can't say yet, for I have not had time to look at anyone. I will now, if you don't mind;" and, to the great amusement of the rest, Mac gravely adjusted his eye-glasses and took an observation.

"Well?" said Phebe, smiling and blushing under his honest stare, yet seeming not to resent it as she did the lordly sort of approval which made her answer the glance of Charlie's audacious blue eyes with a flash of her black ones.

"I think if you were my sister, I should be very proud of you, because your face shows what I admire more than its beauty— truth and courage, Phebe," answered Mac, with a little bow, full of such genuine respect that surprise and pleasure brought a sudden dew to quench the fire of the girl's eyes, and soothe the sensitive pride of the girl's heart.

Rose clapped her hands just as she used to do when anything delighted her, and beamed at Mac approvingly, as she said—

"Now that's a criticism worth having, and we are much obliged. I was sure *you'd* admire my Phebe when you knew her:

but I didn't believe you would be wise enough to see it at once; and you have gone up many pegs in my estimation, I assure you."

"I was always fond of mineralogy you remember, and I've been tapping round a good deal lately, so I've learned to know precious metals when I see them," Mac said with his shrewd smile.

"That is the last hobby, then? Your letters have amused us immensely; for each one had a new theory or experiment, and the latest was always the best. I thought uncle would have died of laughing over the vegetarian mania: it was so funny to imagine you living on bread and milk, baked apples, and potatoes roasted in your own fire," continued Rose, changing the subject again.

"This old chap was the laughing-stock of his class. They called him Don Quixote; and the way he went at windmills of all sorts was a sight to see," put in Charlie, evidently feeling that Mac had been patted on the head quite as much as was good for him.

"But in spite of that the Don got through college with all the honours. Oh, wasn't I proud when Aunt Jane wrote us about it! and didn't she rejoice that her boy kept at the head of his class, and won the medal!" cried Rose, shaking Mac by both hands in a way that caused Charlie to wish "the old chap" had been left behind with Dr. Alec.

"Oh come, that's all mother's nonsense. I began earlier than the other fellows and liked it better: so I don't deserve any praise. Prince is right, though: I did make a regular jack of myself; but, on the whole, I'm not sure that my wild oats weren't better than some I've seen sowed. Anyway, they didn't cost much, and I'm none the worse for them," said Mac placidly.

"I know what 'wild oats' mean. I heard Uncle Mac say Charlie was sowing 'em too fast, and I asked mamma, so she told me. And I know that he was suspelled or expended, I don't remember which, but it was something bad, and Aunt Clara cried," added Jamie all in one breath; for he possessed a fatal gift of making *malapropos* remarks, which caused him to be a terror to his family.

"Do you want to go on the box again?" demanded Prince, with a warning frown.

"No, I don't."

"Then hold your tongue."

"Well Mac needn't kick me; for I was only"—began the culprit, innocently trying to make a bad matter worse.

"That will do," interrupted Charlie, sternly, and James subsided, a crushed boy, consoling himself with Rose's new watch for the indignities he suffered at the hands of the "old fellows," as he vengefully called his elders.

Mac and Charlie immediately began to talk as hard as their tongues could wag, bringing up all sorts of pleasant subjects so successfully that peals of laughter made passers-by look after the merry load with sympathetic smiles.

An avalanche of aunts fell upon Rose as soon as she reached home, and for the rest of the day the old house buzzed like a beehive. Evening found the whole tribe collected in the drawing-rooms, with the exception of Aunt Peace, whose place was empty now.

Naturally enough, the elders settled into one group after a while, and the young fellows clustered about the girls, like butterflies round two attractive flowers. Dr. Alec was the central figure in one room and Rose in the other; for the little girl, whom they had all loved and petted, had bloomed into a woman; and two years of absence had wrought a curious change in the relative positions of the cousins, especially the three elder ones, who eyed her with a mixture of boyish affection and manly admiration that was both new and pleasant.

Something sweet yet spirited about her charmed them and piqued their curiosity; for she was not quite like other girls, and rather startled them now and then by some independent little speech or act, which made them look at one another with a sly smile, as if reminded that Rose was "uncle's girl."

Let us listen, as in duty bound, to what the elders are saying first; for they are already building castles in the air for the boys and girls to inhabit.

"Dear child! how nice it is to see her safely back, so well and happy and like her sweet little self!" said Aunt Plenty, folding her hands as if giving thanks for a great happiness.

"I shouldn't wonder if you found that you'd brought a fire-brand into the family, Alec. Two, in fact; for Phebe is a fine girl, and the lads have found it out already, if I'm not mistaken," added Uncle Mac, with a nod towards the other room.

All eyes followed his, and a highly suggestive tableau pre-

sented itself to the paternal and maternal audience in the back
parlour.

Rose and Phebe, sitting side by side on the sofa, had evidently
assumed at once the places which they were destined to fill by
right of youth, sex, and beauty; for Phebe had long since ceased
to be the maid and become the friend, and Rose meant to have
that fact established at once.

Jamie occupied the rug, on which Will and Geordie stood at
ease, showing their uniforms to the best advantage; for they
were now in a great school, where military drill was the delight
of their souls. Steve posed gracefully in an arm-chair, with Mac
lounging over the back of it; while Archie leaned on one corner
of the low chimney-piece, looking down at Phebe as she listened
to his chat with smiling lips, and cheeks almost as rich in colour
as the carnations in her belt.

But Charlie was particularly effective, although he sat upon
a music-stool, that most trying position for any man not gifted
with grace in the management of his legs. Fortunately Prince
was, and had fallen into an easy attitude, with one arm over
the back of the sofa, his handsome head bent a little, as he
monopolized Rose, with a devoted air and a very becoming
expression of contentment on his face.

Aunt Clara smiled as if well pleased; Aunt Jessie looked
thoughtful; Aunt Jane's keen eyes went from dapper Steve to
broad-shouldered Mac with an anxious glance; Mrs. Myra
murmured something about her "blessed Caroline;" and Aunt
Plenty said warmly—

"Bless the dears! anyone might be proud of such a bonny
flock of bairns as that."

"I am all ready to play chaperon as soon as you please, Alec;
for I suppose the dear girl will come out at once, as she did not
before you went away. My services won't be wanted long, I
fancy; for with her many advantages she will be carried off in
her first season or I'm much mistaken," said Mrs. Clara, with
significant nods and smiles.

"You must settle all those matters with Rose: I am no longer
captain, only first mate now, you know," answered Dr. Alec,
adding soberly, half to himself, half to his brother—"I wonder
people are in such haste to 'bring out' their daughters, as it's
called. To me there is something almost pathetic in the sight
of a young girl standing on the threshold of the world, so

innocent and hopeful, so ignorant of all that lies before her, and usually so ill prepared to meet the ups and downs of life. We do our duty better by the boys; but the poor little women are seldom provided with any armour worth having; and, sooner or later, they are sure to need it, for every one must fight her own battle, and only the brave and strong can win."

"You can't reproach yourself with neglect of that sort, Alec, for you have done your duty faithfully by George's girl; and I envy you the pride and happiness of having such a daughter, for she is that to you," answered old Mac, unexpectedly betraying the paternal sort of tenderness men seldom feel for their sons.

"I've tried, Mac, and I *am* both proud and happy; but with every year my anxiety seems to increase. I've done my best to fit Rose for what may come, as far as I can foresee it; but now she must stand alone, and all my care is powerless to keep her heart from aching, her life from being saddened by mistakes, or thwarted by the acts of others. I can only stand by ready to share her joy and sorrow, and watch her shape her life."

"Why, Alec, what is the child going to do, that you need look so solemn?" exclaimed Mrs. Clara, who seemed to have assumed a sort of right to Rose already.

"Hark! and let her tell you herself," answered Dr. Alec, as Rose's voice was heard saying very earnestly—

"Now you have all told your plans for the future, why don't you ask us ours?"

"Because we know that there is only one thing for a pretty girl to do—break a dozen or so of hearts before she finds one to suit, then marry and settle," answered Charlie, as if no other reply was possible.

"That may be the case with many, but not with us; for Phebe and I believe that it is as much a right and a duty for women to do something with their lives as for men; and we are not going to be satisfied with such frivolous parts as you give us," cried Rose, with kindling eyes. "I mean what I say, and you cannot laugh me down. Would *you* be contented to be told to enjoy yourself for a little while, then marry and do nothing more till you die?" she added, turning to Archie.

"Of course not: that is only a part of a man's life," he answered decidedly.

"A very precious and lovely part, but not *all*," continued Rose; "neither should it be for a woman: for we've got minds and souls as well as hearts; ambition and talents, as well as beauty and accomplishments; and we want to live and learn as well as love and be loved. I'm sick of being told that is all a woman is fit for! I won't have anything to do with love till I prove that I am something beside a housekeeper and baby-tender!"

"Heaven preserve us! here's woman's rights with a vengeance!" cried Charlie, starting up with mock horror, while the others regarded Rose with mingled surprise and amusement, evidently fancying it all a girlish outbreak.

"Ah, you needn't pretend to be shocked: you will be in earnest presently; for this is only the beginning of my strong-mindedness," continued Rose, nothing daunted by the smiles of good-natured incredulity or derision on the faces of her cousins. "I have made up my mind not to be cheated out of the real things that make one good and happy; and, just because I'm a rich girl, fold my hands and drift as so many do. I haven't lived with Phebe all these years in vain: I know what courage and self-reliance can do for one; and I sometimes wish I hadn't a penny in the world so that I could go and earn my bread with her, and be as brave and independent as she will be pretty soon."

It was evident that Rose was in earnest now; for, as she spoke, she turned to her friend with such respect as well as love in her face that the look told better than any words how heartily the rich girl appreciated the virtues hard experience had given the poor girl, and how eagerly she desired to earn what all her fortune could not buy for her.

Something in the glance exchanged between the friends impressed the young men in spite of their prejudices; and it was in a perfectly serious tone that Archie said—

"I fancy you'll find your hands full, cousin, if you want work; for I've heard people say that wealth has its troubles and trials as well as poverty."

"I know it, and I'm going to try and fill my place well. I've got some capital little plans all made, and have begun to study my profession already," answered Rose, with an energetic nod.

"Could I ask what it is to be?" inquired Charlie, in a tone of awe.

"Guess!" and Rose looked up at him with an expression half-earnest, half-merry.

"Well, I should say that you were fitted for a beauty and a belle; but, as that is evidently not to your taste, I am afraid you are going to study medicine and be a doctor. Won't your patients have a heavenly time though? It will be easy dying with an angel to poison them."

"Now, Charlie, that's base of you, when you know how well women have succeeded in this profession, and what a comfort Dr. Mary Kirk was to dear Aunt Peace. I did want to study medicine; but uncle thought it wouldn't do to have so many M.D.'s in one family, since Mac thinks of trying it. Besides, I seem to have other work put into my hands that I am better fitted for."

"You are fitted for anything that is generous and good; and I'll stand by you, no matter what you've chosen," cried Mac heartily; for this was a new style of talk from a girl's lips, and he liked it immensely.

"Philanthropy is a generous, good, and beautiful profession; and I've chosen it for mine because I have much to give. I'm only the steward of the fortune papa left me; and I think, if I use it wisely for the happiness of others, it will be more blest than if I keep it all for myself."

Very sweetly and simply was this said, but it was curious to see how differently the various hearers received it.

Charlie shot a quick look at his mother, who exclaimed, as if in spite of herself—

"Now, Alec, *are* you going to let that girl squander a fine fortune on all sorts of charitable nonsense and wild schemes, for the prevention of pauperism and crime?"

" 'They who give to the poor lend to the Lord,' and practical Christianity is the kind He loves the best," was all Dr. Alec answered; but it silenced the aunts, and caused even prudent Uncle Mac to think with sudden satisfaction of certain secret investments he had made, which paid him no interest but the thanks of the poor.

Archie and Mac looked well pleased, and promised their advice and assistance with the enthusiasm of generous young hearts. Steve shook his head, but said nothing; and the lads on the rug at once proposed founding a hospital for invalid dogs and horses, white mice and wounded heroes.

"Don't you think that will be a better way for a woman to spend her life, than in dancing, dressing, and husband-hunting,

Charlie?" asked Rose, observing his silence and anxious for his approval.

"Very pretty for a little while, and very effective too; for I don't know anything more captivating than a sweet girl in a meek little bonnet, going on charitable errands and glorifying poor people's houses with a delightful mixture of beauty and benevolence. Fortunately, the dear souls soon tire of it, but it's heavenly while it lasts."

Charlie spoke in a tone of mingled admiration and contempt, and smiled a superior sort of smile, as if he understood all the innocent delusions as well as the artful devices of the sex, and expected nothing more from them. It both surprised and grieved Rose, for it did not sound like the Charlie she had left two years ago. But she only said, with a reproachful look and a proud little gesture of head and hand, as if she put the subject aside since it was not treated with respect—

"I am sorry you have so low an opinion of women: there *was* a time when you believed in them sincerely."

"I do still, upon my word I do! They haven't a more devoted admirer and slave in the world than I am. Just try me and see," cried Charlie, gallantly kissing his hand to the sex in general.

But Rose was not appeased, and gave a disdainful shrug, as she answered with a look in her eyes that his lordship did not like—

"Thank you: I don't want admirers or slaves, but friends and helpers. I've lived so long with a wise, good man that I am rather hard to suit, perhaps; but I don't intend to lower my standard, and anyone who cares for my regard must at least try to live up to it."

"Whew! here's a wrathful dove! Come and smooth her ruffled plumage, Mac. I'll dodge before I do further mischief," and Charlie strolled away into the other room, privately lamenting that Uncle Alec had spoiled a fine girl by making her strong-minded.

He wished himself back again in five minutes; for Mac said something that produced a gale of laughter, and when he took a look over his shoulder the "wrathful dove" was cooing so peacefully and pleasantly he was sorely tempted to return and share the fun. But Charlie had been spoiled by too much indulgence, and it was hard for him to own himself in the wrong even when he knew it. He always got what he wanted sooner or later; and, having long ago made up his mind that Rose and her fortune were to be his, he was secretly displeased at the new plans and beliefs of the young lady, but flattered himself that they would soon be changed when she saw how unfashionable and inconvenient they were.

Musing over the delightful future he had laid out, he made himself comfortable in the sofa corner near his mother, till the appearance of a slight refection caused both groups to melt into one. Aunt Plenty believed in eating and drinking; so the slightest excuse for festivity delighted her hospitable soul, and on this joyful occasion she surpassed herself.

It was during this informal banquet that Rose, roaming about from one admiring relative to another, came upon the three younger lads, who were having a quiet little scuffle in a secluded corner.

"Come out here and let me have a look at you," she said enticingly; for she predicted an explosion and public disgrace if peace was not speedily restored.

Hastily smoothing themselves down, the young gentlemen presented three flushed and merry countenances for inspection, feeling highly honoured by the command.

"Dear me, how you two have grown! You big things! how dare you get ahead of me in this way?" she said, standing on tiptoe to pat the curly pates before her; for Will and Geordie had shot up like weeds and now grinned cheerfully down upon her as she surveyed them in comic amazement.

"The Campbells are all fine, tall fellows; and we mean to be the best of the lot. Shouldn't wonder if we were six-footers, like Grandpa," observed Will proudly, looking so like a young Shanghae rooster, all legs and an insignificant head, that Rose kept her countenance with difficulty.

"We shall broaden out when we get our growth. We are taller than Steve now, a half a head, both of us," added Geordie, with his nose in the air.

Rose turned to look at Steve, and, with a sudden smile, beckoned to him. He dropped his napkin, and flew to obey the summons; for she was queen of the hour, and he had openly announced his deathless loyalty.

"Tell the other boys to come here. I've a fancy to stand you all in a row and look you over, as you did me that dreadful day when you nearly frightened me out of my wits," she said, laughing at the memory of it as she spoke.

They came in a body, and, standing shoulder to shoulder, made such an imposing array that the young commander was rather daunted for a moment. But she had seen too much of the world lately to be abashed by a trifle; and the desire to try a girlish test gave her courage to face the line of smiling cousins with dignity and spirit.

"Now I'm going to stare at you as you stared at me. It is my revenge on you seven bad boys for entrapping one poor little girl, and enjoying her alarm, I'm not a bit afraid of you now; so tremble and beware!"

As she spoke, Rose looked up into Archie's face and nodded approvingly; for the steady grey eyes met hers fairly, and softened as they did so—a becoming change, for naturally they were rather keen than kind.

"A true Campbell, bless you!" she said, and shook his hand heartily as she passed on.

Charlie came next, and here she felt less satisfied, though scarcely conscious why; for, as she looked, there came a defiant sort of flash, changing suddenly to something warmer than anger, stronger than pride, making her shrink a little and say, hastily—

"I don't find the Charlie I left; but the Prince is there still, I see."

Turning to Mac with a sense of relief, she gently took off his "winkers," as Jamie called them, and looked straight into the honest blue eyes that looked straight back at her, full of a frank and friendly affection that warmed her heart, and made her own eyes brighten as she gave back the glasses, saying, with a look and tone of cordial satisfaction—

"*You* are not changed, my dear old Mac; and I'm so glad of that!"

"Now say something extra sweet to me, because I'm the flower of the family," said Steve, twirling the blonde moustache, which was evidently the pride of his life.

Rose saw at a glance that Dandy deserved his name more than ever, and promptly quenched his vanities by answering, with a provoking laugh—

"Then the name of the flower of the family is Cock's-comb."

"Ah, ha! who's got it now?" jeered Will.

"Let us off easy, please," whispered Geordie, mindful that their turn came next.

"You blessed beanstalks! I'm proud of you: only don't grow quite out of sight, or ever be ashamed to look a woman in the face," answered Rose, with a gentle pat on the cheek of either bashful young giant; for both were as red as peonies, though their boyish eyes were as clear and calm as summer lakes.

"Now me!" And Jamie assumed his manliest air, feeling that he did not appear to advantage among his tall kinsmen. But he went to the head of the class in everyone's opinion when Rose put her arms round him, saying, with a kiss—

"You must be my boy now; for all the others are too old, and I want a faithful little page to do my errands for me."

"I will, I will! and I'll marry you too, if you'll just hold on till I grow up!" cried Jamie, rather losing his head at this sudden promotion.

"Bless the baby, what is he talking about?" laughed Rose, looking down at her little knight, as he clung about her with grateful ardour.

"Oh, I heard the aunts say that you'd better marry one of us, and keep the property in the family; so I speak first, because you are very fond of me, and I *do* love curls."

Alas for Jamie! this awful speech had hardly left his innocent lips when Will and Geordie swept him out of the room like a whirlwind; and the howls of that hapless boy were heard from the torture-hall, where being shut into the skeleton-case was one of the mildest punishments inflicted upon him.

Dismay fell upon the unfortunates who remained: but their confusion was soon ended; for Rose, with a look which they had never seen upon her face before, dismissed them with the brief command, "Break ranks—the review is over," and walked away to Phebe.

"Confound that boy! You ought to shut him up, or gag him!" fumed Charlie, irritably.

"He shall be attended to," answered poor Archie, who was trying to bring up the little marplot with the success of most parents and guardians.

"The whole thing was deuced disagreeable," growled Steve, who felt that he had not distinguished himself in the late engagement.

"Truth generally is," observed Mac drily as he strolled away with his odd smile.

As if he suspected discord somewhere, Dr. Alec proposed music at this crisis; and the young people felt that it was a happy thought.

"I want you to hear both my birds; for they have improved immensely, and I am very proud of them," said the Doctor, twirling up the stool and pulling out the old music-books.

"I had better come first, for after you have heard the nightingale you won't care for the canary," added Rose, wishing to put Phebe at her ease; for she sat among them looking like a picture, but rather shy and silent, remembering the days when her place was in the kitchen.

"I'll give you some of the dear old songs you used to like so much. This was a favourite, I think;" and sitting down she sang the first familiar air that came, and sang it well in a pleasant, but by no means finished, manner.

It chanced to be "The Birks of Aberfeldie," and vividly recalled the time when Mac was ill, and she took care of him. The memory was sweet to her, and involuntarily her eye wandered in search of him. He was not far away, sitting just as he used to sit when she soothed his most despondent moods—astride of a chair with his head down on his arms, as if the song suggested the attitude. Her heart quite softened to him as she looked, and she decided to forgive *him* if no one else; for she was sure that he had no mercenary plans about her tiresome money.

Charlie had assumed a pensive air, and fixed his fine eyes upon her with an expression of tender admiration, which made her laugh in spite of all her efforts to seem unconscious of it. She was both amused and annoyed at his very evident desire to remind her of certain sentimental passages in the last year of their girl and boyhood, and to change what she had considered a childish joke into romantic earnest. This did not suit her; for, young as she was, Rose had very serious ideas of love, and had no intention of being beguiled into even a flirtation with her handsome cousin.

So Charlie attitudinized unnoticed, and was getting rather out of temper when Phebe began to sing; and he forgot all about himself in admiration of her. It took every one by surprise: for two years of foreign training added to several at home had worked wonders; and the beautiful voice that used to warble cheerily over pots and kettles, now rang out melodiously or melted to a mellow music that woke a sympathetic thrill in those who listened. Rose glowed with pride as she accompanied her friend; for Phebe was in her own world now—a lovely world where no depressing memory of poor-house or kitchen, ignorance or loneliness, came to trouble her; a happy world where she could be herself, and rule others by the magic of her sweet gift.

Yes, Phebe was herself now, and showed it in the change that came over her at the first note of music. No longer shy and silent, no longer the image of a handsome girl, but a blooming woman, alive and full of the eloquence her art gave her, as she laid her hands softly together, fixed her eyes on the light, and just poured out her song as simply and joyfully as the lark does soaring towards the sun.

"My faith, Alec! that's the sort of voice that wins a man's heart out of his breast!" exclaimed Uncle Mac, wiping his eyes after one of the plaintive ballads that never grow old.

"So it would!" answered Dr. Alec, delightedly.

"So it has," added Archie to himself; and he was right: for, just at that moment, he fell in love with Phebe. He actually did, and could fix the time almost to a second: for, at a quarter past nine, he merely thought her a very charming young person; at twenty minutes past, he considered her the loveliest woman he ever beheld; at five and twenty minutes past, she was an angel singing his soul away; and at half after nine he was a lost man, floating over a delicious sea to that temporary heaven on earth where lovers usually land after the first rapturous plunge.

If anyone had mentioned this astonishing fact, nobody would have believed it; nevertheless, it was quite true: and sober, business-like Archie suddenly discovered a fund of romance at the bottom of his hitherto well-conducted heart that amazed him. He was not quite clear what had happened to him at first, and sat about in a dazed sort of way; seeing, hearing, knowing nothing but Phebe: while the unconscious idol found something wanting in the cordial praise so modestly received, because Mr. Archie never said a word.

This was one of the remarkable things which occurred that evening; another was that Mac paid Rose a compliment, which was such an unprecedented fact, it produced a great sensation, though only one person heard it.

Everybody had gone but Mac and his father, who was busy with the Doctor. Aunt Plenty was counting the teaspoons in the dining-room, and Phebe was helping her as of old. Mac and Rose were alone—he apparently in a brown study, leaning his elbows on the chimney-piece; and she lying back in a low chair, looking thoughtfully at the fire. She was tired; and the quiet was grateful to her: so she kept silence and Mac respectfully held his tongue. Presently, however, she became conscious that he was looking at her as intently as eyes and glasses could do it; and, without stirring from her comfortable attitude, she said, smiling up at him—

"He looks as wise as an owl: I wonder what he's thinking about?"

"You, cousin."

"Something good, I hope?"

"I was thinking Leigh Hunt was about right when he said, 'A girl is the sweetest thing God ever made.' "

"Why, Mac!" and Rose sat bolt upright with an astonished face: this was such an entirely unexpected sort of remark for the philosopher to make.

Evidently interested in the new discovery, Mac placidly continued, "Do you know, it seems as if I never really saw a girl before, or had any idea what agreeable creatures they could be. I fancy you are a remarkably good specimen, Rose."

"No, indeed! I'm only hearty and happy; and being safe at home again may make me look better than usual perhaps: but I'm no beauty except to uncle."

" 'Hearty and happy'—that must be it," echoed Mac, soberly investigating the problem. "Most girls are sickly or silly, I think I have observed; and that is probably why I am so struck with you."

"Of all queer boys you are the queerest! Do you really mean that you don't like or notice girls?" asked Rose, much amused at this new peculiarity of her studious cousin.

"Well, no: I am only conscious of two sorts—noisy and quiet ones. I prefer the latter: but, as a general thing, I don't notice any of them much more than I do flies, unless they bother me; then I'd like to flap them away; but, as that won't do, I hide."

Rose leaned back and laughed till her eyes were full: it was so comical to hear Mac sink his voice to a confidential whisper at the last words, and see him smile with sinful satisfaction at the memory of the tormentors he had eluded.

"You needn't laugh: it's a fact, I assure you. Charlie likes the creatures, and they spoil him; Steve follows suit, of course. Archie is a respectful slave when he can't help himself. As for me, I don't often give them a chance; and, when I get caught, I talk science and dead languages till they run for their lives. Now and then I find a sensible one, and then we get on excellently."

"A sad prospect for Phebe and me," sighed Rose, trying to keep sober.

"Phebe is evidently a quiet one. I know she is sensible, or you wouldn't care for her. I can see that she is pleasant to look at, so I fancy I shall like her. As for you, I helped bring you up; therefore I am a little anxious to see how you turn out. I was afraid your foreign polish might spoil you, but I think it has not. In fact, I find you quite satisfactory so far, if you don't mind my saying it. I don't quite know what the charm is, though. Must be the power of inward graces, since you insist that you have no outward ones."

Mac was peering at her with a shrewd smile on his lips, but such a kindly look behind the glasses, that she found both words and glance very pleasant, and answered merrily—

"I am glad you approve of me, and much obliged for your care of my early youth. I hope to be a credit to you, and depend on your keeping me straight; for I'm afraid I shall be spoilt among you all."

"I'll keep my eye on you upon one condition," replied the youthful Mentor.

"Name it."

"If you are going to have a lot of lovers round I wash my hands of you. If not, I'm your man."

"You must be sheep-dog, and help keep them away; for I don't want any yet awhile; and, between ourselves, I don't believe I shall have any if it is known that I am strong-minded. That fact will scare most men away like a yellow flag," said Rose: for, thanks to Dr. Alec's guardianship, she had wasted neither heart nor time in the foolish flirtations so many girls fritter away their youth upon.

"Hum! I rather doubt that," muttered Mac, as he surveyed the damsel before him.

She certainly did not look unpleasantly strong-minded, for

she *was* beautiful in spite of her modest denials. Beautiful with the truest sort of beauty; for nobility of character lent its subtle charm to the bloom of youth, the freshness of health, the innocence of a nature whose sweet maidenliness Mac felt but could not describe. Gentle yet full of spirit, and all aglow with the earnestness that suggests lovely possibilities, and makes one hope that such human flowers may have heaven's purest air and warmest sunshine to blossom in.

"Wait and see," answered Rose; then, as her uncle's voice was heard in the hall, she held out her hand, adding pleasantly, "The old times are to begin again, so come soon and tell me all your doings, and help me with mine just as you used to do."

"You really mean it?" and Mac looked much pleased.

"I really do. You are so little altered, except to grow big, that I don't feel at all strange with you, and want to begin where we left off."

"That will be capital. Good-night, cousin," and to her great amazement he gave her a hearty kiss.

"Oh, but that is not the old way at all!" cried Rose, stepping back in merry confusion; while the audacious youth assumed an air of mild surprise, as he innocently asked—

"Didn't we always say good-night in that way? I had an impression that we did, and were to begin just as we left off."

"Of course not; no power on earth would have bribed you to do it, as you know well enough. I don't mind the first night, but we are too old for that sort of thing now."

"I'll remember. It was the force of habit, I suppose; for I'm sure I must have done it in former times, it seemed so natural. Coming, father!" and Mac retired, evidently convinced that he was right.

"Dear old thing! he is as much a boy as ever, and that is such a comfort; for some of the others have grown up very fast," said Rose to herself, recalling Charlie's sentimental airs, and Archie's beatified expression while Phebe sang.

2

Old Friends With New Faces

"It is *so* good to be at home again! I wonder how we ever made up our minds to go away!" exclaimed Rose, as she went roaming about the old house next morning, full of the satisfaction one feels at revisiting familiar nooks and corners, and finding them unchanged.

"That we might have the pleasure of coming back again," answered Phebe, walking down the hall beside her little mistress, as happy as she.

"Everything seems just as we left it, even to the rose-leaves we used to tuck in here," continued the younger girl, peeping into one of the tall India jars that stood about the hall.

"Don't you remember how Jamie and Pokey used to play Forty Thieves with them, and how you tried to get into that blue one and got stuck, and the other boys found us before I could pull you out?" asked Phebe, laughing.

"Yes, indeed; and speaking of angels one is apt to hear the rustling of their wings," added Rose, as a shrill whistle came up the avenue, accompanied by the clatter of hoofs.

"It is the circus!" cried Phebe, gaily, as they both recalled the red cart and the charge of the Clan.

There was only one boy now, alas! but he made noise enough for half a dozen; and, before Rose could run to the door, Jamie came bouncing in with a "shining morning face," a bat over his shoulder, a red and white jockey cap on his head, one pocket bulging with a big ball, the other overflowing with cookies, and his mouth full of the apple he was just finishing off in hot haste.

"Morning! I just looked in to make sure you'd really come,

and see that you were all right," he observed, saluting with the bat and doffing the gay cap with one effective twitch.

"Good-morning, dear. Yes, we are really here, and getting to rights as fast as possible. But it seems to me you are rather gorgeous, Jamie. What do you belong to—a fire company or a jockey club?" asked Rose, turning up the once chubby face, which now was getting brown, and square about the chin.

"No, *ma'am*! Why, don't you know? I'm captain of the Base Ball Star Club. Look at that, will you?" and, as if the fact was one of national importance, Jamie flung open his jacket to display upon his proudly swelling chest a heart-shaped red-flannel shield, decorated with a white cotton star the size of a tea-plate.

"Superb! I've been away so long I forgot there was such a game. And *you* are the captain?" cried Rose, deeply impressed by the high honour to which her kinsman had arrived.

"I just am, and it's no joke you'd better believe; for we knock our teeth out, black our eyes, and split our fingers almost as well as the big fellows. You come down to the Common between one and two and see us play a match; then you'll understand what hard work it is. I'll teach you to bat now if you'll come out on the lawn," added Jamie, fired with a wish to exhibit his prowess.

"No, thank you, captain. The grass is wet, and you'll be late at school if you stay for us."

"I'm not afraid. Girls are not good for much generally; but you never used to mind a little wet, and played cricket like a good one. Can't you ever do that sort of thing now?" asked the boy, with a pitying look at these hapless creatures debarred from the joys and perils of manly sports.

"I can run still: and I'll get to the gate before you; see if I don't;" and, yielding to the impulse of the moment, Rose darted down the steps before astonished Jamie could mount and follow.

He was off in a moment: but Rose had the start; and, though old Sheltie did his best, she reached the goal just ahead, and stood there laughing and panting, all rosy with the fresh October air, a pretty picture for several gentlemen who were driving by.

"Good for you, Rose!" said Archie, jumping out to shake hands, while Will and Geordie saluted, and Uncle Mac laughed at Jamie, who looked as if girls had risen slightly in his opinion.

"I'm glad it is you, because you won't be shocked. But I'm so happy to be back I forgot I was not little Rose still," said Atalanta, smoothing down her flying hair.

"You look very like her, with the curls on your shoulders in the old way. I missed them last night, and wondered what it was. How is uncle and Phebe?" asked Archie, whose eyes had been looking over Rose's head while he spoke towards the piazza, where a female figure was visible among the reddening woodbines.

"All well, thanks. Won't you come up and see for yourselves?"

"Can't, my dear, can't possibly. Business, you know, business. This fellow is my right-hand man, and I can't spare him a minute. Come, Arch, we must be off, or these boys will miss their train," answered Uncle Mac, pulling out his watch.

With a last look from the light-haired figure at the gate to the dark-haired one among the vines, Archie drove away, and Jamie cantered after, consoling himself for his defeat with apple number two.

Rose lingered a moment, feeling much inclined to continue her run, and pop in upon all the aunts in succession; but, remembering her uncovered head, was about to turn back, when a cheerful "Ahoy! ahoy!" made her look up, to see Mac approaching at a great pace, waving his hat as he came.

"The Campbells are coming thick and fast this morning, and the more the merrier," she said, running to meet him. "You look like a good boy going to school, and virtuously conning your lesson by the way," she added, smiling to see him take his finger out of the book he had evidently been reading, and tuck it under his arm, just as he used to do years ago.

"I *am* a schoolboy going to the school I like best," he answered, waving a plumy spray of asters, as if pointing out the lovely autumn world about them, full of gay hues, fresh airs, and mellow sunshine.

"That reminds me that I didn't get a chance to hear much about your plans last night: the other boys all talked at once, and you only got in a word now and then. What have you decided to be, Mac?" asked Rose, as they went up the avenue side by side.

"A man first, and a good one if possible; after that, what God pleases."

Something in the tone, as well as the words, made Rose look up quickly into Mac's face, to see a new expression there. It was indescribable; but she felt as she had often done when watching the mists part suddenly, giving glimpses of some mountain-top, shining serene and high against the blue.

"I think you *will* be something splendid; for you really look quite glorified, walking under this arch of yellow leaves with the sunshine on your face," she exclaimed, conscious of a sudden admiration never felt before; for Mac was the plainest of all the cousins.

"I don't know about that; but I have my dreams and aspirations, and some of them are pretty high ones. Aim at the best, you know, and keep climbing if you want to get on," he said, looking at the asters with an inward sort of smile, as if he and they had some sweet secret between them.

"You are queerer than ever. But I like your ambition, and hope you will get on. Only mustn't you begin at something soon? I fancied you would study medicine with uncle: that used to be our plan, you know."

"I shall, for the present at least, because I quite agree with you that it is necessary to have an anchor somewhere, and not go floating off into the world of imagination without ballast of the right sort. Uncle and I had some talk about it last night, and I'm going up to begin as soon as possible; for I've mooned long enough," and giving himself a shake, Mac threw down the pretty spray, adding half aloud—

> "Chide me not, laborious band,
>   For the idle flowers I brought:
> Every aster in my hand
>   Goes home laden with a thought."

Rose caught the words and smiled, thinking to herself, "Oh, that's it: he is getting into the sentimental age, and Aunt Jane has been lecturing him. Dear me, how we *are* growing up!"

"You look as if you didn't like the prospect very well," she said aloud; for Mac had rammed the volume of Shelley into his pocket, and the glorified expression was so entirely gone Rose fancied that she had been mistaken about the mountain-top behind the mists.

"Yes, well enough: I always thought the profession a grand one; and where could I find a better teacher than uncle? I've got into lazy ways lately, and it is high time I went at something useful; so here I go," and Mac abruptly vanished into the study, while Rose joined Phebe in Aunt Plenty's room.

The dear old lady had just decided, after long and earnest discussion, which of six favourite puddings should be served for dinner, and thus had a few moments to devote to sentiment; so, when Rose came in, she held out her arms, saying fondly—

"I shall not feel as if I'd got my child back again, until I have her in my lap a minute. No, you're not a bit too heavy; my rheumatism doesn't begin much before November: so sit here, darling, and put your two arms round my neck."

Rose obeyed, and neither spoke for a moment, as the old woman held the young one close, and appeased the two years' longing of a motherly heart by the caresses women give the creatures dearest to them. Right in the middle of a kiss, however, she stopped suddenly; and, holding out one arm, caught Phebe, who was trying to steal away unobserved.

"Don't go: there's room for both in my love, though there isn't in my lap. I'm so grateful to get my dear girls safely home again, that I hardly know what I'm about," said Aunt Plenty, embracing Phebe so heartily that she could not feel left out in the cold, and stood there with her black eyes shining through the happiest tears.

"There, now I've had a good hug, and feel as if I was all right again. I wish you'd set that cap in order, Rose: I went to bed in such a hurry I pulled the strings off and left it all in a heap. Phebe, dear, you shall dust round a mite, just as you used to; for I haven't had anyone to do it as I like since you've been gone, and it will do me good to see all my knick-knacks straightened out in your tidy way," said the elder lady, getting up with a refreshed expression on her rosy old face.

"Shall I dust in here too?" asked Phebe, glancing towards an inner room which used to be her care.

"No, dear, I'd rather do that myself. Go in if you like; nothing is changed. I *must* go and see to my pudding;" and Aunt Plenty trotted abruptly away, with a quiver of emotion in her voice which made even her last words pathetic.

Pausing on the threshold as if it was a sacred place, the girls looked in with eyes soon dimmed by tender tears; for it seemed as if the gentle occupant was still there. Sunshine shone on the old geraniums by the window; the cushioned chair stood in its

B

accustomed place, with the white wrapper hung across it, and the faded slippers lying ready. Books and basket, knitting and spectacles, were all just as she had left them; and the beautiful tranquillity that always filled the room seemed so natural both lookers turned involuntarily towards the bed where Aunt Peace used to greet them with a smile. There was no sweet old face upon the pillow now, yet the tears that wet the blooming cheeks were not for her who had gone, but for her who was left; because they saw something which spoke eloquently of the love which outlives death and makes the humblest thing beautiful and sacred.

A well-worn footstool stood beside the bed, and in the high-piled whiteness of the empty couch there was a little hollow where a gray head nightly rested, while Aunt Plenty said the prayers her mother taught her seventy years ago.

Without a word, the girls softly shut the door: and, while Phebe put the room in the most exquisite order, Rose retrimmed the plain white cap, where pink and yellow ribbons never rustled now; both feeling honoured by their tasks, and better for their knowledge of the faithful love and piety which sanctified a good old woman's life.

"You darling creature, I'm *so* glad to get you back! I know it's shamefully early; but I really couldn't keep away another minute. Let me help you: I'm dying to see all your splendid things; for I saw the trunks pass, and I know you've quantities of treasures," cried Annabel Bliss, all in one breath as she embraced Rose an hour later, and glanced about the room bestrewn with a variety of agreeable objects.

"How well you are looking! Sit down and I'll show you my lovely photographs. Uncle chose all the best for me, and it's a treat to see them," answered Rose, putting a roll on the table and looking about for more.

"Oh, thanks! I haven't time now: one needs hours to study such things. Show me your Paris dresses, there's a dear: I'm perfectly aching to see the last styles," and Annabel cast a hungry eye towards certain large boxes delightfully suggestive of French finery.

"I haven't got any," said Rose, fondly surveying the fine photographs as she laid them away.

"Rose Campbell! you don't mean to say that you didn't get one Paris dress at least?" cried Annabel, scandalized at the bare idea of such neglect.

"Not one for myself: Aunt Clara ordered several and will be charmed to show them when her box comes."

"Such a chance! right there and plenty of money! How *could* you love your uncle after such cruelty?" sighed Annabel, with a face full of sympathy.

Rose looked puzzled for a minute, then seemed to understand, and assumed a superior air which became her very well, as she said, good-naturedly opening a box of laces, "Uncle did not forbid my doing it, and I had money enough; but I chose not to spend it on things of that sort."

"Could and didn't! I can't believe it!" And Annabel sunk into a chair as if the thought was too much for her.

"I did rather want to at first, just for the fun of the thing; in fact, I went and looked at some amazing gowns. But they were very expensive, very much trimmed, and not my style at all; so I gave them up, and kept what I valued more than all the gowns Worth ever made."

"What in the world was it?" cried Annabel, hoping she would say diamonds.

"Uncle's good opinion," answered Rose, looking thoughtfully into the depths of a packing case, where lay the lovely picture that would always remind her of the little triumph over girlish vanity, which not only kept but increased "Uncle's good opinion."

"Oh, indeed!" said Annabel, blankly, and fell to examining Aunt Plenty's lace; while Rose went on with a happy smile in her eyes as she dived into another trunk.

"Uncle thinks one has no right to waste money on such things; but he is very generous, and loves to give useful, beautiful, or curious gifts. See, all these pretty ornaments are for presents; and you shall choose first whatever you like."

"He's a perfect dear!" cried Annabel, revelling in the crystal, filigree, coral, and mosaic trinkets spread before her; while Rose completed her rapture by adding sundry tasteful trifles fresh from Paris.

"Now tell me, when do you mean to have your coming-out party? I ask because I've nothing ready, and want plenty of time; for, I suppose, it will be *the* event of the season," asked Annabel, a few minutes later, as she wavered between a pink coral and a blue lava set.

"I came out when I went to Europe; but I suppose Aunty

Plen will want to have some sort of merry-making to celebrate our return. I shall begin as I mean to go on, and have a simple, sociable sort of party, and invite every one whom I like, no matter in what set they happen to belong. No one shall ever say *I* am aristocratic and exclusive: so prepare yourself to be shocked; for old friends and young, rich and poor, will be asked to all my parties."

"Oh, my heart! you *are* going to be odd just as mamma predicted!" sighed Annabel, clasping her hands in despair, and studying the effect of three bracelets on her chubby arm in the midst of her woe.

"In my own house I'm going to do as I think best; and, if people call me odd, I can't help it. I shall endeavour not to do anything very dreadful; but I seem to inherit uncle's love for experiments, and mean to try some. I dare say they will fail and I shall get laughed at; I intend to do it nevertheless, so you had better drop me now before I begin," said Rose, with an air of resolution that was rather alarming.

"What shall you wear at this new sort of party of yours?" asked Annabel, wisely turning a deaf ear to all delicate or dangerous topics and keeping to matters she understood.

"That white thing over there. It is fresh and pretty, and Phebe has one like it. I never want to dress more than she does; and gowns of that sort are always most appropriate and becoming to girls of our age."

"Phebe! you don't mean to say you are going to make a lady of *her*!" gasped Annabel, upsetting her treasures, as she fell back with a gesture that made the little chair creak again; for Miss Bligh was as plump as a partridge.

"She *is* one already, and anybody who slights her slights me; for she is the best girl I know and the dearest," cried Rose, warmly.

"Yes, of course—I was only surprised—you are quite right; for she *may* turn out to be somebody, and then how glad you'll feel that you were so good to her!" said Annabel, veering round at once, seeing which way the wind blew.

Before Rose could speak again, a cheery voice called from the hall—

"Little mistress, where are you?"

"In my room, Phebe, dear," and up came the girl Rose was going to "make a lady of," looking so like one that Annabel opened her china-blue eyes, and smiled involuntarily as Phebe dropped a little curtsy in playful imitation of her old manner, and said quietly—

"How do you do, Miss Bliss?"

"Glad to see you back, Miss Moore," answered Annabel, shaking hands in a way that settled the question of Phebe's place in *her* mind for ever; for the stout damsel had a kind heart in spite of a weak head, and was really fond of Rose. It was evidently, "Love me, love my Phebe;" so she made up her mind on the spot that Phebe *was* somebody, and that gave an air of romance even to the poor-house.

She could not help staring a little, as she watched the two friends work together, and listened to their happy talk over each new treasure as it came to light; for every look and word plainly showed that years of close companionship had made them very dear to one another. It was pretty to see Rose try to do the hardest part of any little job herself: still prettier to see Phebe circumvent her, and untie the hard knots, fold the stiff papers, or lift the heavy trays with her own strong hands; and prettiest of all to hear her say in a motherly tone, as she put Rose into an easy chair—

"Now, my deary, sit and rest; for you will have to see company all day, and I can't let you get tired out so early."

"That is no reason why I should let you either. Call Jane to help or I'll bob up again directly," answered Rose, with a very bad assumption of authority.

"Jane may take my place downstairs; but no one shall wait on you here except me, as long as I'm with you," said stately Phebe, stooping to put a hassock under the feet of her little mistress.

"It is very nice and pretty to see; but I don't know what people *will* say when she goes into society with the rest of us. I do hope Rose won't be *very* odd," said Annabel to herself as she went away to circulate the depressing news that there was to be no grand ball; and, saddest disappointment of all, that Rose had not a single Paris costume with which to refresh the eyes and rouse the envy of her amiable friends.

"Now I've seen or heard from all the boys but Charlie, and I suppose he is too busy. I wonder what he is about," thought Rose, turning from the hall door, whither she had courteously accompanied her guest.

The wish was granted a moment after; for, going into the parlour to decide where some of her pictures should hang, she saw a pair of boots at one end of the sofa, a tawny-brown head at the other, and discovered that Charlie was busily occupied in doing nothing.

"The voice of the Bliss was heard in the land, so I dodged till she went upstairs, and then took a brief *siesta* while waiting to pay my respects to the distinguished traveller, Lady Hester Stanhope," he said, leaping up to make his best bow.

"The voice of the sluggard would be a more appropriate quotation, I think. Does Annabel still pine for you?" asked Rose, recalling certain youthful jokes upon the subject of unrequited affections.

"Not a bit of it. Fun has cut me out, and the fair Annabella will be Mrs. Tokio before the winter is over, if I'm not much mistaken."

"What, little Fun See? How droll it seems to think of him grown up and married to Annabel of all people! She never said a word about him; but this accounts for her admiring my pretty Chinese things, and being so interested in Canton."

"Little Fun is a great swell now and much enamoured of our fat friend, who will take to chopsticks whenever he says the word. I needn't ask how you do, cousin; for you beat that Aurora all hollow in the way of colour. I should have been up before, but I thought you'd like a good rest after your voyage."

"I was running a race with Jamie before nine o'clock. What were you doing, young man?"

" 'Sleeping I dreamed, love, dreamed, love, of thee,' "

began Charlie; but Rose cut him short by saying as reproachfully as she could, while the culprit stood regarding her with placid satisfaction—

"You ought to have been up and at work like the rest of the boys. I felt like a drone in a hive of very busy bees, when I saw them all hurrying off to their business."

"But, my dear girl, I've got no business. I'm making up my mind, you see, and do the ornamental while I'm deciding. There always ought to be one gentleman in a family, and that seems to be rather my line," answered Charlie, posing for the character, with an assumption of languid elegance which would have been very effective if his twinkling eyes had not spoilt it.

"There are none *but* gentlemen in our family, I hope," answered Rose, with the proud air she always wore when anything was said derogatory to the name of Campbell.

"Of course, of course. I should have said gentleman of leisure. You see it is against my principles to slave as Archie does. What's the use? Don't need the money, got plenty; so why not enjoy it, and keep jolly as long as possible? I'm sure cheerful people are public benefactors in this world of woe."

It was not easy to object to this proposition, especially when made by a comely young man, who looked the picture of health and happiness as he sat on the arm of the sofa, smiling at his cousin in the most engaging manner. Rose knew very well that the Epicurean philosophy was not the true one to begin life upon; but it was difficult to reason with Charlie, because he always dodged sober subjects, and was so full of cheery spirits, one hated to lessen the sort of sunshine which certainly is a public benefactor.

"You have such a clever way of putting things that I don't know how to contradict you, though I still think I'm right," she said gravely. "Mac likes to idle as well as you; but he is not going to do it, because he knows it's bad for him to fritter away his time. He is going to study a profession like a wise boy; though he would much prefer to live among his beloved books, or ride his hobbies in peace."

"That's all very well for *him*, because *he* doesn't care for society, and may as well be studying medicine as philandering about the woods with his pockets full of musty philosophers and old-fashioned poets," answered Charlie, with a shrug which plainly expressed his opinion of Mac.

"I wonder if musty philosophers, like Socrates and Aristotle, and old-fashioned poets, like Shakespeare and Milton, are not safer company for him to keep than some of the more modern friends you have?" said Rose, remembering Jamie's hints about wild oats; for she could be a little sharp sometimes, and had not lectured "the boys" for so long it seemed unusually pleasant.

But Charlie changed the subject skilfully by exclaiming with an anxious expression—

"I do believe you are going to be like Aunt Jane; for that's just the way she comes down on me whenever she gets a chance! Don't take her for a model, I beg: she is a good woman but a mighty disagreeable one, in my humble opinion."

The fear of being disagreeable is a great bugbear to a girl, as this artful young man well knew, and Rose fell into the trap at once; for Aunt Jane was far from being her model, though she could not help respecting her worth.

"Have you given up your painting?" she asked rather abruptly, turning to a gilded Fra Angelico angel which leaned in the sofa corner.

"Sweetest face I ever saw, and very like you about the eyes, isn't it?" said Charlie, who seemed to have a Yankee trick of replying to one question with another.

"I want an answer, not a compliment," and Rose tried to look severe, as she put away the picture more quickly than she took it up.

"Have I given up painting? Oh, no! I daub a little in oils, slop a little in water-colours, sketch now and then, and poke about the studios when the artistic fit comes on."

"How is the music?"

"More flourishing. I don't practise much, but sing a good deal in company. Set up a guitar last summer and went trouba-douring round in great style. The girls like it, and it's jolly among the fellows."

"Are you studying anything?"

"Well, I have some law books on my table—good, big, wise-looking chaps—and I take a turn at them semi-occasionally, when pleasure palls or parents chide. But I doubt if I do more than learn what 'a allybi' is this year," and a sly laugh in Charlie's eye suggested that he sometimes availed himself of this bit of legal knowledge.

"What *do* you do then?"

"Fair catechist, I enjoy myself. Private theatricals have been the rage of late, and I have won such laurels that I seriously think of adopting the stage as my profession."

"Really!" cried Rose, alarmed.

"Why not? if I *must* go to work, isn't that as good as any-thing?"

"Not without more talent than I think you possess. With genius one can do anything: without it one had better let the stage alone."

"There's a quencher for the 'star of the goodlie companie'

to which I belong. Mac hasn't a ray of genius for anything, yet you admire him for trying to be an M.D.," cried Charlie, rather nettled by her words.

"It is respectable, at all events; and I'd rather be a second-rate doctor than a second-rate actor. But I know you don't mean it, and only say so to frighten me."

"Exactly. I always bring it up when anyone begins to lecture, and it works wonders. Uncle Mac turns pale, the aunts hold up their hands in holy horror, and a general panic ensues. Then I magnanimously promise not to disgrace the family; and in the first burst of gratitude the dear souls agree to everything I ask; so peace is restored, and I go on my way rejoicing."

"Just the way you used to threaten to run off to sea, if your mother objected to any of your whims. You are not changed in that respect, though you are in others. You had great plans and projects once, Charlie; and now you seem to be contented with being a 'jack of all trades and master of none.' "

"Boyish nonsense! Time has brought wisdom; and I don't see the sense of tying myself down to one particular thing, and grinding away at it year after year. People of one idea get so deucedly narrow and tame, I've no patience with them. Culture is the thing; and the sort one gets by ranging over a wide field is the easiest to acquire, the handiest to have, and the most successful in the end. At any rate, it is the kind I like, and the only kind I intend to bother myself about."

With this declaration, Charlie smoothed his brow, clasped his hands over his head, and, leaning back, gently warbled the chorus of a college song, as if it expressed his views of life better than he could:—

> "While our rosy fillets shed
>   Blushes o'er each fervid head,
>   With many a cup and many a smile
>   The festal moments we beguile."

"Some of my saints here were people of one idea; and, though they were not very successful in a worldly point of view while alive, they were loved and canonized when dead," said Rose, who had been turning over a pile of photographs upon the table, and, just then, found her favourite, St. Francis, among them.

"This is more to my taste. Those worn-out, cadaverous fellows give me the blues; but here's a gentlemanly saint, who takes things easy, and does good as he goes along, without howling over his own sins, or making other people miserable by telling them of theirs." And Charlie laid a handsome St. Martin beside the brown-frocked monk.

Rose looked at both, and understood why her cousin preferred the soldierly figure with the sword to the ascetic with his crucifix. One was riding bravely through the world in purple and fine linen, with horse and hound, and squires at his back; the other was in a lazar-house, praying over the dead and dying. The contrast was a strong one; and the girl's eyes lingered longest on the knight, though she said thoughtfully—

"Yours is certainly the pleasantest: and yet I never heard of any good deed he did, except divide his cloak with a beggar; while my St. Francis gave himself to charity just when life was most tempting, and spent years working for God without reward. He's old and poor, and in a dreadful place, but I won't give him up; and you may have your gay St. Martin, if you want him."

"No, thank you; saints are not in my line: but I'd like the golden-haired angel in the blue gown, if you'll let me have her. She shall be my little Madonna, and I'll pray to her like a good Catholic," answered Charlie, turning to the delicate, deep-eyed figure, with the lilies in its hand.

"With all my heart, and any others that you like. Choose some for your mother, and give them to her with my love."

So Charlie sat down beside Rose to turn and talk over the pictures for a long and pleasant hour. But when they went away to lunch, if there had been any one to observe so small but significant a trifle, good St. Francis lay face downwards behind the sofa, while gallant St. Martin stood erect upon the chimney-piece.

3

Miss Campbell

WHILE THE TRAVELLERS unpack their trunks, we will pick
up, as briefly as possible, the dropped stitches in the little
romance we are weaving.

Rose's life had been a very busy and quiet one for the four
years following the May-day when she made her choice. Study,
exercise, house-work, and many wholesome pleasures, kept her
a happy, hearty creature, yearly growing in womanly graces,
yet always preserving the innocent freshness girls lose so soon
when too early sent upon the world's stage, and given a part
to play.

Not a remarkably gifted girl in any way, and far from perfect;
full of all manner of youthful whims and fancies; a little spoiled
by much love; rather apt to think all lives as safe and sweet as
her own; and, when want or pain appealed to her, the tender
heart overflowed with a remorseful charity, which gave of its
abundance recklessly. Yet, with all her human imperfections,
the upright nature of the child kept her desires climbing towards
the just and pure and true, as flowers struggle to the light; and
the woman's soul was budding beautifully under the green
leaves behind the little thorns.

At seventeen, Dr. Alec pronounced her ready for the voyage
round the world, which he considered a better finishing off than
any school could give her. But just then Aunt Peace began to
fail, and soon slipped quietly away to rejoin the lover she had
waited for so long. Youth seemed to come back in a mysterious
way to touch the dead face with lost loveliness, and all the
romance of her past to gather round her memory. Unlike most

43

aged women, her friends were among the young; and, at her
funeral, the grey heads gave place to the band of loving girls
who made the sweet old maiden ready for her rest, bore her pall,
and covered her grave with the white flowers she had never
worn.

When this was over, poor Aunt Plenty seemed so lost
without her life-long charge that Dr. Alec would not leave her;
and Rose gladly paid the debt she owed by the tender service
which comforts without words. But Aunt Plenty, having lived
for others all her days, soon rebelled against this willing sacrifice, soon found strength in her own sincere piety, solace in
cheerful occupation, and amusement in nursing Aunt Myra, who
was a capital patient, as she never died and never got well.

So, at last, the moment came when, with free minds, the
travellers could set out; and on Rose's eighteenth birthday, with
Uncle Alec and the faithful Phebe, she sailed away to see and
study the big, beautiful world, which lies ready for us all, if we
only know how to use and to enjoy it.

Phebe was set to studying music in the best schools; and,
while she trained her lovely voice with happy industry, Rose
and her uncle roamed about in the most delightful way, till two
years were gone like a dream, and those at home clamoured for
their return.

Back they came, and now the heiress must make ready
to take her place; for at twenty-one she came into possession
of the fortune she had been trying to learn how to use well.
Great plans fermented in her brain; for, though the heart was as
generous as ever, time had taught her prudence, and observation
shown her that the wisest charity is that which helps the poor to
help themselves.

Dr. Alec found it a little difficult to restrain the ardour of this
young philanthropist, who wanted to begin at once to endow
hospitals, build homes, adopt children, and befriend all mankind.

"Take a little time to look about you and get your bearings,
child; for the world you have been living in is a much simpler,
honester one than that you are now to enter. Test yourself a bit,
and see if the old ways seem best after all; for you are old
enough to decide, and wise enough to discover, what is for your
truest good, I hope," he said trying to feel ready to let the bird
escape from under his wing, and make little flights alone.

'Now, uncle, I'm very much afraid you are going to be disappointed in me," answered Rose, with unusual hesitation, yet a very strong desire visible in her eyes. "You like to have me quite honest, and I've learned to tell you all my foolish thoughts: so I'll speak out, and if you find my wish very wrong and silly, please say so; for I don't want you to cast me off entirely, though I am grown up. You say, wait a little, test myself, and try if the old ways are best. I should like to do that; and can I in a better way than by leading the life other girls lead, just for a little while," she added, as her uncle's face grew grave.

He *was* disappointed; yet acknowledged that the desire was natural, and in a moment saw that a trial of this sort might have its advantages. Nevertheless, he dreaded it; for he had intended to choose her society carefully, and try to keep her unspoiled by the world as long as possible, like many another fond parent and guardian. But the spirit of Eve is strong in all her daughters: forbidden fruit will look rosier to them than any in their own orchards, and the temptation to take just one little bite proves irresistible to the wisest. So Rose, looking out from the safe seclusion of her girlhood into the woman's kingdom which she was about to take possession of, felt a sudden wish to try its pleasures before assuming its responsibilities, and was too sincere to hide the longing.

"Very well, my dear, try it if you like, only take care of your health: be temperate in your gaiety, and don't lose more than you gain; if that is possible," he added under his breath, endeavouring to speak cheerfully and not look anxious.

"I know it is foolish; but I do want to be a regular butterfly for a little while and see what it is like. You know I couldn't help seeing a good deal of fashionable life abroad, though we were not in it; and here at home the girls tell me about all sorts of pleasant things that are to happen this winter; so, if you won't despise me *very* much, I should like to try it."

"For how long?"

"Would three months be too long? New Year is a good time to take a fresh start. Everyone is going to welcome me; so I must be gay in spite of myself, unless I'm willing to seem very ungrateful and morose," said Rose, glad to have so good a reason to offer for her new experiment.

"You may like it so well that the three months may become years. Pleasure is very sweet when we are young."

"Do you think it will intoxicate me?"

"We shall see, my dear."

"We shall!" and Rose marched away; looking as if she had taken a pledge of some sort, and meant to keep it.

It was a great relief to the public mind when it became known that Miss Campbell was really coming out at last; and invitations to Aunt Plenty's party were promptly accepted. Aunt Clara was much disappointed about the grand ball she had planned; but Rose stood firm, and the dear old lady had her way about everything.

The consequence was a delightfully informal gathering of friends to welcome the travellers home. Just a good, old-fashioned, hospitable house-warming; so simple, cordial, and genuine that those who came to criticise remained to enjoy, and many owned the charm they could neither describe nor imitate.

Much curiosity was felt about Phebe, and much gossip went on behind fans that evening; for those who had known her years ago found it hard to recognize the little house-maid in the handsome young woman who bore herself with such quiet dignity, and charmed them all with her fine voice. "Cinderella has turned out a princess," was the general verdict; and Rose enjoyed the little sensation immensely; for she had had many battles to fight for her Phebe since she came among them, and now her faith was vindicated.

Miss Campbell herself was in great demand, and did the honours so prettily that even Miss Bliss forgave her for her sad neglect of Worth; though she shook her head over the white gowns, just alike except that Phebe wore crimson and Rose blue trimmings.

The girls swarmed eagerly round their recovered friend; for Rose had been a favourite before she went away, and found her throne waiting for her now. The young men privately pronounced Phebe the handsomest—"But then you know there's neither family nor money; so it's no use." Phebe, therefore, was admired as one of the ornamental properties belonging to the house, and let respectfully alone.

But bonny Rose was "all right," as these amiable youths expressed it; and many a wistful eye followed the bright head as it flitted about the rooms, as if it were a second Golden Fleece to be won with difficulty; for stalwart kinsmen hedged it round, and watchful aunts kept guard.

Little wonder that the girl found her new world an enchanting

one, and that her first sip of pleasure rather went to her head; for everybody welcomed and smiled on her, flattered and praised, whispered agreeable prophecies in her ear, and looked the compliments and congratulations they dared not utter, till she felt as if she must have left her old self somewhere abroad, and suddenly becoming a new and wonderfully gifted being.

"It is very nice, uncle; and I'm not sure that I mayn't want another three months of it when the first are gone," she whispered to Dr. Alec, as he stood watching the dance she was leading with Charlie in the long hall after supper.

"Steady, my lass, steady; and remember that you are not really a butterfly, but a mortal girl with a head that will ache to-morrow," he answered, watching the flushed and smiling face before him.

"I almost wish there wasn't any tomorrow, but that tonight would last for ever: it is so pleasant, and everyone so kind," she said with a little sigh of happiness, as she gathered up her fleecy skirts like a white bird pluming itself for flight.

"I'll ask your opinion about that at two A.M.," began her uncle, with a warning nod.

"I'll give it honestly," was all Rose had time to say before Charlie swept her away into the parti-coloured cloud before them.

"It's no use, Alec: train a girl as wisely as you choose, she will break loose when the time comes, and go in for pleasure as eagerly as the most frivolous; for ' 'tis their nature to,' " said Uncle Mac, keeping time to the music as if he would not mind "going in" for a bit of pleasure himself.

"My girl shall taste and try; but, unless I'm much mistaken, a little of it will satisfy her. I want to see if she will stand the test; for, if not, all my work is a failure, and I'd like to know it," answered the doctor, with a hopeful smile on his lips, but an anxious look in his eyes.

"She will come out all right—bless her heart! so let her sow her innocent wild oats and enjoy herself till she is ready to settle down. I wish all our young folks were likely to have as small a crop, and get through as safely as she will," added Uncle Mac, with a shake of the head, as he glanced at some of the young men revolving before him.

"Nothing amiss with your lads, I hope?"

"No, thank heaven! So far I've had little trouble with either though Mac is an odd stick, and Steve a puppy. I don't complain; for both will outgrow that sort of thing, and are good fellows at heart, thanks to their mother. But Clara's boy is in a bad way; and she will spoil him as a man as she has as a boy, if his father doesn't interfere."

"I told brother Stephen all about him when I was in Calcutta last year, and he wrote to the boy; but Clara has got no end of plans in her head, and so she insisted on keeping Charlie a year longer when his father ordered him off to India," replied the doctor, as they walked away.

"It is too late to 'order:' Charlie is a man now, and Stephen will find that he has been too easy with him all these years. Poor fellow, it has been hard lines for him, and is likely to be harder, I fancy, unless he comes home and straightens things out."

"He won't do that if he can help it; for he has lost all his energy living in that climate, and hates worry more than ever: so you can imagine what an effort it would be to manage a foolish woman and a headstrong boy. We must lend a hand, Mac, and do our best for poor old Steve."

"The best we can do for the lad is to marry and settle him as soon as possible."

"My dear fellow, he is only three and twenty," began the doctor, as if the idea was preposterous: then a sudden change came over him, as he added with a melancholy smile, "I forget how much one can hope and suffer, even at twenty-three."

"And be all the better for, if bravely outlived," said Uncle Mac, with his hand on his brother's shoulder, and the sincerest approval in his voice. Then, kindly returning to the younger people, he went on inquiringly, "You don't incline to Clara's view of a certain matter, I fancy?"

"Decidedly not. My girl must have the best, and Clara's training would spoil an angel," answered Dr. Alec, quickly.

"But we shall find it hard to let our little Rose go out of the family. How would Archie do? He has been well brought up, and is a thoroughly excellent lad."

The brothers had retired to the study by this time, and were alone; yet Dr. Alec lowered his voice as he said with a tender sort of anxiety pleasant to see—

"You know I do not approve of cousins marrying, so I'm in a

quandary, Mac; for I love the child as if she were my own, and feel as if I could not give her up to any man whom I did not know and trust entirely. It is of no use for us to plan; for she must choose for herself; yet I do wish we could keep her among us, and give one of our boys a wife worth having."

"We must; so never mind your theories, but devote yourself to testing our elder lads, and making one of them a happy fellow. All are heart-whole, I believe, and, though young still for this sort of thing, we can be gently shaping matters for them, since no one knows how soon the moment may come. My faith! it is like living in a powder-mill to be among a lot of young folks nowadays. All looks as calm as possible, till a sudden spark produces an explosion, and heaven only knows where we find ourselves after it is over."

And Uncle Mac sat himself comfortably down to settle Rose's fate; while the doctor paced the room, plucking at his beard and knitting his brows, as if he found it hard to see his way.

"Yes, Archie is a good fellow," he said, answering the question he had ignored before. "An upright, steady, intelligent lad, who will make an excellent husband, if he ever finds out that he has a heart. I suppose I'm an old fool, but I do like a little more romance in a young man than he seems to have; more warmth and enthusiasm, you know. Bless the boy! he might be forty instead of three or four and twenty; he's so sober, calm, and cool. I'm younger now than he is, and could go a-wooing like a Romeo if I had any heart to offer a woman."

The doctor looked rather shamefaced as he spoke, and his brother burst out laughing—

"See here, Alec, it's a pity so much romance and excellence as yours should be lost; so why don't you set these young fellows an example and go a-wooing yourself? Jessie has been wondering how you have managed to keep from falling in love with Phebe all this time; and Clara is quite sure that you only waited till she was safe under Aunt Plenty's wing to offer yourself in the good old-fashioned style."

"I!" and the doctor stood aghast at the mere idea; then he gave a resigned sort of sigh and added like a martyr, "If those dear women would let me alone, I'd thank them for ever. Put the idea out of their minds for heaven's sake, Mac, or I shall be having that poor girl flung at my head, and her comfort destroyed. She is a fine creature, and I'm proud of her; but she deserves a better lot than to be tied to an old fellow like me, whose only merit is his fidelity."

"As you please, I was only joking," and Uncle Mac dropped the subject with secret relief; for the excellent man thought a good deal of family, and had been rather worried at the hints of the ladies. After a moment's silence, he returned to a former topic, which was rather a pet plan of his. "I don't think you do Archie justice, Alec. You don't know him as well as I do; but you'll find that he has heart enough under his cool, quiet manner. I've grown very fond of him, think highly of him, and don't see how you could do better for Rose than to give her to him."

"If she will go," said the doctor, smiling at his brother's business-like way of disposing of the young people.

"She'll do anything to please you," began Uncle Mac, in perfect good faith; for twenty-five years in the society of a very prosaic wife had taken nearly all the romance out of him.

"It is of no use for us to plan, and I shall never interfere except to advise; but, if I *were* to choose one of the boys, I should incline to my godson," answered the doctor, gravely.

"What, my Ugly Duckling!" exclaimed Uncle Mac, in great surprise.

"The Ugly Duckling turned out a swan, you remember. I've always been fond of the boy, because he's so genuine and original. Crude as a green apple now, but sound at the core, and only needs time to ripen. I'm sure he'll turn out a capital specimen of the Campbell variety."

"Much obliged, Alec; but it will never do at all. He's a good fellow, and may do something to be proud of by and by; but he's not the mate for our Rose. She needs someone who can manage her property when we are gone; and Archie is the man for that, depend upon it."

"Confound the property!" cried Dr. Alec, impetuously. "I want her to be *happy*; and I don't care how soon she gets rid of her money if it is going to be a millstone round her neck. I declare to you, I dreaded the thought of this time so much that I've kept her away as long as I could, and trembled whenever a young fellow joined us while we were abroad. Had one or two narrow escapes, and now I'm in for it, as you can see by tonight's 'success,' as Clara calls it. Thank heaven, I haven't *many* daughters to look after!"

"Come, come, don't be anxious: take Archie, and settle it right up safely and happily. That's my advice, and you'll find it sound," replied the elder conspirator, like one having experience.

"I'll think of it; but mind you, Mac, not a word of this to the sisters. We are a couple of old fools to be match-making so soon; but I see what is before me, and it's a comfort to free my mind to someone."

"So it is. Depend on me; not a breath even to Jane," answered Uncle Mac, with a hearty shake and a sympathetic slap on the shoulder.

"Why, what dark and awful secrets are going on here? Is it a Freemasons' Lodge, and those the mystic signs?" asked a gay voice at the door; and there stood Rose, full of smiling wonder at the sight of her two uncles hand in hand, whispering and nodding to one another mysteriously.

They started, like schoolboys caught plotting mischief, and looked so guilty that she took pity on them, innocently imagining that the brothers were indulging in a little sentiment on this joyful occasion; so she added quickly, as she beckoned, without crossing the threshold—

"Women not allowed, of course: but both of you dear Odd Fellows are wanted; for Aunt Plenty begs we will have an old-fashioned contra dance, and I'm to lead off with Uncle Mac. I chose you, sir, because you do it in style, pigeon-wings and all. So, please come; and Phebe is waiting for you, Uncle Alec. She is rather shy you know, but will enjoy it with you to take care of her."

"Thank you, thank you!" cried both gentlemen, following with great alacrity.

Unconscious Rose enjoyed that Virginia reel immensely; for the pigeon-wings were superb, and her partner conducted her through the convolutions of the dance without a fault, going down the middle in his most gallant style. Landing safely at the bottom, she stood aside to let him get his breath; for stout Uncle Mac was bound to do or die on that occasion, and would have danced his pumps through without a murmur if she had desired it.

Leaning against the wall with his hair in his eyes, and a decidedly bored expression of countenance, was Mac, Jr., who had been surveying the gymnastics of his parent with respectful astonishment.

"Come and take a turn, my lad. Rose is as fresh as a daisy; but we old fellows soon get enough of it, so you shall have my place," said his father, wiping his face, which glowed like a cheerful peony.

"No, thank you, sir: I can't stand that sort of thing. I'll race you round the piazza with pleasure, cousin; but this oven is too much for me," was Mac's uncivil reply, as he backed towards the open window, as if glad of an excuse to escape.

"Fragile creature, don't stay on my account, I beg. *I* can't leave my guests for a moonlight run, even if I dared to take it on a frosty night in a thin dress," said Rose, fanning herself, and not a bit ruffled by Mac's refusal; for she knew his ways, and they amused her.

"Not half so bad as all this dust, gas, heat, and noise. What do you suppose lungs are made of?" demanded Mac, ready for a discussion then and there.

"I used to know, but I've forgotten now. Been so busy with other things that I've neglected the hobbies I used to ride five or six years ago," she said, laughing.

"Ah, those were times worth having! Are you going in for much of this sort of thing, Rose?" he asked, with a disapproving glance at the dancers.

"About three months of it, I think."

"Then good-bye till New Year," and Mac vanished behind the curtains.

"Rose, my dear, you really must take that fellow in hand before he gets to be quite a bear. Since you have been gone, he has lived in his books, and got on so finely that we have let him alone, though his mother groans over his manners. Polish him up a bit, I beg of you; for it is high time he mended his odd ways, and did justice to the fine gifts he hides behind them," said Uncle Mac, scandalized at the bluntness of his son.

"I know my chestnut-burr too well to mind his prickles. But others do not; so I *will* take him in hand and make him a credit to the family," answered Rose, readily.

"Take Archie for your model: he's one of a thousand; and the girl who gets him gets a prize I do assure you," added Uncle Mac, who found match-making to his taste, and thought that closing remark a deep one.

"Oh me, how tired I am!" cried Rose, dropping into a chair as the last carriage rolled away, somewhere between one and two.

"What is your opinion now, Miss Campbell?" asked the
doctor, addressing her for the first time by the name which had
been uttered so often that night.

"My opinion is that Miss Campbell is likely to have a gay
life if she goes on as she has begun; and that she finds it very
delightful so far," answered the girl, with lips still smiling from
their first taste of what the world calls pleasure.

4

Thorns among the Roses

FOR A TIME everything went smoothly, and Rose was a happy girl; for the world seemed a beautiful and friendly place, and the fulfilment of her brightest dreams appeared to be a possibility. Of course, this could not last, and disappointment was inevitable; because young eyes look for a Paradise, and weep when they find a work-a-day world, which seems full of care and trouble, till one learns to gladden and glorify it with high thoughts and holy living.

Those who loved her waited anxiously for the disillusion which must come in spite of all their cherishing; for, till now, Rose had been so busy with her studies, travels, and home duties, that she knew very little of the triumphs, trials, and temptations of fashionable life. Birth and fortune placed her where she could not well escape some of them; and Doctor Alec, knowing that experience is the best teacher, wisely left her to learn this lesson as she must many another, devoutly hoping that it would not be a hard one.

October and November passed rapidly; and Christmas was at hand, with all its merry mysteries, home-gatherings, and good wishes.

Rose sat in her own little sanctum, opening from the parlour, busily preparing gifts for the dear five hundred friends who seemed to grow fonder and fonder as the holidays drew near. The drawers of her commode stood open, giving glimpses of dainty trifles, which she was tying up with bright ribbons.

A young girl's face at such moments is apt to be a happy one; but Rose's was very grave as she worked, and now and then she

55

threw a parcel into the drawer with a careless toss, as if no love made the gift precious. So unusual was this expression that it struck Dr. Alec as he came in, and brought an anxious look to his eyes; for any cloud on that other countenance dropped its shadow over his.

"Can you spare a minute from your pretty work to take a stitch in my old glove?" he asked, coming up to the table strewn with ribbon, lace, and coloured papers.

"Yes, uncle, as many as you please."

The face brightened with sudden sunshine; both hands were put out to receive the shabby driving-glove; and the voice was full of that affectionate alacrity which makes the smallest service sweet.

"My Lady Bountiful is hard at work, I see. Can I help in any way?" he asked, glancing at the display before him.

"No, thank you; unless you can make me as full of interest and pleasure in these things as I used to be. Don't you think preparing presents a great bore, except for those you love, and who love you?" she added, in a tone which had a slight tremor in it as she uttered the last words.

"I don't give to people whom I care nothing for. Can't do it; especially at Christmas, when good-will should go into everything one does. If all these 'pretties' are for dear friends, you must have a great many."

"I thought they were friends; but I find many of them are not, and that's the trouble, sir."

"Tell me all about it, dear, and let the old glove go," he said, sitting down beside her with his most sympathetic air.

But she held the glove fast, saying eagerly, "No, no, I love to do this! I don't feel as if I could look at you while I tell what a bad, suspicious girl I am," she added, keeping her eyes upon her work.

"Very well, I'm ready for confessions of any iniquity, and glad to get them; for sometimes lately I've seen a cloud in my girl's eyes, and caught a worried tone in her voice. Is there a bitter drop in the cup that promised to be so sweet, Rose?"

"Yes, uncle. I've tried to think there was not; but it *is* there, and I don't like it. I'm ashamed to tell; and yet I want to, because you will show me how to make it sweet, or assure me that I shall be the better for it, as you used to do when I took medicine."

She paused a minute, sewing swiftly; then out came the trouble all in one burst of girlish grief and chagrin.

"Uncle, half the people who are so kind to me don't care a bit for me, but for what I can give them; and that makes me unhappy, because I was so glad and proud to be liked. I do wish I hadn't a penny in the world, then I should know who my true friends were."

"Poor little lass! she has found out that all that glitters is not gold, and the disillusion has begun," said the doctor to himself, adding aloud, smiling yet pitiful, "And so all the pleasure is gone out of the pretty gifts, and Christmas is a failure?"

"Oh, no! not for those whom nothing can make me doubt. It is sweeter than ever to make *these* things, because my heart is in every stitch; and I know that, poor as they are, they will be dear to you, Aunty Plen, Aunt Jessie, Phebe, and the boys."

She opened a drawer where lay a pile of pretty gifts, wrought with loving care by her own hands; touching them tenderly as she spoke, and patting the sailor's knot of blue ribbon on one fat parcel with a smile that told how unshakable her faith in some one was. "But *these*," she said, pulling open another drawer, and tossing over its gay contents with an air half sad, half scornful, "these I *bought* and give because they are expected. *These* people only care for a rich gift, not one bit for the giver, whom they will secretly abuse if she is not as generous as they expect. How *can* I enjoy that sort of thing, uncle?"

"You cannot; but perhaps you do some of them injustice, my dear. Don't let the envy or selfishness of a few poison your faith in all. Are you sure that none of these girls care for you?" he asked, reading a name here and there on the parcels scattered about.

"I'm afraid I am. You see I heard several talking together the other evening at Annabel's, only a few words, but it hurt me very much; for nearly everyone was speculating on what I would give them, and hoping it would be something fine. 'She's so rich she ought to be generous,' said one. 'I've been perfectly devoted to her for weeks and hope she won't forget it,'' said another. 'If she doesn't give me some of her gloves, I shall think she's very mean; for she has heaps, and I tried on a pair in fun so she could see they fitted and take a hint,' added a third. I did take the hint, you see;" and Rose opened a handsome box in which lay several pairs of her best gloves, with buttons enough to satisfy the heart of the most covetous.

"Plenty of silver paper and perfume, but not much love went into *that* bundle, I fancy?" and Dr. Alec could not help smiling at the disdainful little gesture with which Rose pushed away the box.

"Not a particle, nor in most of these. I have given them what they wanted, and taken back the confidence and respect they didn't care for. It is wrong, I know; but I can't bear to think all the seeming good-will and friendliness I've been enjoying was insincere and for a purpose. That's not the way *I* treat people."

"I am sure of it. Take things for what they are worth, dear, and try to find the wheat among the tares; for there is plenty if one knows how to look. Is that all the trouble?"

"No, sir, that is the lightest part of it. I shall soon get over my disappointment in those girls, and take them for what they are worth as you advise; but being deceived in them makes me suspicious of others, and that is hateful. If I cannot trust people, I'd rather keep by myself and be happy. I do detest manœuvring and underhand plots and plans!"

Rose spoke petulantly, and twitched her silk till it broke; while regret seemed to give place to anger as she spoke.

"There is evidently another thorn pricking. Let us have it out, and then 'I'll kiss the place to make it well,' as I used to do when I took the splinters from the fingers you are pricking so unmercifully," said the doctor, anxious to relieve his pet patient as soon as possible.

Rose laughed, but the colour deepened in her cheeks, as she answered with a pretty mixture of maidenly shyness and natural candour.

"Aunt Clara worries me by warning me against half the young men I meet, and insisting that they only want my money. Now that is dreadful, and I won't listen: but I can't help thinking of it sometimes; for they *are* very kind to me, and I'm not vain enough to think it is my beauty. I suppose I am foolish, but I do like to feel that I am something besides an heiress."

The little quiver was in Rose's voice again as she ended; and Dr. Alec gave a quick sigh as he looked at the downcast face so full of the perplexity ingenuous spirits feel when doubt first mars their faith, and dims the innocent beliefs still left from childhood. He had been expecting this, and knew that what the girl just began to perceive and try modestly to tell, had long ago been plain to worldlier eyes. The heiress *was* the attraction to most of the young men whom she met. Good fellows enough, but educated, as nearly all are nowadays, to believe that girls with beauty or money are brought to market to sell or buy as the case may be.

Rose could purchase anything she liked, as she combined both advantages; and was soon surrounded by many admirers, each striving to secure the prize. Not being trained to believe that the only end and aim of a woman's life was a good match, she was a little disturbed, when the first pleasing excitement was over, to discover that her fortune was her chief attraction.

It was impossible for her to help seeing, hearing, guessing this from a significant glance, a stray word, a slight hint here and there; and the quick instinct of a woman felt even before it understood the self-interest which chilled for her so many opening friendships. In her eyes love was a very sacred thing, hardly to be thought of till it came, reverently received, and cherished faithfully to the end. Therefore it is not strange that she shrunk from hearing it flippantly discussed, and marriage treated as a bargain to be haggled over, with little thought of its high duties, great responsibilities, and tender joys. Many things perplexed her, and sometimes a doubt of all that till now she had believed and trusted made her feel as if at sea without a compass; for the new world was so unlike the one she had been living in that it bewildered while it charmed the novice.

Dr. Alec understood the mood in which he found her, and did his best to warn without saddening by too much worldly wisdom.

"You are something besides an heiress to those who know and love you; so take heart, my girl, and hold fast to the faith that is in you. There is a touchstone for all these things, and whatever does not ring true doubt and avoid. Test and try men and women as they come along; and I am sure conscience, instinct, and experience will keep you from any dire mistake," he said, with a protecting arm about her, and a trustful look that was very comforting.

After a moment's pause she answered, while a sudden smile dimpled round her mouth, and the big glove went up to half hide her tell-tale cheeks—

"Uncle, if I must have lovers, I do wish they'd be more interesting. How can I like or respect men who go on as some of them do, and then imagine women *can* feel honoured by the offer of their hands? hearts are out of fashion, so they don't say much about them."

"Ah, ha! that is the trouble is it? and we begin to have delicate distresses do we?" said Dr. Alec, glad to see her brightening, and full of interest in the new topic; for he *was* a romantic old fellow, as he confessed to his brother.

Rose put down the glove, and looked up with a droll mixture of amusement and disgust in her face. "Uncle, it is perfectly disgraceful! I've wanted to tell you, but I was ashamed, because I never could boast of such things as some girls do; and they were so absurd I couldn't feel as if they were worth repeating even to you. Perhaps I ought, though; for you may think proper to command me to make a good match, and of course I should have to obey," she added, trying to look meek.

"Tell, by all means. Don't I always keep your secrets, and give you the best advice, like a model guardian? You must have a confidant, and where find a better one than here?" he asked, tapping his waistcoat with an inviting gesture.

"Nowhere: so I'll tell all but the names. I'd best be prudent; for I'm agraid you may get a little fierce; you do sometimes when people vex me," began Rose, rather liking the prospect of a confidential chat with uncle; for he had kept himself a good deal in the background lately.

"You know our ideas are old-fashioned; so I was not prepared to have men propose at all times and places, with no warning but a few smiles and soft speeches. I expected things of that sort would be very interesting and proper, not to say thrilling, on my part: but they are not; and I find myself laughing instead of crying, feeling angry instead of glad, and forgetting all about it very soon. Why, uncle, one absurd boy proposed when we'd only met half a dozen times. But he was dreadfully in debt, so that accounted for it perhaps," and Rose dusted her fingers, as if she had soiled them.

"I know him, and I thought he'd do it," observed the doctor with a shrug.

"You see and know everything; so there's no need of going on, is there?"

"Do, do! who else? I won't even guess."

"Well, another went down upon his knees in Mrs. Van's greenhouse and poured forth his passion manfully, with a great cactus pricking his poor legs all the while. Kitty found him there, and it was impossible to keep sober; so he has hated me ever since."

The doctor's "Ha! ha!" was good to hear, and Rose joined him; for it was impossible to regard these episodes seriously, since no true sentiment redeemed them from absurdity.

"Another one sent me reams of poetry, and went on so Byronically, that I began to wish I had red hair and my name was Betsey Ann. I burnt all the verses: so don't expect to see them; and he, poor fellow, is consoling himself with Emma. But the worst of all was the one who would make love in public, and insisted on proposing in the middle of a dance. I seldom dance round dances except with our boys; but that night I did, because the girls laughed at me for being so 'prudish,' as they called it. I don't mind them now; for I found I *was* right, and felt that I deserved my fate."

"Is that all?" asked her uncle, looking "fierce," as she predicted, at the idea of his beloved girl obliged to listen to a declaration, twirling about on the arm of a lover.

"One more: but him I shall not tell about; for I know *he* was in earnest and really suffered, though I was as kind as I knew how to be. I'm young in these things yet, so I grieved for him, and treat his love with the tenderest respect."

Rose's voice sunk almost to a whisper as she ended; and Dr. Alec bent his head, as if involuntarily saluting a comrade in misfortune. Then he got up, saying with a keen look into the face he lifted by a finger under the chin—

"Do you want another three months of this?"

"I'll tell you on New Year's day, uncle."

"Very well: try to keep a straight course, my little captain, and, if you see dirty weather ahead, call on your first mate."

"Ay, ay, sir; I'll remember."

5

Prince Charming

THE OLD GLOVE lay upon the floor forgotten, while Rose sat musing, till a quick step sounded in the hall, and a voice drew near tunefully humming.

"As he was walkin' doun the street
    The city for to view,
Oh, there he spied a bonny lass,
    The window lookin' through."

"Sae licht he jumpèd up the stair,
    And tirled at the pin;
Oh, wha sae ready as hersel'
    To let the laddie in?"

sung Rose, as the voice paused and a tap came at the door.

"Good morning, Rosamunda; here are your letters, and your most devoted ready to execute any commissions you may have for him," was Charlie's greeting, as he came in looking comely, gay, and debonair as usual.

"Thanks: I've no errands unless you mail my replies, if these need answering; so by your leave, Prince," and Rose began to open the handful of notes he threw into her lap.

"Ha! what sight is this to blast mine eyes?" ejaculated Charlie, as he pointed to the glove with a melodramatic start; for, like most accomplished amateur actors, he was fond of introducing private theatricals into his "daily walk and conversation."

"Uncle left it."

" 'Tis well; methought perchance a rival had been here" and, picking it up, Charlie amused himself with putting it on the

62

head of a little Psyche, which ornamented the mantelpiece, humming, as he did so, another verse of the old song—

> "He set his Jenny on his knee,
>   All in his Highland dress;
> For brawly well he kenned the way
>   To please a bonny lass."

Rose went on reading her letters, but all the while was thinking of her conversation with her uncle, and something else, suggested by the newcomer and his ditty.

During the three months since her return, she had seen more of this cousin than any of the others; for he seemed to be the only one who had leisure to "play with Rose," as they used to say years ago. The other boys were all at work, even little Jamie, many of whose play hours were devoted to manful struggles with Latin grammar, the evil genius of his boyish life. Dr. Alec had many affairs to arrange after his long absence; Phebe was busy with her music; and Aunt Plenty still actively superintended her housekeeping. Thus it fell out, quite naturally that Charlie should form the habit of lounging in at all hours with letters, messages, bits of news, and agreeable plans for Rose. He helped her with her sketching, rode with her, sung with her, and took her to parties, as a matter of course; for Aunt Clara, being the gayest of the sisters, played chaperon on all occasions.

For a time it was very pleasant; but, by and by, Rose began to wish Charlie would find something to do like the rest, and not make dawdling after her the business of his life. The family were used to his self-indulgent ways: and there was an amiable delusion in the minds of the boys that he had a right to the best of everything; for to them he was still the Prince, the flower of the flock, and in time to be an honour to the name. No one exactly knew how: for, though full of talent, he seemed to have no especial gift or bias; and the elders began to shake their heads, because, in spite of many grand promises and projects, the moment for decisive action never came.

Rose saw all this, and longed to inspire her brilliant cousin with some manful purpose which should win for him respect as well as admiration. But she found it very hard: for, though he listened with imperturbable good humour, and owned his short-comings with delightful frankness, he always had some argument, reason, or excuse to offer, and out-talked her in five minutes; leaving her silenced, but unconvinced.

Of late she had observed that he seemed to feel as if her time and thoughts belonged exclusively to him, and rather resented the approach of any other claimant. This annoyed her, and suggested the idea that her affectionate interest and efforts were misunderstood by him, misrepresented and taken advantage of by Aunt Clara, who had been most urgent that she should "use her influence with the dear boy," though the fond mother resented all other interference. This troubled Rose, and made her feel as if caught in a snare; for, while she owned to herself that Charlie was the most attractive of her cousins, she was not ready to be taken possesson of in this masterful way, especially since other and sometimes better men sought her favour more humbly.

These thoughts were floating vaguely in her mind as she read her letters, and unconsciously influenced her in the chat that followed.

"Only invitations, and I can't stop to answer them now, or I shall never get through this job," she said, returning to her work.

"Let me help. You do up, and I'll direct. Have a secretary; do now, and see what a comfort it will be," proposed Charlie, who could turn his hand to anything, and had made himself quite at home in the sanctum.

"I'd rather finish this myself, but you may answer the notes if you will. Just regrets to all but two or three. Read the names as you go along, and I'll tell you which."

"To hear is to obey. Who says I'm a 'frivolous idler' now?" and Charlie sat down at the writing table with alacrity; for these hours in the little room were his best and happiest.

"Order is heaven's first law, and the view a lovely one, but I *don't* see any notepaper," he added, opening the desk and surveying its contents with interest.

"Right-hand drawer: violet monogram for the notes; plain paper for the business letter. I'll see to that, though," answered Rose, trying to decide whether Annabel or Emma should have the laced handkerchief.

"Confiding creature! Suppose I open the wrong drawer, and come upon the tender secrets of your soul?" continued the new secretary, rummaging out the delicate notepaper with masculine disregard of order.

"I haven't got any," answered Rose, demurely.

"What, not one despairing scrawl, one cherished miniature, one faded floweret, etc., etc.? I can't believe it, cousin," and he shook his head incredulously.

"If I had, I certainly should not show them to you, impertinent person! There *are* a few little souvenirs in that desk, but nothing very sentimental or interesting."

"How I'd like to see 'em! But I should never dare to ask," observed Charlie, peering over the top of the half-open lid with a most persuasive pair of eyes.

"You may if you want to, but you'll be disappointed, Paul Pry. Lower left-hand drawer with the key in it."

" 'Angel of goodness, how shall I requite thee? Interesting moment, with what palpitating emotions art thou fraught!' " and, quoting from the "Mysteries of Udolpho," he unlocked and opened the drawer with a tragic gesture.

"Seven locks of hair in a box, all light; for 'here's your straw colour, your orange tawny, your French crown colour, and your perfect yellow' Shakespeare. They look very familiar, and I fancy I know the heads they thatched."

"Yes, you all gave me one when I went away, you know; and I carried them round the world with me in that very box."

"I wish the heads had gone too. Here's a jolly little amber god, with a gold ring in his back and a most balmy breath," continued Charlie, taking a long sniff at the scent-bottle.

"Uncle brought me that long ago, and I'm very fond of it."

"This now looks suspicious—a man's ring with a lotus cut on the stone and a note attached. I tremble as I ask, Who, when, and where?"

"A gentleman, on my birthday, in Calcutta."

"I breathe again: it was my sire?"

"Don't be absurd. Of course it was, and he did everything to make my visit pleasant. I wish you'd go and see him like a dutiful son, instead of idling here."

"That's what Uncle Mac is eternally telling me; but I don't intend to be lectured into the tread-mill till I've had my fling first," muttered Charlie, rebelliously.

"If you fling yourself in the wrong direction, you may find it hard to get back again," began Rose, gravely.

"No fear, if you look after me as you seem to have promised to do, judging by the thanks you get in this note. Poor old

c

governor! I *should* like to see him; for it's almost four years since he came home last, and he must be getting on."

Charlie was the only one of the boys who ever called his father "governor:" perhaps because the others knew and loved their fathers, while he had seen so little of his that the less respectful name came more readily to his lips; since the elder man seemed in truth a governor issuing requests or commands, which the younger too often neglected or resented.

Long ago Rose had discovered that Uncle Stephen found home made so distasteful by his wife's devotion to society, that he preferred to exile himself, taking business as an excuse for his protracted absences.

The girl was thinking of this, as she watched her cousin turn the ring about with a sudden sobriety which became him well; and, believing that the moment was propitious, she said earnestly—

"He *is* getting on. Dear Charlie, do think of duty more than pleasure in this case, and I'm sure you never will regret it."

"Do *you* want me to go?" he asked quickly.

"I think you ought."

"And I think you'd be much more charming if you wouldn't always be worrying about right and wrong! Uncle Alec taught you that along with the rest of his queer notions."

"I'm glad he did!" cried Rose, warmly; then checked herself, and said with a patient sort of sigh, "You know women always want the men they care for to be good, and can't help trying to make them so."

"So they do; and we ought to be a set of angels; but I've a strong conviction that, if we were, the dear souls wouldn't like us half as well. Would they now?" asked Charlie, with an insinuating smile.

"Perhaps not; but that is dodging the point. Will you go?" persisted Rose, unwisely.

"No, I will not."

That was sufficiently decided; and an uncomfortable pause followed, during which Rose tied a knot unnecessarily tight, and Charlie went on exploring the drawer with more energy than interest.

"Why, here's an old thing I gave you ages ago!" he suddenly exclaimed in a pleased tone, holding up a little agate heart on a faded blue ribbon. "Will you let me take away the heart of stone and give you a heart of flesh?" he asked, half in earnest, half in jest, touched by the little trinket and the recollections it awakened.

"No, I will not," answered Rose, bluntly, much displeased by the irreverent and audacious question.

Charlie looked rather abashed for a moment; but his natural light-heartedness made it easy for him to get the better of his own brief fits of waywardness, and put others in good humour with him and themselves.

"Now we are even: let's drop the subject and start afresh," he said with irresistible affability, as he coolly put the little heart in his pocket, and prepared to shut the drawer. But something caught his eye, and exclaiming, "What's this? what's this?" he snatched up a photograph which lay half under a pile of letters with foreign post-marks.

"Oh! I forgot that was there," said Rose, hastily.

"Who is the man!" demanded Charlie, eyeing the good-looking countenance before him with a frown.

"That is the Honourable Gilbert Murry, who went up the Nile with us, and shot crocodiles and other small deer, being a mighty hunter, as I told you in my letters," answered Rose gaily, though ill-pleased at the little discovery just then; for this had been one of the narrow escapes her uncle spoke of.

"And they haven't eaten him yet, I infer from that pile of letters?" said Charlie, jealously.

"I hope not. His sister did not mention it when she wrote last."

"Ah! then she is your correspondent? Sisters are dangerous things sometimes." And Charlie eyed the packet suspiciously.

"In this case, a very convenient thing; for she tells me all about her brother's wedding as no one else would take the trouble to do."

"Oh! well, if he's married, I don't care a straw about him. I fancied I'd found out why you are such a hard-hearted charmer. But, if there is no secret idol, I'm all at sea again." And Charlie tossed the photograph into the drawer, as if it no longer interested him.

"I'm hard-hearted because I'm particular, and, as yet, do not find anyone at all to my taste."

"No one?" with a tender glance.

"No one," with a rebellious blush, and the truthful addition,

"I see much to admire and like in many persons, but none quite strong and good enough to suit me. My heroes are old-fashioned, you know."

"Prigs, like Guy Carleton, Count Altenberg, and John Halifax: I know the pattern you goody girls like," sneered Charlie, who preferred the Guy Livingston, Beauclerc, and Rochester style.

"Then I'm not a 'goody girl,' for I don't like prigs. I want a gentleman in the best sense of the word, and I can wait; for I've seen one, and know there are more in the world."

"The deuce you have! Do I know him?" asked Charlie, much alarmed.

"You think you do," answered Rose, with a mischievous sparkle in her eye.

"If it isn't Pem, I give it up. He is the best-bred fellow I know."

"Oh, dear, no! far superior to Mr. Pemberton, and many years older," said Rose, with so much respect that Charlie looked perplexed as well as anxious.

"Some apostolic minister, I fancy. You pious creatures always like to adore a parson. But all we know are married."

"He isn't."

"Give a name, for pity's sake: I'm suffering tortures of suspense," begged Charlie.

"Alexander Campbell."

"Uncle? Well, upon my word, that's a relief, but mighty absurd all the same. So, when you find a young saint of that sort, you intend to marry him, do you?" demanded Charlie, much amused and rather disappointed.

"When I find any man half as honest, good, and noble as uncle, I shall be proud to marry him, if he asks me," answered Rose, decidedly.

"What odd tastes women have!" And Charlie leaned his chin on his hand, to muse pensively for a moment over the blindness of one woman who could admire an excellent old uncle more than a dashing young cousin.

Rose, meanwhile, tied up her parcels industriously, hoping she had not been too severe; for it was very hard to lecture Charlie, though he seemed to like it sometimes, and came to confession voluntarily, knowing that women love to forgive when the sinners are of his sort.

"It will be mail-time before you are done," she said presently; for silence was less pleasant than his rattle.

Charlie took the hint, and dashed off several notes in his best manner. Coming to the business-letter, he glanced at it, and asked, with a puzzled expression—

"What is all this? Cost of repairs, &c., from a man named Buffum?"

"Never mind that: I'll see to it by and by."

"But I do mind, for I'm interested in all your affairs; and, though you think I've no head for business, you'll find I have, if you'll try me."

"This is only about my two old houses in the city, which are being repaired and altered so that the rooms can be let singly."

"Going to make tenement-houses of them? Well, that's not a bad idea: such places pay well, I've heard."

"That is just what I'm *not* going to do. I wouldn't have a tenement-house on my conscience for a million of dollars—not as they are now," said Rose, decidedly.

"Why, what do *you* know about it, except that poor people live in them, and the owners turn a penny on the rents?"

"I know a good deal about them; for I've seen many such, both here and abroad. It was not all pleasure with us, I assure you. Uncle was interested in hospitals and prisons, and I sometimes went with him: but they made me sad; so he suggested other charities, that I could help about when we came home. I visited Infant Schools, Working-women's Homes, Orphan Asylums, and places of that sort. You don't know how much good it did me, and how glad I am that I have the means of lightening a little some of the misery in the world."

"But, my dear girl, you needn't make ducks and drakes of your fortune trying to feed and cure and clothe all the poor wretches you see. Give, of course: everyone should do something in that line, and no one likes it better than I. But don't, for mercy's sake, go at it as some women do, and get so desperately earnest, practical, and charity-mad that there is no living in peace with you," protested Charlie, looking alarmed at the prospect.

"You can do as you please. *I* intend to do all the good I can by asking the advice and following the example of the most 'earnest,' 'practical,' and 'charitable' people I know: so, if you don't approve, you can drop my acquaintance," answered Rose, emphasizing the obnoxious words, and assuming the resolute air she always wore when defending her hobbies.

"You'll be laughed at."

"I'm used to that."

"And criticised and shunned."

"Not by people whose opinion I value."

"Women shouldn't go poking into such places."

"I've been taught that they should."

"Well, you'll get some dreadful disease and lose your beauty, and then where are you?" added Charlie, thinking that might daunt the young philanthropist.

But it did not; for Rose answered, with a sudden kindling of the eyes as she remembered her talk with Uncle Alec—

"I shouldn't like it: but there would be one satisfaction in it; for, when I'd lost my beauty and given away my money, I should know who really cared for me."

Charlie nibbled his pen in silence for a moment, then asked, meekly—

"Could I respectfully inquire what great reform is to be carried on in the old houses which their amiable owner is repairing?"

"I am merely going to make them comfortable homes for poor but respectable women to live in. There is a class who cannot afford to pay much, yet suffer a great deal from being obliged to stay in noisy, dirty, crowded places like tenement-houses and cheap lodgings. I can help a few of them, and I'm going to try."

"May I humbly ask if these decayed gentlewomen are to inhabit their palatial retreat rent-free?"

"That was my first plan; but uncle showed me that it was wiser not to make genteel paupers of them, but let them pay a small rent and feel independent. I don't want the money of course, and shall use it in keeping the houses tidy, or helping other women in like case," said Rose, entirely ignoring her cousin's covert ridicule.

"Don't expect any gratitude, for you won't get it; nor much comfort with a lot of forlornities on your hands; and be sure that when it is too late you will tire of it all, and wish you had done as other people do."

"Thanks for your cheerful prophecies; but I think I'll venture."

She looked so undaunted that Charlie was a little nettled, and fired his last shot rather recklessly—

"Well, one thing I do know: you'll never get a husband if you go on in this absurd way; and, by Jove! you need one to take care of you and keep the property together!"

Rose had a temper, but seldom let it get the better of her; now, however, it flashed up for a moment. Those last words were peculiarly unfortunate, because Aunt Clara had used them more than once, when warning her against impecunious suitors and generous projects. She was disappointed in her cousin, annoyed at having her little plans laughed at, and indignant with him for his final suggestion.

"I'll never have one, if I must give up the liberty of doing what I know is right; and I'd rather go into the poor-house tomorrow than 'keep the property together' in the selfish way you mean!"

That was all: but Charlie saw that he had gone too far, and hastened to make his peace with the skill of a lover; for, turning to the little cabinet piano behind him, he sung in his best style the sweet old song—

"Oh were thou in the cauld blast,"

dwelling with great effect, not only upon the tender assurance that

"My plaid should shelter thee,"

but also that, even if a king,

"The brightest jewel in my crown
Wad be my queen, wad be my queen."

It was very evident that Prince Charming had not gone troubadouring in vain; for Orpheus himself could not have restored harmony more successfully. The tuneful apology was accepted with a forgiving smile, and a frank—

"I'm sorry I was cross; but you haven't forgotten how to tease, and I'm rather out of sorts today. Late hours don't agree with me."

"Then you won't feel like going to Mrs. Hope's tomorrow night, I'm afraid," and Charlie took up the last note with an expression of regret which was very flattering.

"I must go, because it is made for me; but I can come away early, and make up lost sleep. I do hate to be so fractious," and Rose rubbed the forehead that ached with too much racketing.

"But the German does not begin till late: I'm to lead, and depend upon you. Just stay this once to oblige me," pleaded Charlie; for he had set his heart on distinguishing himself.

"No: I promised uncle to be temperate in my pleasures, and I must keep my word. I'm so well now, it would be very foolish to get ill and make him anxious: not to mention losing my beauty, as you are good enough to call it; for that depends on health, you know."

"But the fun doesn't begin till after supper. Everything will be delightful, I assure you; and we'll have a gay old time as we did last week at Emma's."

"Then I certainly will not; for I'm ashamed of myself when I remember what a romp that was, and how sober uncle looked, as he let me in at three in the morning, all fagged out; my dress in rags, my head aching, my feet so tired I could hardly stand, and nothing to show for five hours' hard work but a pocketful of bonbons, artificial flowers, and tissue-paper fool's-caps. Uncle said I'd better put one on and go to bed; for I looked as if I'd been to a French Bal Masqué. I never want to hear him say so again, and I'll never let dawn catch me out in such a plight any more."

"You were all right enough; for mother didn't object, and I got you both home before daylight. Uncle is notional about such things, so I shouldn't mind; for we had a jolly time, and we were none the worse for it."

"Indeed we were, every one of us! Aunt Clara hasn't got over her cold yet; I slept all the next day, and you looked like a ghost, for you'd been out every night for weeks, I think."

"Oh, nonsense! everyone does it during the season, and you'll get used to the pace very soon," began Charlie, bent on making her go; for he was in his element in a ballroom, and never happier than when he had his pretty cousin on his arm.

"Ah! but I don't want to get used to it; for it costs too much in the end. I don't wish to get used to being whisked about a hot room by men who have taken too much wine; to turn day into night, wasting time that might be better spent; and grow into a fashionable fast girl who can't get on without excitement. I don't deny that much of it is pleasant, but don't try to make me too fond of gaiety. Help me to resist what I know is hurtful, and please don't laugh me out of the good habits uncle has tried so hard to give me."

Rose was quite sincere in her appeal, and Charlie knew she was right: but he always found it hard to give up anything he had set his heart upon, no matter how trivial; for the maternal indulgence which had harmed the boy had fostered the habit of self-indulgence which was ruining the man. So when Rose looked up at him, with a very honest desire to save him as well as herself from being swept into the giddy vortex which keeps so many young people revolving aimlessly, till they go down or are cast upon the shore wrecks of what they might have been, he gave a shrug and answered briefly—

"As you please. I'll bring you home as early as you like, and Effie Waring can take your place in the German. What flowers shall I send you?"

Now, that was an artful speech of Charlie's; for Miss Waring was a fast and fashionable damsel, who openly admired Prince Charming, and had given him the name. Rose disliked her, and was sure her influence was bad; for youth made frivolity forgivable, wit hid want of refinement, and beauty always covers a multitude of sins in a man's eyes. At the sound of Effie's name, Rose wavered, and would have yielded but for the memory of the "first mate's" last words. She did desire to "keep a straight course;" so, though the current of impulse set strongly in a southerly direction, principle, the only compass worth having, pointed due north, and she tried to obey it like a wise young navigator, saying steadily, while she directed to Annabel the parcel containing a capacious pair of slippers intended for Uncle Mac—

"Don't trouble yourself about me. I can go with uncle, and slip away without disturbing anybody."

"I don't believe you'll have the heart to do it," said Charlie, incredulously, as he sealed the last note.

"Wait and see."

"I will, but shall hope to the last," and, kissing his hand to her, departed to post her letters, quite sure that Miss Waring would not lead the German.

It certainly looked for a moment as if Miss Campbell *would*, because she ran to the door with the words "I'll go" upon her lips. But she did not open it till she had stood a minute staring hard at the old glove on Psyche's head; then, like one who had suddenly got a bright idea, she gave a decided nod and walked slowly out of the room.

c*

6

Polishing Mac

"Please could I say one word?" was the question three times repeated before a rough head bobbed out from the grotto of books in which Mac usually sat when he studied.

"Did anyone speak?" he asked, blinking in the flood of sunshine that entered with Rose.

"Only three times, thank you. Don't disturb yourself, I beg; for I merely want to say a word," answered Rose, as she prevented him from offering the easy chair in which he sat.

"I was rather deep in a compound fracture, and didn't hear. What can I do for you, cousin?' and Mac shoved a stack of pamphlets off the chair near him, with a hospitable wave of the hand that sent his papers flying in all directions.

Rose sat down, but did not seem to find her "word" an easy one to utter; for she twisted her handkerchief about her fingers in embarrassed silence, till Mac put on his glasses, and, after a keen look, asked soberly—

"Is it a splinter, a cut, or a whitlow, ma'am?"

"It is neither; do forget your tiresome surgery for a minute, and be the kindest cousin that ever was," answered Rose, beginning rather sharply and ending with her most engaging smile.

"Can't promise in the dark," said the wary youth.

"It is a favour, a great favour, and one I don't choose to ask any of the other boys," answered the artful damsel.

Mac looked pleased, and leaned forward, saying more affably—

"Name it, and be sure I'll grant it if I can."

74

"Go with me to Mrs. Hope's party tomorrow night."

"What!" and Mac recoiled as if she had put a pistol to his head.

"I've left you in peace a long time: but it is your turn now; so do your duty like a man and a cousin."

"But I never go to parties!" cried the unhappy victim in great dismay.

"High time you began, sir."

"But I don't dance fit to be seen."

"I'll teach you."

"My dress-coat isn't decent, I know."

"Archie will lend you one: he isn't going."

"I'm afraid there's a lecture that I ought not to cut."

"No, there isn't: I asked uncle."

"I'm always so tired and dull in the evening."

"This sort of thing is just what you want to rest and freshen up your spirits."

Mac gave a groan and fell back vanquished; for it was evident that escape was impossible.

"What put such a perfectly wild idea into your head?" he demanded, rather roughly; for hitherto he *had* been "left in peace," and this sudden attack decidedly amazed him.

"Sheer necessity; but don't do it if it is so very dreadful to you. I must go to several more parties because they are made for me; but after that I'll refuse, and then no one need be troubled with me."

Something in Rose's voice made Mac answer penitently, even while he knit his brows in perplexity—

"I didn't mean to be rude; and of course I'll go anywhere if I'm really needed. But I don't understand where the sudden necessity is, with three other fellows at command, all better dancers and beaux than I am."

"I don't want them, and I do want you; for I haven't the heart to drag uncle out any more and you know I never go with any gentleman but those of my own family."

"Now look here, Rose: if Steve has been doing anything to tease you just mention it, and I'll attend to him," cried Mac, plainly seeing that something was amiss and fancying that Dandy was at the bottom of it, as he had done escort duty several times lately.

"No, Steve has been very good: but I know he had rather be

with Kitty Van; so of course I feel like a marplot, though he is too polite to hint it."

"What a noodle that boy is! But there's Archie, he's as steady as a church, and has no sweetheart to interfere," continued Mac, bound to get at the truth, and half suspecting what it was.

"He is on his feet all day, and Aunt Jessie wants him in the evening. He does not care for dancing as he used, and I suppose he really does prefer to rest and read." Rose might have added, "and hear Phebe sing;" for Phebe did not go out as much as Rose did, and Aunt Jessie often came in to sit with the old lady when the young folks were away; and, of course, dutiful Archie came with her; so willingly of late!

"What's amiss with Charlie? I thought *he* was the prince of cavaliers. Annabel says he dances 'like an angel,' and I know a dozen mothers couldn't keep him at home of an evening. Have you had a tiff with Adonis, and so fall back on poor me?" asked Mac, coming last to the person of whom he thought first, but did not mention, feeling shy about alluding to a subject often discussed behind her back.

"Yes, we have; and I don't intend to go with him any more for some time. His ways do not suit me, and mine do not suit him; so I want to be quite independent, and you can help me if you will," said Rose, rather nervously spinning the big globe close by.

Mac gave a low whistle, looking wide awake all in a minute, as he said with a gesture, as if he brushed a cobweb off his face—

"Now, see here, cousin: I'm not good at mysteries, and shall only blunder if you put me blindfold into any nice manœuvre. Just tell me straight out what you want, and I'll do it if I can. Play I'm uncle, and free your mind; come now."

He spoke so kindly, and the honest eyes were so full of merry good-will, that Rose felt she might confide in him, and answered as frankly as he could desire—

"You are right, Mac; and I don't mind talking to you almost as freely as to uncle, because you are such a reliable fellow, and won't think me silly for trying to do that I believe to be right. Charlie does, and so makes it hard for me to hold to my resolutions. I want to keep early hours, dress simply, and behave properly; no matter what fashionable people do. You will agree to that, I'm sure; and stand by me through thick and thin for principle's sake."

"I will; and begin by showing you that I understand the case. I don't wonder you are not pleased; for Charlie is too presuming, and you do need someone to help you head him off a bit. Hey, cousin?"

"What a way to put it!" and Rose laughed in spite of herself, adding with an air of relief, "That *is* it; and I do want someone to help me make him understand that I don't choose to be taken possession of in that lordly way, as if I belonged to him more than to the rest of the family. I don't like it; for people begin to talk, and Charlie won't see how disagreeable it is to me."

"Tell him so," was Mac's blunt advice.

"I have; but he only laughs and promises to behave, and then he does it again, when I am so placed that I can't say anything. You will never understand and I cannot explain; for it is only a look, or a word, or some little thing: but I won't have it, and the best way to cure him is to put it out of his power to annoy me so."

"He is a great flirt, and wants to teach you how, I suppose. I'll speak to him if you like and tell him you don't want to learn. Shall I?" asked Mac, finding the case rather an interesting one.

"No, thank you: that would only make trouble. If you will kindly play escort a few times, it will show Charlie that I am in earnest without more words, and put a stop to the gossip,' said Rose, colouring like a poppy at the recollection of what she had heard one young man whisper to another, as Charlie led her through a crowded supper-room with his most devoted air, "Lucky dog! he is sure to get the heiress, and we are nowhere."

"There's no danger of people's gossiping about us, is there?" and Mac looked up, with the oddest of all his odd expressions.

"Of course not: you're only a boy."

"I'm twenty-one, thank you; and Prince is but a couple of years older," said Mac, promptly resenting the slight put upon his manhood.

"Yes; but he is like other young men, while you are a dear old bookworm. No one would ever mind what *you* did; so you may go to parties with me every night, and not a word would be said; or, if there was, I shouldn't mind since it is 'only Mac,' " answered Rose, smiling as she quoted a household word often used to excuse his vagaries.

"Then *I* am nobody?" lifting his brows, as if the discovery surprised and rather nettled him.

"Nobody in society as yet; but my very best cousin in private, and I've just proved my regard by making you my confidant, and choosing you for my knight," said Rose, hastening to soothe the feelings her careless words seemed to have ruffled slightly.

"Much good *that* is likely to do me," grumbled Mac.

"You ungrateful boy, not to appreciate the honour I've conferred upon you! I know a dozen who would be proud of the place: but you only care for compound fractures; so I won't detain you any longer, except to ask if I may consider myself provided with an escort for tomorrow night?" said Rose, a trifle hurt at his indifference; for she was not used to refusals.

"If I may hope for the honour," and, rising, he made her a bow which was such a capital imitation of Charlie's grand manner that she forgave him at once, exclaiming with amused surprise—

"Why, Mac! I didn't know you *could* be so elegant!"

"A fellow can be almost anything he likes, if he tries hard enough," he answered, standing very straight, and looking so tall and dignified that Rose was quite impressed, and with a stately curtsy she retired, saying graciously—

"I accept with thanks. Good morning, Doctor Alexander Mackenzie Campbell."

When Friday evening came, and word was sent up that her escort had arrived, Rose ran down, devoutly hoping that he had not come in a velveteen jacket, top-boots, black gloves, or made any trifling mistake of that sort. A young gentleman was standing before the long mirror, apparently intent on the arrangement of his hair; and Rose paused suddenly as her eye went from the glossy broadcloth to the white-gloved hands, busy with an unruly lock that would not stay in place.

"Why, Charlie, I thought—" she began with an accent of surprise in her voice, but got no further; for the gentleman turned and she beheld Mac in immaculate evening costume, with his hair parted sweetly on his brow, a superior posy at his button-hole, and the expression of a martyr upon his face.

"Ah, don't you wish it was? No one but yourself to thank that it isn't he. Am I right? Dandy got me up, and he ought to know what is what," demanded Mac, folding his hands and standing as stiff as a ramrod.

"You are so regularly splendid that I don't know you."

"Neither do I."

"I really had no idea you could look so like a gentleman," added Rose, surveying him with approval.

"Nor I that I could feel so like a fool."

"Poor boy! he does look rather miserable. What can I do to cheer him up, in return for the sacrifice he is making?"

"Stop calling me a boy. It will soothe my agony immensely, and give me courage to appear in a low-necked coat and a curl on my forehead; for I'm not used to such elegancies, and find them no end of a trial."

Mac spoke in such a pathetic tone, and gave such a gloomy glare at the aforesaid curl, that Rose laughed in his face, and added insult to his woe by handing him her cloak. He surveyed it gravely for a minute, then carefully put it on wrong side out, and gave the swan's-down hood a good pull over her head, to the utter destruction of all smoothness to the curls inside.

Rose uttered a cry and cast off the cloak, bidding him learn to do it properly, which he meekly did, and then led her down the hall without walking on her skirts more than three times by the way. But at the door she discovered that she had forgotten her furred overshoes, and bade Mac get them.

"Never mind: it's not wet," he said, pulling his cap over his eyes and plunging into his coat, regardless of the "elegancies" that afflicted him.

"But I can't walk on cold stones with thin slippers, can I?" began Rose, showing a little white foot.

"You needn't, for—there you are, my lady;" and, unceremoniously picking her up, Mac landed her in the carriage before she could say a word.

"What an escort!" she exclaimed in comic dismay, as she rescued her delicate dress from the rug in which he was about to tuck her up like a mummy.

"It's 'only Mac,' so don't mind," and he cast himself into an opposite corner, with the air of a man who had nerved himself to the accomplishment of many painful duties, and was bound to do them or die.

"But gentlemen don't catch up ladies like bags of meal, and poke them into carriages in this way. It is evident that you need looking after, and it is high time I undertook your society manners. Now, do mind what you are about, and don't get yourself or me into a scrape if you can help it," besought Rose, feeling that on many accounts she had gone farther and fared worse.

"I'll behave like a Turveydrop: see if I don't."

Mac's idea of the immortal Turveydrop's behaviour seemed to be a peculiar one; for, after dancing once with his cousin, he left her to her own devices, and soon forgot all about her in a long conversation with Professor Stumph, the learned geologist. Rose did not care; for one dance proved to her that that branch of Mac's education *had* been sadly neglected, and she was glad to glide smoothly about with Steve, though he was only an inch or two taller than herself. She had plenty of partners, however, and plenty of chaperons; for all the young men were her most devoted, and all the matrons beamed upon her with maternal benignity.

Charlie was not there; for when he found that Rose stood firm, and had moreover engaged Mac as a permanency, he would not go at all, and retired in high dudgeon to console himself with more dangerous pastimes. Rose feared it would be so; and, even in the midst of the gaiety about her, an anxious mood came over her now and then, and made her thoughtful for a moment. She felt her power, and wanted to use it wisely; but did not know how to be kind to Charlie without being untrue to herself and giving him false hopes.

"I wish we were all children again, with no hearts to perplex us and no great temptations to try us," she said to herself, as she rested a moment in a quiet nook while her partner went to get a glass of water. Right in the midst of this half-sad, half-sentimental reverie, she heard a familiar voice behind her say earnestly—

"And allophite is the new hydrous silicate of alumina and magnesia, much resembling pseudophite, which Websky found in Silesia."

"What *is* Mac talking about!" she thought: and, peeping behind a great azalea in full bloom, she saw her cousin in deep converse with the professor, evidently having a capital time; for his face had lost its melancholy expression and was all alive with interest while the elder man was listening as if his remarks were both intelligent and agreeable.

"What is it?" asked Steve, coming up with the water, and seeing a smile on Rose's face.

She pointed out the scientific *tête-à-tête* going on behind the azalea, and Steve grinned as he peeped, then grew sober and said in a tone of despair—

"If you had seen the pains I took with that fellow, the patience with which I brushed his wig, the time I spent trying to convince him that he must wear thin boots, and the fight I had to get him into that coat; you'd understand my feelings when I see him now."

"Why, what is the matter with him?" asked Rose.

"Will you take a look, and see what a spectacle he has made of himself. He'd better be sent home at once, or he will disgrace the family by looking as if he'd been in a row."

Steve spoke in such a tragic tone that Rose took another peep and did sympathize with Dandy; for Mac's elegance was quite gone. His tie was under one ear, his posy hung upside down, his gloves were rolled into a ball, which he absently squeezed and pounded as he talked, and his hair looked as if a whirlwind had passed over it; for his ten fingers set it on end now and then, as they had a habit of doing when he studied or talked earnestly. But he looked so happy and wide awake, in spite of his dishevelment, that Rose gave an approving nod, and said behind her fan—

"It *is* a trying spectacle, Steve: yet, on the whole, I think his own odd ways suit him best; and I fancy we shall yet be proud of him, for he knows more than all the rest of us put together. Hear that now," and Rose paused, that they might listen to the following burst of eloquence from Mac's lips:—

"You know Frenzel has shown that the globular forms of silicate of bismuth at Schneeburg and Johanngeorgenstadt are not isometric, but monoclinic in crystalline form; and consequently he separates them from the old eulytite, and gives them the new name Agricolite."

"Isn't it awful? Let us get out of this before there's another avalanche, or we shall be globular silicates and isometric crystals in spite of ourselves," whispered Steve with a panic-stricken air; and they fled from the hail-storm of hard words that rattled about their ears, leaving Mac to enjoy himself in his own way.

But when Rose was ready to go home, and looked about for

her escort he was nowhere to be seen; for the professor had
departed, and Mac with him, so absorbed in some new topic
that he entirely forgot his cousin, and went placidly home, still
pondering on the charms of geology. When this pleasing fact
dawned upon Rose, her feelings may be imagined. She was both
angry and amused: it was so like Mac to go mooning off and
leave her to her fate. Not a hard one, however; for, though
Steve was gone with Kitty before her flight was discovered,
Mrs. Bliss was only too glad to take the deserted damsel under
her wing, and bear her safely home.

Rose was warming her feet, and sipping the chocolate which
Phebe always had ready for her, as she never ate suppers; when
a hurried tap came at the long window whence the light
streamed, and Mac's voice was heard softly asking to be let in
"just for one minute."

Curious to know what had befallen him Rose bade Phebe
obey his call; and the delinquent cavalier appeared, breathless,
anxious, and more dilapidated than ever: for he had forgotten
his overcoat; his tie was at the back of his neck now; and his
hair as rampantly erect as if all the winds of heaven had been
blowing freely through it, as they had; for he had been tearing
to and fro the last half-hour trying to undo the dreadful deed
he had so innocently committed.

"Don't take any notice of me; for I don't deserve it. I only
came to see that you were safe, cousin, and then go hang myself,
as Steve advised," he began, in a remorseful tone, that would
have been very effective, if he had not been obliged to catch his
breath with a comical gasp now and then.

"I never thought *you* would be the one to desert me," said
Rose, with a reproachful look; thinking it best not to relent too
soon, though she was quite ready to do it when she saw how
sincerely distressed he was.

"It was that confounded man! He was a regular walking
encyclopædia; and, finding I could get a good deal out of him,
I went in for general information, as the time was short. You
know I always forget everything else when I get hold of such
a fellow."

"That is evident. I wonder how you came to remember me
at all" answered Rose, on the brink of a laugh: it was so absurd.

"I didn't till Steve said something that reminded me: then
it burst upon me, in one awful shock, that I'd gone and left you;

and you might have knocked me down with a feather," said honest Mac, hiding none of his iniquity.

"Do! I went off like a shot, and never stopped till I reached the Hopes"—

"You didn't walk all that way?" cried Rose.

"Bless you, no: I ran. But you were gone with Mrs. Bliss: so I pelted back again to see with my own eyes that you were safe at home," answered Mac, wiping his hot forehead, with a sigh of relief.

"But it is three miles at least each way; and twelve o'clock, and dark and cold. O Mac! how could you!" exclaimed Rose, suddenly realizing what he had done, as she heard his laboured breathing, saw the state of the thin boots, and detected the absence of an overcoat.

"Couldn't do less, could I?" asked Mac, leaning up against the door and trying not to pant.

"There was no need of half-killing yourself for such a trifle. You might have known I could take care of myself for once, at least, with so many friends about. Sit down this minute. Bring another cup, please, Phebe: this boy isn't going home till he is rested and refreshed after such a run as that," commanded Rose.

"Don't be good to me: I'd rather take a scolding than a chair, and drink hemlock instead of chocolate if you happen to have any ready," answered Mac, with a pathetic puff, as he subsided on to the sofa, and meekly took the draught Phebe brought him.

"If you had anything the matter with your heart, sir, a race of this sort might be the death of you: so never do it again," said Rose, offering her fan to cool his heated countenance.

"Haven't got any heart."

"Yes, you have, for I hear it beating like a trip-hammer, and it is my fault: I ought to have stopped as we went by, and told you I was all right."

"It's the mortification, not the miles, that upsets me. I often take that run for exercise, and think nothing of it; but tonight I was so mad I made extra good time, I fancy. Now don't you worry, but compose your mind, and 'sip your dish of tea,' as Evelina says," answered Mac, artfully turning the conversation from himself.

"What do you know about Evelina?" asked Rose, in great surprise.

"All about her. Do you suppose I never read a novel?"

"I thought you read nothing but Greek and Latin, with an occasional glance at Websky's pseudophites and the monoclinics of Johanngeorgenstadt."

Mac opened his eyes wide at this reply, then seemed to see the joke, and joined in the laugh with such heartiness that Aunt Plenty's voice was heard demanding from above, with sleepy anxiety—

"*Is* the house afire?"

"No, ma'am, everything is safe, and I'm only saying goodnight," answered Mac, diving for his cap.

"Then go at once, and let that child have her sleep," added the old lady, retiring to her bed.

Rose ran into the hall, and, catching up her uncle's fur coat, met Mac as he came out of the study, absently looking about for his own.

"You haven't got any, you benighted boy! so take this, and have your wits about you next time, or I won't let you off so easily," she said, holding up the heavy garment, and peeping over it, with no sign of displeasure in her laughing eyes.

"Next time! Then you do forgive me? You will try me again, and give me a chance to prove that I'm not a fool?" cried Mac, embracing the big coat with emotion.

"Of course I will; and, so far from thinking you a fool, I was much impressed with your learning tonight, and told Steve that we ought to be proud of our philosopher."

"Learning be hanged! I'll show you that I'm *not* a bookworm, but as much a man as any of them; and then you may be proud or not, as you like!" cried Mac, with a defiant nod, that caused the glasses to leap wildly off his nose, as he caught up his hat and departed as he came.

A day or two later, Rose went to call upon Aunt Jane, as she dutifully did once or twice a week. On her way upstairs, she heard a singular sound in the drawing-room, and involuntarily stopped to listen.

"One, two, three, slide! One, two, three, turn! Now then, come on!" said one voice, impatiently.

"It's very easy to say 'come on;' but what the dickens do I do with my left leg while I'm turning and sliding with my right?" demanded another voice, in a breathless and mournful tone.

Then the whistling and thumping went on more vigorously

than before; and Rose, recognizing the voices, peeped through the half-open door to behold a sight which made her shake with suppressed laughter. Steve, with a red tablecloth tied round his waist, languished upon Mac's shoulder, dancing in perfect time to the air he whistled; for Dandy was a proficient in the graceful art, and plumed himself upon his skill. Mac, with flushed face and dizzy eye, clutched his brother by the small of his back, vainly endeavourng to steer him down the long room without entangling his own legs in the tablecloth, treading on his partner's toes, or colliding with the furniture. It was very droll; and Rose enjoyed the spectacle, till Mac, in a frantic attempt to swing round, dashed himself against the wall, and landed Steve upon the floor. Then it was impossible to restrain her laughter any longer; and she walked in upon them, saying merrily—

"It was splendid! Do it again, and I'll play for you."

Steve sprung up, and tore off the tablecloth in great confusion; while Mac, still rubbing his head, dropped into a chair, trying to look quite calm and cheerful as he gasped out—

"How are you, cousin? When did you come? John should have told us."

"I'm glad he didn't, for then I should have missed this touching tableau of cousinly devotion and brotherly love. Getting ready for our next party, I see."

"Trying to; but there are so many things to remember all at once—keep time, steer straight, dodge the petticoats, and manage my confounded legs—that it isn't easy to get on at first," answered Mac, wiping his hot forehead, with a sigh of exhaustion.

"Hardest job *I* ever undertook; and, as I'm not a battering-ram, I decline to be knocked round any longer," growled Steve, dusting his knees, and ruefully surveying the feet that had been trampled on till they tingled; for his boots and broadcloth were dear to the heart of the dapper youth.

"Very good of you, and I'm much obliged. I've got the pace, I think, and can practise with a chair to keep my hand in," said Mac, with such a comic mixture of gratitude and resignation that Rose went off again so irresistibly that her cousins joined her with a hearty roar.

"As you are making a martyr of yourself in my service, the least I can do is to lend a hand. Play for us, Steve, and I'll give Mac a lesson, unless he prefers the chair." And, throwing off

hat and cloak, Rose beckoned so invitingly that the gravest philosopher would have yielded.

"A thousand thanks, but I'm afraid I shall hurt you," began Mac, much gratified, but mindful of past mishaps.

"I'm not. Steve didn't manage his train well, for good dancers always loop theirs up. I have none at all: so that trouble is gone; and the music will make it much easier to keep step. Just do as I tell you, and you'll go beautifully after a few turns."

"I will, I will! Pipe up, Steve! Now, Rose!" And, brushing his hair out of his eyes with an air of stern determination, Mac grasped Rose, and returned to the charge, bent on distinguishing himself if he died in the attempt.

The second lesson prospered: for Steve marked the time by a series of emphatic bangs; Mac obeyed orders as promptly as if his life depended on it; and, after several narrow escapes at exciting moments, Rose had the satisfaction of being steered safely down the room, and landed with a grand pirouette at the bottom. Steve applauded, and Mac, much elated, exclaimed with artless candour—

"There really is a sort of inspiration about you Rose. I always detested dancing before; but now, do you know, I rather like it."

"I knew you would; only you mustn't stand with your arm round your partner in this way when you are done. You must seat and fan her, if she likes it," said Rose, anxious to perfect a pupil who seemed so lamentably in need of a teacher.

"Yes, of course, I know how they do it;' and, releasing his cousin, Mac raised a small whirlwind round her with a folded newspaper, so full of grateful zeal that she had not the heart to chide him again.

"Well done, old fellow. I begin to have hopes of you, and will order you a new dress-coat at once, since you are really going in for the proprieties of life," said Steve from the music-stool, with the approving nod of one who was a judge of said proprieties. "Now, Rose, if you will just coach him a little in his small-talk, he won't make a laughing-stock of himself as he did the other night," added Steve. "I don't mean his geological gabble: that was bad enough, but his chat with Emma Curtis was much worse. Tell her, Mac, and see if she doesn't think poor Emma had a right to think you a first-class bore."

"I don't see why, when I merely tried to have a little sensible conversation," began Mac, with reluctance; for he had been unmercifully chaffed by his cousins, to whom his brother had betrayed him.

"What did you say? I won't laugh if I can help it," said Rose, curious to hear; for Steve's eyes were twinkling with fun.

"Well, I knew she was fond of theatres; so I tried that first and got on pretty well till I began to tell her how they managed those things in Greece. Most interesting subject, you know?"

"Very. Did you give her one of the choruses or a bit of Agamemnon, as you did when you described it to me?" asked Rose keeping sober with difficulty as she recalled that serio-comic scene.

"Of course not; but I was advising her to read Prometheus, when she gaped behind her fan, and began to talk about Phebe. What a 'nice creature' she was, 'kept her place,' 'dressed according to her station,' and that sort of twaddle. I suppose it *was* rather rude, but being pulled up so short confused me a bit, and I said the first thing that came into my head, which was that I thought Phebe the best-dressed woman in the room, because she wasn't all fuss and feathers like most of the girls."

"O Mac! that to Emma, who makes it the labour of her life to be always in the height of the fashion, and was particularly splendid that night. What *did* she say?" cried Rose, full of sympathy for both parties.

"She bridled and looked daggers at me."

"And what did you do?"

"I bit my tongue, and tumbled out of one scrape into another. Following her example, I changed the subject by talking about the Charity Concert for the orphans; and, when she gushed about the 'little darlings,' I advised her to adopt one, and wondered why young ladies didn't do that sort of thing, instead of cuddling cats and lapdogs."

"Unhappy boy! her pug is the idol of her life, and she hates babies," said Rose.

"More fool she! Well, she got my opinion on the subject, anyway, and she's very welcome; for I went on to say that I thought it would not only be a lovely charity, but excellent training for the time when they had little darlings of their own. No end of poor things die through the ignorance of mothers, you know," added Mac, so seriously that Rose dared not smile at what went before.

"Imagine Emma trotting round with a pauper baby under her arm instead of her cherished Toto," said Steve, with an ecstatic twirl on the stool.

"Did she seem to like your advice, Monsieur Malapropos?" asked Rose, wishing she had been there.

"No, she gave a little shriek and said, 'Good gracious, Mr. Campbell, how droll you are! Take me to mamma, please,' which I did with a thankful heart. Catch me setting her pug's leg again," ended Mac, with a grim shake of the head.

"Never mind. You were unfortunate in your listener that time. Don't think all girls are so foolish. I can show you a dozen sensible ones, who would discuss dress reform and charity with you, and enjoy Greek tragedy if you did the chorus for them as you did for me," said Rose, consolingly; for Steve would only jeer.

"Give me a list of them, please; and I'll cultivate their acquaintance. A fellow must have some reward for making a teetotum of himself."

"I will with pleasure; and if you dance well they will make it very pleasant for you, and you'll enjoy parties in spite of yourself."

"I cannot be a 'glass of fashion and a mould of form' like Dandy here, but I'll do my best: only, if I had my choice, I'd much rather go round the streets with an organ and a monkey," answered Mac, despondently.

"Thank you kindly for the compliment," and Rose made him a low curtsy, while Steve cried—

"Now you *have* done it!" in a tone of reproach which reminded the culprit, all too late, that he was Rose's chosen escort.

"By the gods, so I have!" and, casting away the newspaper with a gesture of comic despair, Mac strode from the room, chanting tragically the words of Cassandra—

" 'Woe! woe! O Earth! O Apollo! I will dare to die; I will accost the gates of Hades, and make my prayer that I may receive a mortal blow!' "

7

Phebe

WHILE ROSE was making discoveries and having experiences, Phebe was doing the same in a quieter way: but, though they usually compared notes during the bedtime *tête-à-tête* which always ended their day, certain topics were never mentioned; so each had a little world of her own into which even the eye of friendship did not peep.

Rose's life just now was the gayest, but Phebe's the happiest. Both went out a good deal; for the beautiful voice was welcomed everywhere, and many were ready to patronize the singer who would have been slow to recognize the woman. Phebe knew this, and made no attempt to assert herself; content to know that those whose regard she valued felt her worth, and hopeful of a time when she could gracefully take the place she was meant to fill.

Proud as a princess was Phebe about some things, though in most as humble as a child; therefore, when each year lessened the service she loved to give, and increased the obligations she would have refused from any other source, dependence became a burden which even the most fervent gratitude could not lighten. Hitherto the children had gone on together, finding no obstacles to their companionship in the secluded world in which they lived: now that they were women their paths inevitably diverged, and both reluctantly felt that they must part before long.

It had been settled, when they went abroad, that on their return Phebe should take her one gift in her hand, and try her fortunes. On no other terms would she accept the teaching which

90

was to fit her for the independence she desired. Faithfully had she used the facilities so generously afforded both at home and abroad, and now was ready to prove that they had not been in vain. Much encouraged by the small successes she won in drawing-rooms, and the praise bestowed by interested friends, she began to feel that she might venture on a larger field, and begin her career as a concert singer; for she aimed no higher.

Just at this time, much interest was felt in a new asylum for orphan girls, which could not be completed for want of funds. The Campbells "well had borne their part," and still laboured to accomplish the much-needed charity. Several fairs had been given for this purpose, followed by a series of concerts. Rose had thrown herself into the work with all her heart, and now proposed that Phebe should make her *début* at the last concert which was to be a peculiarly interesting one, as all the orphans were to be present, and were expected to plead their own cause by the sight of their innocent helplessness, as well as touch hearts by the simple airs they were to sing.

Some of the family thought Phebe would object to so humble a beginning: but Rose knew her better, and was not disappointed; for, when she made her proposal, Phebe answered readily—

"Where could I find a fitter time and place to come before the public than here among my little sisters in misfortune? I'll sing for them with all my heart: only I must be one of them, and have no flourish made about me."

"You shall arrange it as you like; and, as there is to be little vocal music but yours and the children's, I'll see that you have everything as you please," promised Rose.

It was well she did; for the family got much excited over the prospect of "our Phebe's *début*," and *would* have made a flourish if the girls had not resisted. Aunt Clara was in despair about the dress; because Phebe decided to wear a plain claret-coloured merino with frills at neck and wrists, so that she might look as much as possible, like the other orphans in their stuff gowns and white aprons. Aunt Plenty wanted to have a little supper afterwards in honour of the occasion; but Phebe begged her to change it to a Christmas dinner for the poor children. The boys planned to throw bushels of flowers, and Charlie claimed the honour of leading the singer in. But Phebe, with tears in her eyes, declined their kindly offers, saying earnestly—

"I had better begin as I am to go on, and depend upon myself entirely. Indeed, Mr. Charlie, I'd rather walk in alone; for you'd be out of place among us, and spoil the pathetic effect we wish to produce," and a smile sparkled through the tears, as Phebe looked at the piece of elegance before her, and thought of the brown gowns and pinafores.

So, after much discussion, it was decided that she should have her way in all things, and the family content themselves with applauding from the front.

"We'll blister our hands every man of us, and carry you home in a chariot and four: see if we don't, you perverse prima donna!" threatened Steve, not at all satisfied with the simplicity of the affair.

"A chariot and two will be very acceptable as soon as I'm done. I shall be quite steady till my part is all over, and then I may feel a little upset; so I'd like to get away before the confusion begins. Indeed I don't mean to be perverse: but you are all so kind to me, my heart is full whenever I think of it; and that wouldn't do if I'm to sing," said Phebe, dropping one of the tears on the little frill she was making.

No diamond could have adorned it better Archie thought, as he watched it shine there for a moment; and felt like shaking Steve for daring to pat the dark head with an encouraging—

"All right. I'll be on hand, and whisk you away while the rest are splitting their gloves. No fear of your breaking down. If you feel the least bit like it, though, just look at me; and I'll glare at you and shake my fist, since kindness upsets you."

"I wish you would because one of my ballads is rather touching, and I always want to cry when I sing it. The sight of you trying to glare will make me want to laugh, and that will steady me nicely: so sit in front, please, ready to slip out when I come off the last time."

"Depend upon me!" And the little man departed, taking great credit to himself for his influence over tall, handsome Phebe.

If he had known what was going on in the mind of the silent young gentleman behind the newspaper, Steve would have been much astonished; for Archie, though apparently engrossed by business, was fathoms deep in love by this time. No one suspected this but Rose; for he did his wooing with his eyes, and only Phebe knew how eloquent they could be. He had discovered what the matter was long ago—had made many attempts to reason himself out of it; but, finding it a hopeless task, had given up trying, and let himself drift deliciously. The knowledge that the family would not approve only seemed to add ardour to his love and strength to his purpose: for the same energy and persistence which he brought to business went into everything he did; and, having once made up his mind to marry Phebe, nothing could change his plan except a word from her.

He watched and waited for three months, so that he might not be accused of precipitation, though it did not take him one to decide that this was the woman to make him happy. Her steadfast nature; quiet, busy ways; and the reserved power and passion betrayed sometimes by a flash of the black eyes, a quiver of the firm lips—suited Archie, who possessed many of the same attributes himself: while the obscurity of her birth and isolation of her lot, which would have deterred some lovers, not only appealed to his kindly heart, but touched the hidden romance which ran like a vein of gold through his strong common-sense, and made practical, steady-going Archie a poet when he fell in love. If Uncle Mac had guessed what dreams and fancies went on in the head bent over his ledgers, and what emotions were fermenting in the bosom of his staid "right-hand man," he would have tapped his forehead, and suggested a lunatic asylum. The boys thought Archie had sobered down too soon. His mother began to fear that the air of the counting-room did not suit him: and Dr. Alec was deluded into the belief that the fellow really began to "think of Rose;" he came so often in the evening, seeming quite contented to sit beside her work-table, and snip tape, or draw patterns, while they chatted.

No one observed that, though he talked to Rose on these occasions, he looked at Phebe, in her low chair close by, busy but silent; for she always tried to efface herself when Rose was near, and often mourned that she was too big to keep out of sight. No matter what he talked about, Archie always saw the glossy black braids on the other side of the table, the damask cheek curving down into the firm white throat, and the dark lashes, lifted now and then, showing eyes so deep and soft he dared not look into them long. Even the swift needle charmed him, the little brooch which rose and fell with her quiet breath, the plain work she did, and the tidy way she gathered her bits of thread into a tiny bag. He seldom spoke to her; never touched her basket, though he ravaged Rose's if he wanted string or scissors; very rarely ventured to bring her some curious or pretty thing when ships came in from China: only sat and thought of her; imagined that this was *his* parlour, this *her* work-table, and they two sitting there alone a happy man and wife.

At this stage of the little evening drama, he would be conscious of such a strong desire to do something rash that he took refuge in a new form of intoxication, and proposed music, sometimes so abruptly that Rose would pause in the middle of a sentence and look at him, surprised to meet a curiously excited look in the usually cool, grey eyes.

Then Phebe, folding up her work, would go to the piano, as if glad to find a vent for the inner life which she seemed to have no power of expressing except in song. Rose would follow to accompany her; and Archie, moving to a certain shady corner whence he could see Phebe's face as she sang would give himself up to unmitigated rapture for half an hour. Phebe never sang so well as at such times: for the kindly atmosphere was like sunshine to a bird, criticisms were few and gentle, praises hearty and abundant; and she poured out her soul as freely as a spring gushes up when its hidden source is full.

Always comely, with a large and wholesome growth, in moments such as these Phebe was beautiful with the beauty that makes a man's eye brighten with honest admiration, and thrills his heart with a sense of womanly nobility and sweetness. Little wonder, then, that the chief spectator of this agreeable tableau grew nightly more enamoured; and, while the elders were deep in whist, the young people were playing that still more absorbing game in which hearts are always trumps.

Rose, having Dummy for a partner, soon discovered the fact, and lately had begun to feel as she fancied Wall must have done when Pyramus wooed Thisbe through its chinks. She was a little startled at first, then amused, then anxious, then heartily interested, as every woman is in such affairs, and willingly continued to be a medium, though sometimes she quite tingled with the electricity which seemed to pervade the air. She said nothing, waiting for Phebe to speak; but Phebe was silent, seeming to doubt the truth, till doubt became impossible, then to shrink as if suddenly conscious of wrong-doing, and seize every possible pretext for absenting herself from the "girls' corner," as the pretty recess was called.

The concert plan afforded excellent opportunities for doing

this; and evening after evening she slipped away to practise her
songs upstairs, while Archie sat staring disconsolately at the
neglected work-basket and mute piano. Rose pitied him, and
longed to say a word of comfort, but felt shy—he was such a
reserved fellow—so left him to conduct his quiet wooing in his
own way, feeling that the crisis would soon arrive.

She was sure of this, as she sat beside him on the evening of
the concert; for while the rest of the family nodded and smiled,
chatted and laughed in great spirits, Archie was as mute as a fish,
and sat with his arms tightly folded, as if to keep in any unruly
emotions which might attempt to escape. He never looked at the
programme; but Rose knew when Phebe's turn came by the
quick breath he drew, and the intent look that came into his eyes
so absent before.

But her own excitement prevented much notice of his; for
Rose was in a flutter of hope and fear, sympathy and delight,
about Phebe and her success. The house was crowded; the
audience sufficiently mixed to make the general opinion im-
partial; and the stage full of little orphans with shining faces, a
most effective reminder of the object in view.

"Little dears, how nice they look!" "Poor things, so young
to be fatherless and motherless." "It will be a disgrace to the
city, if those girls are not taken proper care of." "Subscriptions
are always in order, you know; and pretty Miss Campbell will
give you her sweetest smile if you hand her a handsome cheque."
"I've heard this Phebe Moore, and she really has a delicious
voice: such a pity she won't fit herself for opera!" "Only sings
three times tonight; that's modest I'm sure, when she is the
chief attraction; so we must give her an encore after the Italian
piece." "The orphans lead off, I see: stop your ears if you like;
but don't fail to applaud, or the ladies will never forgive
you."

Chat of this sort went on briskly, while fans waved, pro-
grammes rustled, and ushers flew about distractedly; till an
important gentleman appeared, made his bow, skipped upon the
leader's stand, and with a wave of his bâton caused a general
uprising of white pinafores, as the orphans led off with that
much-enduring melody, "America," in shrill small voices, but
with creditable attention to time and tune. Pity and patriotism
produced a generous round of applause; and the little girls sat
down, beaming with innocent satisfaction.

An instrumental piece followed, and then a youthful gentleman, with his hair in picturesque confusion, and what his friends
called a "musical brow," bounded up the steps, and, clutching a
roll of music with a pair of tightly gloved hands, proceeded to
inform the audience, in a husky tenor voice, that

"It was a lovely violet."

What else the song contained in the way of sense or sentiment it was impossible to discover; as the three pages of music
appeared to consist of variations upon that one line, ending with
a prolonged quaver, which flushed the musical brow, and left the
youth quite breathless when he made his bow.

"Now she's coming! O uncle, my heart beats as if it was
myself!" whispered Rose, clutching Dr. Alec's arm with a little
gasp, as the piano was rolled forward, the leader's stand pushed
back, and all eyes turned towards the anteroom door.

She forgot to glance at Archie, and it was as well perhaps; for
his heart was thumping almost audibly, as he waited for his
Phebe. Not from the anteroom, but out from among the children,
where she had sat unseen in the shadow of the organ, came stately
Phebe in her wine-coloured dress, with no ornament but her fine
hair and a white flower at her throat. Very pale, but quite composed, apparently; for she stepped slowly through the narrow
lane of upturned faces, holding back her skirts, lest they should
rudely brush against some little head. Straight to the front she
went, bowed hastily, and, with a gesture to the accompanist,
stood waiting to begin, her eyes fixed on the great gilt clock at
the opposite end of the hall.

They never wandered from that point while she sung; but,
as she ended, they dropped for an instant on an eager, girlish
countenance, bending from a front seat; then, with her hasty little
bow, she went quickly back among the children, who clapped
and nodded as she passed, well pleased with the ballad she had
sung.

Every one courteously followed their example; but there was
no enthusiasm, and it was evident that Phebe had not produced a
particularly favourable impression.

"Never sang so badly in her life," muttered Charlie, irefully.

"She was frightened, poor thing. Give her time, give her
time," said Uncle Mac, kindly.

"I saw she was, and I glared like a gorgon, but she never

looked at me," added Steve, smoothing his gloves and his brows at the same time.

"That first song was the hardest, and she got through much better than I expected," put in Dr. Alec, bound not to show the disappointment he felt.

"Don't be troubled. Phebe has courage enough for anything, and she'll astonish you before the evening's over," prophesied Mac, with unabated confidence; for he knew something that the rest did not.

Rose said nothing, but, under cover of her burnous, gave Archie's hand a sympathetic squeeze; for his arms were unfolded now, as if the strain was over, and one lay on his knee, while with the other he wiped his hot forehead with an air of relief.

Friends about them murmured complimentary fibs, and affected great delight and surprise at Miss Moore's "charming style," "exquisite simplicity," and "undoubted talent." But strangers freely criticized, and Rose was so indignant at some of their remarks she could not listen to anything upon the stage, though a fine overture was played, a man with a remarkable bass voice growled and roared melodiously, and the orphans sang a lively air with a chorus of "Tra, la, la," which was a great relief to little tongues unused to long silence.

"I've often heard that women's tongues were hung in the middle and went at both ends: now I'm sure of it," whispered Charlie, trying to cheer her up by pointing out the comical effect of some seventy-five open mouths, in each of which the unruly member was wagging briskly.

Rose laughed and let him fan her, leaning from his seat behind with the devoted air he always assumed in public; but her wounded feelings were not soothed, and she continued to frown at the stout man on the left, who had dared to say with a shrug and a glance at Phebe's next piece, "That young woman can no more sing this Italian thing than she can fly, and they ought not to let her attempt it."

Phebe did, however; and suddenly changed the stout man's opinion by singing it grandly; for the consciousness of her first failure pricked her pride and spurred her to do her best with the calm sort of determination which conquers fear, fires ambition, and changes defeat to success. She looked steadily at Rose now, or the flushed, intent face beside her; and throwing all her soul into the task let her voice ring out like a silver clarion, filling

D

the great hall and setting the hearers' blood a-tingle with the exulting strain.

That settled Phebe's fate as cantatrice; for the applause was genuine and spontaneous this time, and broke out again and again with the generous desire to atone for former coldness. But she would not return, and the shadow of the great organ seemed to have swallowed her up; for no eye could find her, no pleasant clamour win her back.

"Now I can die content," said Rose, beaming with heart-felt satisfaction; while Archie looked steadfastly at his programme, trying to keep his face in order, and the rest of the family assumed a triumphant air, as if *they* had never doubted from the first.

"Very well, indeed," said the stout man, with an approving nod. "Quite promising for a beginner. Shouldn't wonder if in time they made a second Cary or Kellogg of her."

"Now you'll forgive him, won't you?" murmured Charlie, in his cousin's ear.

"Yes; and I'd like to pat him on the head. But take warning and never judge by first appearances again," whispered Rose, at peace now with all mankind.

Phebe's last song was another ballad; for she meant to devote her talent to that much neglected but always attractive branch of her art. It was a great surprise, therefore, to all but one person in the hall, when, instead of singing "Auld Robin Grey," she placed herself at the piano, and, with a smiling glance over her shoulder at the children, broke out in the old bird-song which first won Rose. But the chirping, twittering, and cooing were now the burden to three verses of a charming little song, full of springtime and the awakening life that makes it lovely. A rippling accompaniment flowed through it all, and a burst of delighted laughter from the children filled up the first pause with a fitting answer to the voices that seemed calling to them from the vernal woods.

It was very beautiful, and novelty lent its charm to the surprise; for art and nature worked a pretty miracle, and the clever imitation, first heard from a kitchen hearth, now became the favourite in a crowded concert room. Phebe was quite herself again; colour in the cheeks now; eyes that wandered smiling to and fro; and lips that sang as gaily and far more sweetly than when she kept time to her blithe music with a scrubbing brush.

This song was evidently intended for the children, and they appreciated the kindly thought; for, as Phebe went back among them, they clapped ecstatically, flapped their pinafores, and some caught her by the skirts with audible requests to "do it again, please; do it again."

But Phebe shook her head and vanished; for it was getting late for such small people, several of whom "lay sweetly slumbering there," till roused by the clamour round them. The elders, however, were not to be denied, and applauded persistently, especially Aunt Plenty, who seized Uncle Mac's cane and pounded with it as vigorously as "Mrs. Nubbles" at the play.

"Never mind your gloves, Steve! keep it up till she comes," cried Charlie, enjoying the fun like a boy; while Jamie lost his head with excitement, and standing up called "Phebe! Phebe!" in spite of his mother's attempts to silence him.

Even the stout man clapped, and Rose could only laugh delightedly as she turned to look at Archie, who seemed to have let himself loose at last, and was stamping with a dogged energy funny to see.

So Phebe had to come, and stood there meekly bowing, with a moved look on her face, that showed how glad and grateful she was, till a sudden hush came; then, as if inspired by the memory of the cause that brought her there, she looked down into the sea of friendly faces before her, with no trace of fear in her own, and sung the song that never will grow old.

That went straight to the hearts of those who heard her: for there was something inexpressibly touching in the sight of this sweet-voiced woman singing of home for the little creatures who were homeless; and Phebe made her tuneful plea irresistible by an almost involuntary gesture of the hands which had hung loosely clasped before her; till, with the last echo of the beloved word, they fell apart and were half-outstretched as if pleading to be filled.

It was the touch of nature that works wonders; for it made full purses suddenly weigh heavily in pockets slow to open, brought tears to eyes unused to weep, and caused that group of red-gowned girls to grow very pathetic in the sight of fathers and mothers who had left little daughters safe asleep at home. This was evident from the stillness that remained unbroken for an instant after Phebe ended; and before people could get rid of

their handkerchiefs she would have been gone, if the sudden
appearance of a mite in a pinafore, climbing up the stairs from
the anteroom, with a great bouquet grasped in both hands, had
not arrested her.

Up came the little creature, intent on performing the mission
for which rich bribes of sugar-plums had been promised, and
trotting bravely across the stage, she held up the lovely nosegay,
saying in her baby voice, "Dis for you, ma'am;" then, startled by
the sudden outburst of applause, she hid her face in Phebe's
gown, and began to sob with fright.

An awkward minute for poor Phebe; but she showed unexpected presence of mind, and left behind her a pretty picture
of the oldest and the youngest orphan, as she went quickly down
the step, smiling over the great bouquet with the baby on her
arm.

Nobody minded the closing piece; for people began to go,
sleepy children to be carried off, and whispers grew into a buzz
of conversation. In the general confusion, Rose looked to see if
Steve had remembered his promise to help Phebe slip away
before the rush began. No, there he was putting on Kitty's cloak,
quite oblivious of any other duty; and, turning to ask Archie to
hurry out, Rose found that he had already vanished, leaving his
gloves behind him.

"Have you lost anything?" asked Dr. Alec, catching a glimpse
of her face.

"No, sir, I've found something," she whispered back, giving
him the gloves to pocket along with her fan and glass, adding
hastily as the concert ended, "Please, uncle, tell them all not to
come with us. Phebe has had enough excitement, and ought to
rest."

Rose's word was law to the family in all things concerning
Phebe. So word was passed that there were to be no congratulations till tomorrow, and Dr. Alec got his party off as soon as
possible. But all the way home, while he and Aunt Plenty were
prophesying a brilliant future for the singer, Rose sat rejoicing
over the happy present of the woman. She was sure that Archie
had spoken, and imagined the whole scene with feminine delight
—how tenderly he had asked the momentous question, how
gratefully Phebe had given the desired reply, and now how both
were enjoying that delicious hour which Rose had been given
to understand never came but once. Such a pity to shorten it, she

thought; and begged her uncle to go home the longest way: the
night was so mild, the moonlight so clear, and herself so in need
of fresh air after the excitement of the evening.

"I thought you would want to rush into Phebe's arms the
instant she got done," said Aunt Plenty, innocently wondering
at the whims girls took into their heads.

"So I should if I consulted my own wishes; but as Phebe asked
to be let alone I want to gratify her," answered Rose, making
the best excuse she could.

"A little piqued," thought the doctor, fancying he understood
the case.

As the old lady's rheumatism forbade their driving about till
midnight, home was reached much too soon, Rose thought,
and tripped away to warn the lovers the instant she entered the
house. But study, parlour, and boudoir were empty; and, when
Jane appeared with cake and wine, she reported that "Miss
Phebe went right upstairs, and wished to be excused, please,
being very tired."

"That isn't at all like Phebe: I hope she isn't ill," began Aunt
Plenty, sitting down to toast her feet.

"She may be a little hysterical; for she is a proud thing, and
represses her emotions as long as she can. I'll step up and see
if she doesn't need a soothing draught of some sort," and Dr.
Alec threw off his coat as he spoke.

"No, no, she's only tired. I'll run up to her: she won't mind
me; and I'll report if anything is amiss."

Away went Rose, quite trembling with suspense; but Phebe's
door was shut, no light shone underneath, and no sound came
from the room within. She tapped, and, receiving no answer,
went on to her own chamber, thinking to herself—

"Love always makes people queer, I've heard; so I suppose
they settled it all in the carriage, and the dear thing ran away
to think about her happiness alone. I'll not disturb her. Why,
Phebe!" added Rose, surprised; for, entering her room, there
was the cantatrice, busy about the nightly services she always
rendered her little mistress.

"I'm waiting for you, dear. Where have you been so long?"
asked Phebe, poking the fire as if anxious to get some colour
into cheeks that were unnaturally pale.

The instant she spoke, Rose knew that something was wrong,
and a glance at her face confirmed the fear. It was like a dash of

cold water, and quenched her happy fancies in a moment; but being a delicate-minded girl she respected Phebe's mood, and asked no questions, made no comments, and left her friend to speak or be silent as she chose.

"I was so excited I would take a turn in the moonlight to calm my nerves. O dearest Phebe, I am *so* glad, so proud, so full of wonder at your courage and skill and sweet ways altogether, that I cannot half tell you how I love and honour you!" she cried, kissing the white cheeks with such tender warmth they could not help glowing faintly, as Phebe held her little mistress close, sure that nothing could disturb this innocent affection.

"It is all your work, dear; because but for you I might still be scrubbing floors and hardly dare to dream of anything like this," she said, in her old grateful way; but in her voice there was a thrill of something deeper than gratitude, and at the last two words her head went up with a gesture of soft pride as if it had been newly crowned.

Rose heard and saw and guessed the meaning of both tone and gesture; feeling that her Phebe deserved both the singer's laurel and the bride's myrtle wreath. But she only looked up, saying very wistfully—

"Then it *has* been a happy night for you as well as for us."

"The happiest of my life, and the hardest," answered Phebe briefly, as she looked away from the questioning eyes.

"You should have let us come nearer and help you through. I'm afraid you are very proud, my Jenny Lind."

"I have to be; for sometimes I feel as if I had nothing else to keep me up." She stopped short there, fearing that her voice would prove traitorous if she went on. In a moment, she asked in a tone that was almost hard—

"You think I did well tonight?"

"They all think so, and were so delighted they wanted to come in a body and tell you so; but I sent them home, because I knew you'd be tired out. Perhaps I ought not to have done it, and you'd rather have had a crowd about you than just me?"

"It was the kindest thing you ever did, and what could I like better than 'just you,' my darling?"

Phebe seldom called her that, and when she did her heart was in the little word, making it so tender that Rose thought it the sweetest in the world, next to Uncle Alec's "my little girl." Now it was almost passionate, and Phebe's face grew rather tragical as she looked down at Rose. It was impossible to seem unconscious any longer, and Rose said, caressing Phebe's cheek, which burned with a feverish colour now—

"Then don't shut me out if you have a trouble; but let me share it as I let you share all mine."

"I will! Little mistress, I've got to go away, sooner even than we planned."

"Why, Phebe?"

"Because—Archie loves me."

"That's the very reason you should stay and make him happy."

"Not if it caused dissension in the family, and you know it would."

Rose opened her lips to deny this impetuously, but checked herself and answered honestly—

"Uncle and I would be heartily glad; and I'm sure Aunt Jessie never could object, if you loved Archie as he does you."

"She has other hopes, I think; and kind as she is it *would* be a disappointment if he brought me home. She is right; they all are, and I alone am to blame. I should have gone long ago: I knew I should; but it was so pleasant I couldn't bear to go away alone."

"I kept you, and I am to blame if anyone; but indeed, dear Phebe, I cannot see why you should care even if Aunt Myra croaks, and Aunt Clara exclaims, or Aunt Jane makes disagreeable remarks. Be happy, and never mind them," cried Rose; so much excited by all this that she felt the spirit of revolt rise up within her, and was ready to defy even that awe-inspiring institution "the family" for her friend's sake.

But Phebe shook her head with a sad smile; and answered, still with the hard tone in her voice as if forcing back all emotion that she might see her duty clearly—

"*You* could do that, but *I* never can. Answer me this, Rose, and answer truly as you love me. If you had been taken into a house, a friendless, penniless, forlorn girl, and for years been heaped with benefits, trusted, taught, loved, and made, oh, so happy! could you think it right to steal away something that these good people valued very much? To have them feel that you have been ungrateful, had deceived them, and meant to thrust yourself into a high place not fit for you; when they had been generously helping you in other ways, far more than you deserved. Could you then say as you do now, 'Be happy and never mind them'?"

Phebe held Rose by the shoulders now, and searched her face so keenly that the other shrunk a little; for the black eyes were full of fire, and there was something almost grand about this girl who seemed suddenly to have become a woman. There was no need of words to answer the questions so swiftly asked; for Rose put herself in Phebe's place in the drawing of a breath and her own pride made her truthfully reply—

"No; I could not!"

"I knew you'd say that and help me to do my duty;" and all the coldness melted out of Phebe's manner, as she hugged her little mistress close, feeling the comfort of sympathy even through the blunt sincerity of Rose's words.

"I will if I know how. Now come and tell me all about it;" and, seating herself in the great chair which had often held them both, Rose stretched out her hands as if glad and ready to give help of any sort.

But Phebe would not take her accustomed place; for, as if coming to confession, she knelt down upon the rug, and, leaning on the arm of the chair, told her love-story in the simplest words.

"I never thought he cared for me until a little while ago. I fancied it was you, and even when I knew he liked to hear me sing I supposed it was because you helped; and so I did my best, and was glad you were to be a happy girl. But his eyes told the truth; then I saw what I had been doing, and was frightened. He did not speak, so I believed, what is quite true, that he felt I was not a fit wife for him, and would never ask me. It was right: I was glad of it, yet I *was* proud; and, though I did not ask or hope for anything, I did want him to see that I respected myself, remembered my duty, and could do right as well as he. I kept away; I planned to go as soon as possible, and resolved that at this concert I would do so well he should not be ashamed of poor Phebe and her one gift."

"It was this that made you so strange, then; preferring to go alone, and refusing every little favour at our hands?" asked Rose, feeling very sure now about the state of Phebe's heart.

"Yes; I wanted to do everything myself, and not owe one jot of my success, if I had any, to even the dearest friend I've got. It was bad and foolish of me, and I was punished by that first

dreadful failure. I was so frightened, Rose! My breath was all
gone, my eyes so dizzy I could hardly see, and that great crowd
of faces seemed so near I dared not look. If it had not been for
the clock I never should have got through; and when I did, not
knowing in the least how I'd sung, one look at your distressed
face told me that I'd failed."

"But I smiled, Phebe—indeed I did—as sweetly as I could;
for I was sure it was only fright," protested Rose, eagerly.

"So you did, but the smile was full of pity, not of pride, as I
wanted it to be; and I rushed into a dark place behind the organ,
feeling ready to kill myself. How angry and miserable I was!
I set my teeth, clenched my hands, and vowed that I would do
well next time, or never sing another note. I was quite desperate when my turn came, and felt as if I could do almost anything; for I remembered that *he* was there. I'm not sure how it
was, but it seemed as if I was all voice; for I let myself go,
trying to forget everything except that two people must *not* be
disappointed, though I died when the song was done."

"O Phebe, it was splendid! I nearly cried, I was so proud and
glad to see you do yourself justice at last."

"And he?" whispered Phebe, with her face half hidden on the
arm of the chair.

"Said not a word: but I saw his lips tremble and his eyes
shine; and I knew he was the happiest creature there, because *I*
was sure he did think you fit to be his wife, and did mean to
speak very soon."

Phebe made no answer for a moment, seeming to forget the
small success in the greater one which followed, and to comfort
her sore heart with the knowledge that Rose was right.

"*He* sent the flowers; *he* came for me, and on the way home,
showed me how wrong I had been to doubt him for an hour.
Don't ask me to tell that part, but be sure *I* was the happiest
creature in the world then." And Phebe hid her face again, all
wet with tender tears, that fell soft and sudden as a summer
shower.

Rose let them flow undisturbed, while she silently caressed
the bent head; wondering, with a wistful look in her own wet
eyes, what this mysterious passion was, which could so move,
ennoble, and beautify the beings whom it blessed.

An impertinent little clock upon the chimney-piece striking
eleven broke the silence, and reminded Phebe that she could not

indulge in love-dreams there. She started up, brushed off her
tears, and said resolutely—

"That is enough for tonight. Go happily to bed, and leave the
troubles for tomorrow."

"But, Phebe, I must know what you said," cried Rose, like a
child defrauded of half its bedtime story.

"I said 'No.' "

"Ah! but it will change to 'Yes' by and by; I'm sure of that:
so I'll let you go to dream of 'him'. The Campbells *are* rather
proud of being descendants of Robert Bruce; but they have
common-sense and love you dearly, as you'll see tomorrow."

"Perhaps." And, with a good-night kiss, poor Phebe went
away, to lie awake till dawn.

8

Breakers Ahead

ANXIOUS TO smooth the way for Phebe, Rose was up betimes, and slipped into Aunt Plenty's room before the old lady had got her cap on.

"Aunty, I've something pleasant to tell you; and, while you listen, I'll brush your hair, as you like to have me," she began, well aware that the proposed process was a very soothing one.

"Yes, dear: only don't be too particular, because I'm late and must hurry down, or Jane won't get things straight; and it does fidget me to have the salt-cellars uneven, the tea-strainer forgotten, and your uncle's paper not aired," returned Miss Plenty, briskly unrolling the two grey curls she wore at her temples.

Then Rose, brushing away at the scanty back-hair led skilfully up to the crisis of her tale by describing Phebe's panic and brave efforts to conquer it; all about the flowers Archie sent her; and how Steve forgot, and dear, thoughtful Archie took his place. So far it went well, and Aunt Plenty was full of interest, sympathy, and approbation; but when Rose added, as if it was quite a matter of course, "So, on the way home, he told her he loved her," a great start twitched the grey locks out of her hands as the old lady turned round, with the little curls standing erect, exclaiming, in undisguised dismay—

"Not seriously, Rose?"

"Yes, Aunty, very seriously. He never jokes about such things."

"Mercy on us! what *shall* we do about it?"

"Nothing, ma'am, but be as glad as we ought, and congratulate him as soon as she says 'Yes.' "

"Do you mean to say she didn't accept at once?"

"She never will if we don't welcome her as kindly as if she belonged to one of our best families, and I don't blame her."

"I'm glad the girl has so much sense. Of course we can't do anything of the sort; and I'm surprised at Archie's forgetting what he owes to the family in this rash manner. Give me my cap, child: I must speak to Alec at once." And Aunt Plenty twisted her hair into a button at the back of her head with one energetic twirl.

"Do speak kindly, Aunty, and remember that it was not Phebe's fault. She never thought of this till very lately, and began at once to prepare for going away," said Rose, pleadingly.

"She ought to have gone long ago. I told Myra we should have trouble somewhere as soon as I saw what a good-looking creature she was; and here it is as bad as can be. Dear, dear! why can't young people have a little prudence?"

"I don't see that anyone need object if Uncle Jem and Aunt Jessie approve; and I do think it will be very, very unkind to scold poor Phebe for being well-bred, pretty, and good, after doing all we could to make her so."

"Child, you don't understand these things yet; but you ought to feel your duty towards your family, and do all you can to keep the name as honourable as it always has been. What do you suppose our blessed ancestress, Lady Marget, would say to our oldest boy taking a wife from the poor-house?"

As she spoke, Miss Plenty looked up, almost apprehensively, at one of the wooden-faced old portraits with which her room was hung, as if asking pardon of the severe-nosed matron, who stared back at her from under the sort of blue dish-cover which formed her head-gear.

"As Lady Marget died about two hundred years ago, I don't care a pin what she would say; especially as she looks like a very narrow-minded, haughty woman. But I do care very much what Miss Plenty Campbell says; for *she* is a very sensible, generous, discreet, and dear old lady, who wouldn't hurt a fly, much less a good and faithful girl who has been a sister to me. Would she?" entreated Rose, knowing well that the elder aunt led all the rest more or less.

But Miss Plenty had her cap on now, and consequently felt

herself twice the woman she was without it; so she not only gave it a somewhat belligerent air by setting it well up, but she shook her head decidedly, smoothed down her stiff white apron, and stood up as if ready for battle.

"I shall do my duty, Rose, and expect the same of others. Don't say any more now: I must turn the matter over in my mind; for it has come upon me suddenly, and needs serious consideration."

With which unusually solemn address, she took up her keys and trotted away, leaving her niece to follow with an anxious countenance, uncertain whether her championship had done good or ill to the cause she had at heart.

She was much cheered by the sound of Phebe's voice in the study; for Rose was sure that if Uncle Alec was on their side all would be well. But the clouds lowered again when they came in to breakfast: for Phebe's heavy eyes and pale cheeks did not look encouraging; while Dr. Alec was as sober as a judge, and sent an inquiring glance towards Rose now and then as if curious to discover how she bore the news.

An uncomfortable meal, though all tried to seem as usual, and talked over last night's events with all the interest they could. But the old peace was disturbed by a word, as a pebble thrown into a quiet pool sends tell-tale circles rippling its surface far and wide. Aunt Plenty, while "turning the subject over in her mind," also seemed intent on upsetting everything she touched, and made sad havoc in her tea-tray; Dr. Alec unsociably read his paper; Rose, having salted instead of sugared her oatmeal, absently ate it feeling that the sweetness had gone out of everything; and Phebe, after choking down a cup of tea and crumbling a roll, excused herself, and went away, sternly resolving not to be a bone of contention to this beloved family.

As soon as the door was shut, Rose pushed away her plate, and going to Dr. Alec peeped over the paper with such an anxious face that he put it down at once.

"Uncle, this is a serious matter, and *we* must take our stand at once; for you are Phebe's guardian and I am her sister," began Rose, with pretty solemnity. "You have often been disappointed in me," she continued, "but I know I never shall be in you; because you are too wise and good to let any worldly pride or prudence spoil your sympathy with Archie and our Phebe. You won't desert them, will you?"

"Never!" answered Dr. Alec, with gratifying energy.

"Thank you! thank you!" cried Rose. "Now, if I have you and aunty on my side, I'm not afraid of anybody."

"Gently, gently, child. I don't intend to desert the lovers; but I certainly shall advise them to consider well what they are about. I'll own I *am* rather disappointed; because Archie is young to decide his life in this way, and Phebe's career seemed settled in another fashion. Old people don't like to have their plans upset, you know," he added, more lightly; for Rose's face fell as he went on.

"Old people shouldn't plan too much for the young ones then. We are very grateful, I'm sure; but we cannot always be disposed of in the most prudent and sensible way; so don't set your hearts on little arrangements of that sort, I beg," and Rose looked wondrous wise; for she could not help suspecting even her best uncle of "plans" in her behalf.

"You are quite right: we shouldn't; yet it is very hard to help it," confessed Dr. Alec, with a conscious air; and, returning hastily to the lovers, he added kindly—

"I was much pleased with the straightforward way in which Phebe came to me this morning, and told me all about it, as if I really was her guardian. She did not own it in words: but it was perfectly evident that she loves Archie with all her heart; yet, knowing the objections which will be made, very sensibly and bravely proposes to go away at once, and end the matter—as if that were possible, poor child," and the tender-hearted man gave a sigh of sympathy that did Rose good to hear, and mollified her rising indignation at the bare idea of ending Phebe's love affairs in such a summary way.

"You don't think she ought to go, I hope?"

"I think she will go."

"We must not let her."

"We have no right to keep her."

"O uncle! surely we have! Our Phebe, whom we all love so much."

"You forget that she is a woman now, and we have no claim upon her. Because we've befriended her for years is the very reason we should not make our benefits a burden, but leave her free; and, if she chooses to do this in spite of Archie, we must let her with a God-speed."

Before Rose could answer, Aunt Plenty spoke out like one

having authority; for old-fashioned ways were dear to her soul, and she thought even love affairs should be conducted with a proper regard to the powers that be.

"The family must talk the matter over and decide what is best for the children, who of course will listen to reason and do nothing ill-advised. For my part, I am quite upset by the news, but shall not commit myself till I've seen Jessie and the boy. Jane, clear away, and bring me the hot water."

That ended the morning conference; and, leaving the old lady to soothe her mind by polishing spoons and washing cups, Rose went away to find Phebe, while the doctor retired to laugh over the downfall of brother Mac's match-making schemes.

The Campbells did not gossip about their concerns in public; but, being a very united family, it had long been the custom to "talk over" any interesting event which occurred to any member thereof, and everyone gave his or her opinion, advice or censure, with the utmost candour. Therefore the first engagement, if such it could be called, created a great sensation, among the aunts especially; and they were in as much of a flutter as a flock of maternal birds when their young begin to hop out of the nest. So at all hours the excellent ladies were seen excitedly nodding their caps together, as they discussed the affair in all its bearings, without ever arriving at any unanimous decision.

The boys took it much more calmly. Mac was the only one who came out strongly in Archie's favour. Charlie thought the Chief ought to do better, and called Phebe "a siren, who had bewitched the sage youth." Steve was scandalized, and delivered long orations upon one's duty to society, keeping the old name up, and the danger of *mésalliances* while all the time he secretly sympathized with Archie, being much smitten with Kitty Van himself. Will and Geordie, unfortunately home for the holidays, considered it "a jolly lark;" and little Jamie nearly drove his elder brother distracted by curious inquiries as to "how folks felt when they were in love."

Uncle Mac's dismay was so comical that it kept Dr. Alec in good spirits; for he alone knew how deep was the deluded man's chagrin at the failure of the little plot which he fancied was prospering finely.

"I'll never set my heart on anything of the sort again; and the young rascals may marry whom they like. I'm prepared for anything now: so if Steve brings home the washerwoman's daughter, and Mac runs away with our pretty chamber-maid I shall say, 'Bless you my children,' with mournful resignation; for, upon my soul, that is all that's left for a modern parent to do."

With which tragic burst, poor Uncle Mac washed his hands of the whole affair, and buried himself in the counting-house while the storm raged.

About this time, Archie might have echoed Rose's childish wish that she had not *quite* so many aunts; for the tongues of those interested relatives made sad havoc with his little romance, and caused him to long fervently for a desert island, where he could woo and win his love in delicious peace. That nothing of the sort was possible soon became evident; since every word uttered only confirmed Phebe's resolution to go away and proved to Rose how mistaken she had been in believing that she could bring everyone to her way of thinking.

Prejudices are unmanageable things; and the good aunts, like most women, possessed a plentiful supply; so Rose found it like beating her head against a wall to try and convince them that Archie was wise in loving poor Phebe. His mother, who had hoped to have Rose for her daughter—not because of her fortune, but the tender affection she felt for her—put away her disappointment without a word, and welcomed Phebe as kindly as she could for her boy's sake. But the girl felt the truth with the quickness of a nature made sensitive by love, and clung to her resolve all the more tenaciously, though grateful for the motherly words that would have been so sweet if genuine happiness had prompted them.

Aunt Jane called it romantic nonsense, and advised strong measures—"kind, but firm, Jessie." Aunt Clara was sadly distressed about "what people would say" if one of "our boys" married a nobody's daughter. And Aunt Myra not only seconded her views by painting portraits of Phebe's unknown relations in the darkest colours, but uttered direful prophecies regarding the disreputable beings who would start up in swarms the moment the girl made a good match.

These suggestions so wrought upon Aunt Plenty that she turned a deaf ear to the benevolent emotions native to her breast, and taking refuge behind "our blessed ancestress, Lady Marget" refused to sanction any engagement which could bring discredit upon the stainless name which was her pride.

So it all ended where it began; for Archie steadily refused to listen to anyone but Phebe and she as steadily reiterated her bitter "No"; fortifying herself half unconsciously with the hope that, by and by, when she had won a name, fate might be kinder.

While the rest talked, she had been working; for every hour showed her that her instinct had been a true one, and pride would not let her stay, though love pleaded eloquently. So, after a Christmas anything but merry, Phebe packed her trunks, rich in gifts from those who generously gave her all but the one thing she desired; and, with a pocketful of letters to people who could further her plans, she went away to seek her fortune, with a brave face and a very heavy heart.

"Write often, and let me know all you do, my Phebe; and remember I shall never be contented till you come back again," whispered Rose, clinging to her till the last.

"She *will* come back; for in a year I'm going to bring her home, please God," said Archie, pale with the pain of parting, but as resolute as she.

"I'll earn my welcome: then perhaps it will be easier for them to give and me to receive it," answered Phebe, with a backward glance at the group of caps in the hall as she went down the steps on Dr. Alec's arm.

"You earned it long ago, and it is always waiting for you while I am here. Remember that, and God bless you, my good girl," he said, with a paternal kiss that warmed her heart.

"I never shall forget it!" and Phebe never did.

9

New Year's Calls

"Now I'm going to turn over a new leaf, as I promised. I wonder what I shall find on the next page?" said Rose, coming down on New Year's morning, with a serious face, and a thick letter in her hand.

"Tired of frivolity, my dear?" asked her uncle, pausing, in his walk up and down the hall, to glance at her with the quick, bright look she liked to bring into his eyes.

"No, sir, and that's the sad part of it; but I've made up my mind to stop while I can, because I'm sure it is not good for me. I've had some very sober thoughts lately; for, since my Phebe went away, I've had no heart for gaiety: so it is a good place to stop and make a fresh start," answered Rose, taking his arm, and walking on with him.

"An excellent time! Now, how are you going to fill the aching void?" he asked, well pleased.

"By trying to be as unselfish, brave, and good as she is." and Rose held the letter against her bosom with a tender touch, for Phebe's strength had inspired her with a desire to be as self-reliant. "I'm going to set about living in earnest, as she has; though I think it will be harder for me than for her, because she stands alone, and has a career marked out for her. I'm nothing but a commonplace sort of girl, with no end of relations to be consulted every time I wink, and a dreadful fortune hanging like a millstone round my neck, to weigh me down if I try to fly. It is a hard case, uncle, and I get low in my mind when I think about it," sighed Rose, oppressed with her blessings.

"Afflicted child! how can I relieve you?" And there was

115

amusement as well as sympathy in Dr. Alec's face, as he patted the hand upon his arm.

"Please don't laugh, for I really *am* trying to be good. In the first place, help me to wean myself from foolish pleasures, and show me how to occupy my thoughts and time so that I may not idle about and dream, instead of doing great things."

"Good! we'll begin at once. Come to town with me this morning, and see your houses. They are all ready, and Mrs. Gardener has half a dozen poor souls waiting to go in as soon as you give the word," answered the doctor, promptly, glad to get his girl back again, though not surprised that she still looked with regretful eyes at the Vanity Fair, always so enticing when we are young.

"I'll give it today, and make the new year a happy one to those poor souls at least. I'm so sorry that it's impossible for me to go with you, but you know I must help Aunty Plen receive. We haven't been here for so long that she has set her heart on having a grand time today; and I particularly want to please her, because I have not been as amiable as I ought lately. I really couldn't forgive her for siding against Phebe."

"She did what she thought was right: so we must not blame her. I am going to make my New Year's calls today; and, as my friends live down that way, I'll get the list of names from Mrs. G., and tell the poor ladies, with Miss Campbell's compliments, that their new home is ready. Shall I?"

"Yes, uncle, but take all the credit to yourself; for I never should have thought of it if you had not proposed the plan."

"Bless your heart! I'm only your agent, and suggest now and then. I've nothing to offer but advice: so I lavish that on all occasions."

"You have nothing because you've given your substance all away as generously as you do your advice. Never mind: you shall never come to want while I live. I'll save enough for us two, though I do make 'ducks and drakes of my fortune.'"

Dr. Alec laughed at the toss of the head with which she quoted Charlie's offensive words, then offered to take the letter, saying, as he looked at his watch—

"I'll post that for you in time for the early mail. I like a run before breakfast."

But Rose held her letter fast, dimpling with sudden smiles, half merry and half shy.

"No, thank you, sir: Archie likes to do that, and never fails to call for all I write. He gets a peep at Phebe's in return, and I cheer him up a bit; for, though he says nothing, he has a hard time of it, poor fellow."

"How many letters in five days?"

"Four, sir, to me: she doesn't write to him, uncle."

"As yet. Well, you show hers: so it's all right; and you are a set of sentimental youngsters." And the doctor walked away, looking as if he enjoyed the sentiment as much as any of them.

Old Miss Campbell was nearly as great a favourite as young Miss Campbell; so a succession of black coats and white gloves flowed in and out of the hospitable mansion pretty steadily all day. The clan were out in great force, and came by instalments to pay their duty to Aunt Plenty, and wish the compliments of the season to "our cousin." Archie appeared first, looking sad but steadfast, and went away with Phebe's letter in his left breast-pocket; feeling that life was still endurable, though his love was torn from him: for Rose had many comfortable things to say, and read him delicious bits from the voluminous correspondence lately begun.

Hardly was he gone, when Will and Geordie came marching in, looking as fine as grey uniforms with much scarlet piping could make them, and feeling peculiarly important, as this was their first essay in New Year's call-making. Brief was their stay, for they planned to visit every friend they had; and Rose could not help laughing at the droll mixture of manly dignity and boyish delight with which they drove off in their own carriage, both as erect as ramrods, arms folded, and caps stuck at exactly the same angle on each blond head.

"Here comes the other couple—Steve, in full feather, with a big bouquet for Kitty; and poor Mac looking like a gentleman and feeling like a martyr, I'm sure," said Rose, watching one carriage turn in as the other turned out of the great gate, with its arch of holly, ivy, and evergreen.

"Here he is: I've got him in tow for the day, and want you to cheer him up with a word of praise; for he came without a struggle, though planning to bolt somewhere with uncle" cried Steve, falling back to display his brother, who came in, looking remarkably well in his state and festival array; for polishing began to tell.

"A happy New Year, aunty; same to you, cousin, and best wishes for as many more as you deserve," said Mac, heeding Steve no more than if he had been a fly, as he gave the old lady a hearty kiss, and offered Rose a quaint little nosegay of pansies.

"Heart's-ease: do you think I need it?" she asked, looking up with sudden sobriety.

"We all do. Could I give you anything better on a day like this?"

"No: thank you very much," and a sudden dew came to Rose's eyes; for, though often blunt in speech, when Mac did do a tender thing, it always touched her; because he seemed to understand her moods so well.

"Has Archie been here? He said he shouldn't go anywhere else; but I hope you talked that nonsense out of his head," said Steve, settling his tie before the mirror.

"Yes, dear, he came; but looked so out of spirits, I really felt reproached. Rose cheered him up a little: but I don't believe he will feel equal to making calls, and I hope he won't; for his face tells the whole story much too plainly," answered Aunt Plenty, rustling about her bountiful table in her richest black silk, with all her old lace on.

"Oh, he'll get over it in a month or two, and Phebe will soon find another lover; so don't be worried about him, aunty," said Steve, with the air of a man who knew all about that sort of thing.

"If Archie does forget, I shall despise him; and I know Phebe won't try to find another lover, though she'll probably have them: she is so sweet and good!" cried Rose, indignantly; for, having taken the pair under her protection, she defended them valiantly.

"Then you'd have Arch hope against hope, and never give up, would you?" asked Mac, putting on his glasses to survey the thin boots which were his especial abomination.

"Yes, I would! for a lover is not worth having if he's not in earnest."

"Exactly: so you'd like them to wait and work and keep on loving till they made you relent, or plainly proved that it was no use."

"If they were good as well as constant, I think I should relent in time."

"I'll mention that to Pemberton; for he seemed to be hit the hardest, and a ray of hope will do him good, whether he is equal to the ten years' wait or not," put in Steve, who liked to rally Rose about her lovers.

"I'll never forgive you if you say a word to anyone. It is only Mac's odd way of asking questions, and I ought not to answer them. You *will* talk about such things, and I can't stop you; but I don't like it," said Rose, much annoyed.

"Poor little Penelope! she shall not be teased about her suitors, but left in peace till her Ulysses comes home," said Mac, sitting down to read the mottoes sticking out of certain fanciful bonbons on the table.

"It is this fuss about Archie which has demoralized us all. Even the owl waked up, and hasn't got over the excitement yet, you see. He's had no experience, poor fellow; so he doesn't know how to behave," observed Steve, regarding his bouquet with tender interest.

"That's true; and I asked for information, because I may be in love myself some day, and all this will be useful, don't you see?"

"You in love!" and Steve could not restrain a laugh at the idea of the bookworm a slave to the tender passion.

Quite unruffled, Mac leaned his chin in both hands, regarding them with a meditative eye, as he answered in his whimsical way—

"Why not? I intend to study love as well as medicine; for it is one of the most mysterious and remarkable diseases that afflict mankind, and the best way to understand it is to have it. I may catch it some day, and then I should like to know how to treat and cure it."

"If you take it as badly as you did measles and whooping-cough, it will go hard with you, old fellow," said Steve, much amused with the fancy.

"I want it to: no great experience comes or goes easily; and this is the greatest we can know, I believe, except death."

Something in Mac's quiet tone and thoughtful eyes made Rose look at him in surprise; for she had never heard him speak in that way before. Steve also stared for an instant, equally amazed; then said below his breath, with an air of mock anxiety—

"He's been catching something at the hospital, typhoid probably, and is beginning to wander. I'll take him quietly away before he gets any wilder. Come, old lunatic, we must be off."

"Don't be alarmed: I'm all right and much obliged for your advice; for I fancy I shall be a desperate lover when my time comes, if it ever does. You don't think it impossible, do you?" and Mac put the question so soberly that there was a general smile.

"Certainly not: you'll be a regular Douglas, tender and true," answered Rose, wondering what queer question would come next.

"Thank you. The fact is, I've been with Archie so much in his trouble lately that I've got interested in this matter, and very naturally want to investigate the subject as every rational man must, sooner or later: that's all. Now, Steve, I'm ready," and Mac got up as if the lesson was over.

"My dear, that boy is either a fool or a genius, and I'm sure I should be glad to know which," said Aunt Plenty, putting her bonbons to rights with a puzzled shake of her best cap.

"Time will show; but I incline to think that he is not a fool by any means," answered the girl, pulling a cluster of white roses out of her bosom to make room for the pansies, though they did not suit the blue gown half so well.

Just then Aunt Jessie came in to help them receive, with Jamie to make himself generally useful; which he proceeded to do by hovering round the table like a fly about a honey-pot, when not flattening his nose against the window-panes, to announce excitedly, "Here's another man coming up the drive!"

Charlie arrived next, in his most sunshiny humour; for anything social and festive was his delight, and when in this mood the Prince was quite irresistible. He brought a pretty bracelet for Rose, and was graciously allowed to put it on, while she chid him gently for his extravagance.

"I am only following your example; for, you know, 'nothing is too good for those we love, and giving away is the best thing one can do,' " he retorted, quoting words of her own.

"I wish you would follow my example in some other things as well as you do in this," said Rose, soberly, as Aunt Plenty called him to come and see if the punch was right.

"Must conform to the customs of society. Aunty's heart would be broken, if we did not drink her health in the good old fashion.

But don't be alarmed: I've a strong head of my own, and that's lucky; for I shall need it before I get through," laughed Charlie, showing a long list, as he turned away to gratify the old lady with all sorts of merry and affectionate compliments as the glasses touched.

Rose did feel rather alarmed; for, if he drank the health of all the owners of those names, she felt sure that Charlie would need a very strong head indeed. It was hard to say anything, then and there, without seeming disrespect to Aunt Plenty: yet she longed to remind her cousin of the example she tried to set him in this respect; for Rose never touched wine, and the boys knew it. She was thoughtfully turning the bracelet with its pretty device of turquoise forget-me-nots, when the giver came back to her, still bubbling over with good spirits.

"Dear little saint, you look as if you'd like to smash all the punch-bowls in the city, and save us jolly young fellows from tomorrow's headache."

"I should; for such headaches sometimes end in heartaches, I'm afraid. Dear Charlie, don't be angry; but you know better than I that this is a dangerous day for such as you: so do be careful for my sake," she added, with an unwonted touch of tenderness in her voice; for, looking at the gallant figure before her, it was impossible to repress the womanly longing to keep it always as brave and blithe as now.

Charlie saw that new softness in the eyes that never looked unkindly on him, fancied that it meant more than it did, and, with a sudden fervour in his own voice, answered quickly—

"My darling, I will!"

The glow which had risen to his face was reflected in hers; for at that moment it seemed as if it would be possible to love this cousin, who was so willing to be led by her, and so much needed some helpful influence to make a noble man of him. The thought came and went like a flash; but gave her a quick heart-throb, as if the old affection was trembling on the verge of some warmer sentiment and left her with a sense of responsibility never felt before. Obeying the impulse, she said, with a pretty blending of earnestness and playfulness—

"If I wear the bracelet to remember you by, you must wear this to remind you of your promise."

"And you," whispered Charlie, bending his head to kiss the hands that put a little white rose in his button-hole.

Just at that most interesting moment, they became aware of an arrival in the front drawing-room, whither Aunt Plenty had discreetly retired. Rose felt grateful for the interruption; because, not being at all sure of the state of her heart as yet, she was afraid of letting a sudden impulse lead her too far. But Charlie, conscious that a very propitious instant had been spoilt, regarded the newcomer with anything but a benignant expression of countenance; and whispering, "Good-bye, my Rose, I shall look in this evening to see how you are after the fatigues of the day," he went away, with such a cool nod to poor Fun See that the amiable Asiatic thought he must have mortally offended him.

Rose had little leisure to analyse the new emotions of which she was conscious: for Mr. Tokio came up at once to make his compliments with a comical mingling of Chinese courtesy and American awkwardness and before he had got his hat on Jamie shouted with admiring energy—

"Here's another! Oh, such a swell!"

They now came thick and fast for many hours; and the ladies stood bravely at their posts till late into the evening. Then Aunt Jessie went home, escorted by a very sleepy little son, and Aunt Plenty retired to bed used up. Dr. Alec had returned in good season; for *his* friends were not fashionable ones: but Aunt Myra had sent up for him in hot haste, and he had good-naturedly obeyed the summons. In fact, he was quite used to them now; for Mrs. Myra, having tried a variety of dangerous diseases, had finally decided upon heart-complaint as the one most likely to keep her friends in a chronic state of anxiety, and was continually sending word that she was dying. One gets used to palpitations as well as everything else, so the doctor felt no alarm, but always went, and prescribed some harmless remedy with the most amiable sobriety and patience.

Rose was tired, but not sleepy, and wanted to think over several things; so instead of going to bed she sat down before the open fire in the study to wait for her uncle, and perhaps Charlie, though she did not expect him so late.

Aunt Myra's palpitations must have been unusually severe; for the clock struck twelve before Dr. Alec came, and Rose was preparing to end her reverie, when the sound of someone fumbling at the hall-door made her jump up, saying to herself—

"Poor man! his hands are so cold he can't get his latch-key in. Is that you, uncle?" she added, running to admit him; for Jane was slow, and the night as bitter as it was brilliant.

A voice answered "Yes," and as the door swung open in walked—not Dr. Alec, but Charlie, who immediately took one of the hall chairs, and sat there with his hat on, rubbing his gloveless hands, and blinking as if the light dazzled him, as he said in a rapid, abrupt sort of tone—

"I told you I'd come—left the fellows keeping it up gloriously—going to see the old year out, you know. But I promised—never break my word—and here I am. Angel in blue, did you slay your thousands?"

"Hush! the waiters are still about: come to the study fire and warm yourself; you must be frozen," said Rose, going before to roll up the easy-chair.

"Not at all—never warmer—looks very comfortable, though. Where's uncle?" asked Charlie, following with his hat still on, his hands in his pockets, and his eye fixed steadily on the bright head in front of him.

"Aunt Myra sent for him, and I was waiting up to see how she was," answered Rose, busily mending the fire.

Charlie laughed, and sat down upon a corner of the library table. "Poor old soul! what a pity she doesn't die before he is quite worn out. A little too much ether some of these times would send her off quite comfortably, you know."

"Don't speak in that way. Uncle says imaginary troubles are often as hard to bear as real ones," said Rose, turning round displeased.

Till now she had not fairly looked at him; for recollections of the morning made her a little shy. His attitude and appearance surprised her as much as his words, and the quick change in her face seemed to remind him of his manners. Getting up, he hastily took off his hat, and stood looking at her with a curiously fixed yet absent look, as he said in the same rapid, abrupt way, as if, when once started, he found it hard to stop—

"I beg pardon—only joking—very bad taste I know, and won't do it again. The heat of the room makes me a little dizzy, and I think I got a chill coming out. It *is* cold—I *am* frozen, I dare say—though I drove like the devil."

"Not that bad horse of yours, I hope? I know it is dangerous, so late and alone," said Rose, shrinking behind the big chair, as

Charlie approached the fire, carefully avoiding a footstool in his way.

"Danger is exciting—that's why I like it. No man ever called me a coward—let him try it once. I never give in—and that horse shall *not* conquer me. I'll break his neck, if he breaks my spirit doing it. No—I don't mean that—never mind—it's all right," and Charlie laughed in a way that troubled her, because there was no mirth in it.

"Have you had a pleasant day?" asked Rose, looking at him intently, as he stood pondering over the cigar and match which he held, as if doubtful which to strike and which to smoke.

"Day? oh, yes, capital. About two thousand calls, and a nice little supper at the Club. Randal can't sing any more than a crow; but I left him with a glass of champagne upside-down trying to give them my old favourite—

"' 'Tis better to laugh than be sighing;' "

and Charlie burst forth in that bacchanalian melody at the top of his voice, waving an allumette-holder over his head to represent Randal's inverted wine-glass.

"Hush! you'll wake aunty," cried Rose, in a tone so commanding that he broke off in the middle of a *roulade* to stare at her with a blank look, as he said apologetically—

"I was merely showing how it should be done. Don't be angry, dearest—look at me as you did this morning, and I'll swear never to sing another note if you say so. I'm only a little gay— we drank your health handsomely, and they all congratulated me. Told 'em it wasn't out yet. Stop, though—I didn't mean to mention that. No matter—I'm always in a scrape; but you always forgive me in the sweetest way. Do it now, and don't be angry, little darling;" and, dropping the vase, he went towards her with a sudden excitement that made her shrink behind the chair.

She was not angry, but shocked and frightened; for she knew now what the matter was, and grew so pale he saw it, and asked pardon before she could utter a rebuke.

"We'll talk of that tomorrow: it is very late; go home, now, please, before uncle comes," she said, trying to speak naturally; yet betraying her distress by the tremor of her voice, and the sad anxiety in her eyes.

"Yes, yes, I will go—you are tired—I'll make it all right

tomorrow;" and, as if the sound of his uncle's name steadied him for an instant, Charlie made for the door with an unevenness of gait which would have told the shameful truth, if his words had not already done so. Before he reached it, however, the sound of wheels arrested him; and, leaning against the wall, he listened with a look of dismay mingled with amusement creeping over his face. "Brutus has bolted—now I *am* in a fix. Can't walk home with this horrid dizziness in my head. It's the cold, Rose, nothing else, I do assure you; and a chill—yes, a chill. See here! let one of those fellows there lend me an arm— no use to go after that brute. Won't mother be frightened though, when he gets home?" and with that empty laugh again, he fumbled for the door-handle.

"No, no: don't let them see you! don't let anyone know! Stay here till uncle comes, and he'll take care of you. O Charlie! how could you do it! how could you when you promised?" and, forgetting fear in the sudden sense of shame and anguish that came over her, Rose ran to him, caught his hand from the lock, and turned the key; then, as if she could not bear to see him standing there with that vacant smile upon his lips, she dropped into a chair and covered up her face.

The cry, the act, and more than all, the sight of the bowed head would have sobered poor Charlie, if it had not been too late. He looked about the room, with a vague, despairing look, as if to find the reason fast slipping from his control: but heat and cold, excitement and reckless pledging of many healths, had done their work too well to make instant sobriety possible; and owning his defeat with a groan, he turned away and threw himself face-downward on the sofa; one of the saddest sights the new year looked upon as it came in.

As she sat there with hidden eyes, Rose felt that something dear to her was dead for ever. The ideal, which all women cherish, look for, and too often think they have found when love glorifies a mortal man, is hard to give up, especially when it comes in the likeness of the first lover who touches a young girl's heart. Rose had just begun to feel that perhaps this cousin, despite his faults, might yet become the hero that he sometimes looked; and the thought that she might be his inspiration was growing sweet to her, although she had not entertained it until very lately. Alas, how short the tender dream had been, how rude the awakening! how impossible it would be ever again to surround that fallen figure with all the romance of an innocent fancy, or gift it with the high attributes beloved by a noble nature!

Breathing heavily in the sudden sleep that kindly brought a brief oblivion of himself, he lay with flushed cheeks, disordered hair, and at his feet the little rose, that never would be fresh and fair again—a pitiful contrast now to the brave, blithe young man who went so gaily out that morning to be so ignominiously overthrown at night.

Many girls would have made light of a trespass so readily forgiven by the world; but Rose had not yet learned to offer temptation with a smile, and shut her eyes to the weakness that makes a man a brute. It always grieved or disgusted her to see it in others, and now it was very terrible to have it brought so near—not in its worst form, by any means, but bad enough to wring her heart with shame and sorrow, and fill her mind with dark forebodings for the future. So she could only sit mourning for the Charlie that might have been, while watching the Charlie that was, with an ache at her heart which found no relief till, putting her hands there as if to ease the pain, they touched the pansies, faded, but still showing gold among the sombre purple; and then two great tears dropped on them as she sighed—

"Ah me! I do need heart's-ease sooner than I thought!"

Her uncle's step made her spring up and unlock the door, showing him such an altered face that he stopped short, ejaculating in dismay—

"Good heavens, child! what's the matter?" adding, as she pointed to the sofa in pathetic silence, "Is he hurt?—ill?—dead?"

"No, uncle: he is—" She could not utter the ugly word, but whispered, with a sob in her throat, "Be kind to him," and fled away to her own room, feeling as if a great disgrace had fallen on the house.

10

The Sad and Sober Part

"How will he look? what will he say? can anything make us forget and be happy again?" were the first questions Rose asked herself as soon as she woke from the brief sleep which followed a long, sad vigil. It seemed as if the whole world must be changed, because a trouble darkened it for her. She was too young to know how possible it is to forgive much greater sins than this, forget far heavier disappointments, outlive higher hopes, and bury loves compared to which hers was but a girlish fancy. She wished it had not been so bright a day, wondered how her birds could sing with such shrill gaiety, put no ribbon in her hair, and said, as she looked at the reflection of her own tired face in the glass—

"Poor thing! you thought the new leaf would have something pleasant on it. The story has been very sweet and easy to read so far, but the sad and sober part is coming now."

A tap at the door reminded her that, in spite of her afflictions, breakfast must be eaten; and the sudden thought that Charlie might still be in the house made her hurry to the door, to find Dr. Alec waiting for her with his morning smile. She drew him in, and whispered anxiously, as if someone lay dangerously ill near by—

"Is he better, uncle? Tell me all about it: I can bear it now."

Some men would have smiled at her innocent distress, and told her this was only what was to be expected and endured; but Dr. Alec believed in the pure instincts that make youth beautiful, desired to keep them true, and hoped his girl would never learn

127

to look unmoved by pain and pity upon any human being vanquished by a vice, no matter how trivial it seemed, how venial it was held. So his face grew grave, though his voice was cheerful as he answered—

"All right, I dare say, by this time; for sleep is the best medicine in such cases. I took him home last night, and no one knows he came but you and I."

"No one ever shall. How did you do it, uncle?"

"Just slipped out of the long study-window, and got him cannily off; for the air and motion, after a dash of cold water, brought him round, and he was glad to be safely landed at home. His rooms are below, you know: so no one was disturbed, and I left him sleeping nicely."

"Thank you so much," sighed Rose. "And Brutus? weren't they frightened when he got back alone?"

"Not at all: the sagacious beast went quietly to the stable, and the sleepy groom asked no questions; for Charlie often sends the horse round by himself when it is late or stormy. Rest easy, dear: no eye but ours saw the poor lad come and go, and we'll forgive it for love's sake."

"Yes, but not forget it. *I* never can; and he will never be again to me the Charlie I've been so proud and fond of all these years. O uncle, such a pity! such a pity!"

"Don't break your tender heart about it, child; for it is not incurable, thank God! I don't make light of it; but I am sure that under better influences Charlie will redeem himself, because his impulses are good, and this his only vice. I can hardly blame him for what he is, because his mother did the harm. I declare to you, Rose, I sometimes feel as if I must break out against that woman, and thunder in her ears that she is ruining the immortal soul for which she is responsible to heaven."

Dr. Alec seldom spoke in this way, and when he did it was rather awful; for his indignation was of the righteous sort, and such thunder often rouses up a drowsy soul when sunshine has no effect. Rose liked it, and sincerely wished Aunt Clara had been there to get the benefit of the outbreak; for she needed just such an awakening from the self-indulgent dream in which she lived.

"Do it, and save Charlie before it is too late!" she cried, kindling herself as she watched him; for he looked like a roused lion, as he walked about the room, with his hand clenched and a spark in his eye, evidently in desperate earnest, and ready to do almost anything.

"Will you help?" he asked, stopping suddenly, with a look that made her stand up straight and strong as she answered with an eager voice—

"I will."

"Then don't love him—yet."

That startled her; but she asked steadily, though her heart began to beat and her colour to come—

"Why not?"

"Firstly, because no woman should give her happiness into the keeping of a man without fixed principles; secondly, because the hope of being worthy of you will help him more than any prayers or preaching of mine. Thirdly, because it will need all our wit and patience to undo the work of nearly four and twenty years. You understand what I mean?"

"Yes, sir."

"Can you say 'No' when he asks you to say 'Yes', and wait a little for your happiness?"

"I can."

"And will you?"

"I will."

"Then I'm satisfied, and a great weight taken off my heart. I can't help seeing what goes on, or trembling when I think of you setting sail with no better pilot than poor Charlie. Now you answer as I hoped you would, and I am proud of my girl!"

They had been standing with the width of the room between them, Dr. Alec looking very much like a commander issuing orders, Rose like a well-drilled private obediently receiving them; and both wore the air of soldiers getting ready for a battle with the bracing of nerves and quickening of the blood brave souls feel as they put on their armour. At the last words he went to her, brushed back the hair and kissed her on the forehead with a tender sort of gravity, and a look that made her feel as if he had endowed her with the Victoria cross for courage on the field.

No more was said then; for Aunt Plenty called them down, and the day's duties began. But that brief talk showed Rose what to do, and fitted her to do it; for it set her to thinking of the duty one owes one's self in loving as in all the other great passions or experiences which make or mar a life.

E

She had plenty of time for quiet meditation that day, because everyone was resting after yesterday's festivity; and she sat in her little room planning out a new year, so full of good works, grand successes, and beautiful romances, that if it could have been realized the Millennium would have begun. It was a great comfort to her, however, and lightened the long hours haunted by a secret desire to know when Charlie would come, and a secret fear of the first meeting. She was sure he would be bowed down with humiliation and repentance, and a struggle took place in her mind between the pity she could not help feeling, and the disapprobation she ought to show. She decided to be gentle, but very frank; to reprove, but also to console, and try to improve the softened moment by inspiring the culprit with a wish for all the virtues which make a perfect man.

This fond delusion grew quite absorbing, and her mind was full of it as she sat watching the sun set from her western window, and admiring with dreamy eyes the fine effect of the distant hills clear and dark against a daffodil sky, when the bang of a door made her sit suddenly erect in her low chair, and say with a catch in her breath—

"He is coming! I must remember what I promised uncle, and be very firm."

Usually Charlie announced his approach with music of some sort: now he neither whistled, hummed, nor sung, but came so quietly Rose was sure that he dreaded the meeting as much as she did, and, compassionating his natural confusion, did not look round as the steps drew near. She thought perhaps he would go down upon his knees, as he used to after a boyish offence, but hoped not; for too much humility distressed her: so she waited for the first demonstration anxiously.

It was rather a shock when it came, however; for a great nosegay dropped into her lap, and a voice, bold and gay as usual, said lightly—

"Here she is, as pretty and pensive as you please. Is the world hollow, our doll stuffed with sawdust, and do we want to go into a nunnery today, cousin?"

Rose was so taken aback by this unexpected coolness that the flowers lay unnoticed, as she looked up with a face so full of surprise, reproach, and something like shame, that it was impossible to mistake its meaning. Charlie did not; and had the grace to redden deeply, and his eyes fell, as he said quickly, though in the same light tone—

"I humbly apologize for—coming so late last night. Don't be hard upon me, cousin: you know America expects every man to do his duty on New Year's day."

"I am tired of forgiving! You make and break promises as easily as you did years ago, and I shall never ask you for another," answered Rose, putting the bouquet away; for the apology did not satisfy her, and she would not be bribed to silence.

"But, my dear girl, you are so very exacting, so peculiar in your notions, and so angry about trifles, that a poor fellow can't please you, try as he will," began Charlie, ill at ease, but too proud to show half the penitence he felt, not so much for the fault as for her discovery of it.

"I am not angry: I am grieved and disappointed; for *I* expect every man to do his duty in another way, and keep his word to the uttermost, as I try to do. If that is exacting, I'm sorry, and won't trouble you with my old-fashioned notions any more."

"Bless my soul! what a rout about nothing! I own that I forgot: I know I acted like a fool, and I beg pardon; what more *can* I do?"

"Act like a man, and never let me be so terribly ashamed of you again as I was last night," and Rose gave a little shiver as she thought of it.

That involuntary act hurt Charlie more than her words, and it was his turn now to feel "terribly ashamed;" for the events of the previous evening were very hazy in his mind, and fear magnified them greatly. Turning sharply away, he went and stood by the fire, quite at a loss how to make his peace this time, because Rose was so unlike herself. Usually a word of excuse sufficed, and she seemed glad to pardon and forget; now, though very quiet, there was something almost stern about her that surprised and daunted him; for how could he know that all the while her pitiful heart was pleading for him, and the very effort to control it made her seem a little hard and cold? As he stood there, restlessly fingering the ornaments upon the chimney-piece, his eye brightened suddenly; and, taking up the pretty bracelet lying there, he went slowly back to her, saying in a tone that was humble and serious enough now—

"I *will* act like a man, and you shall never be ashamed again.

Only be kind to me: let me put this on, and promise afresh; this time I swear I'll keep it. Won't you trust me, Rose?"

It was very hard to resist the pleading voice and eyes: for this humility was dangerous; and, but for Uncle Alec, Rose would have answered "Yes." The blue forget-me-nots reminded her of her own promise; and she kept it with difficulty now, to be glad always afterwards. Putting back the offered trinket with a gentle touch, she said firmly, though she dared not look up into the anxious face bending towards her—

"No, Charlie: I can't wear it yet. My hands must be free if I'm to help you as I ought. I will be kind; I will trust you: but don't swear anything, only try to resist temptation, and we'll all stand by you."

Charlie did not like that, and lost the ground he had gained by saying impetuously—

"I don't want anyone but you to stand by me, and I must be sure you won't desert me, else, while I'm mortifying soul and body to please you, some stranger will come and steal your heart away from me. I couldn't bear that; so I give you fair warning, in such a case I'll break the bargain, and go straight to the devil."

The last sentence spoilt it all; for it was both masterful and defiant. Rose had the Campbell spirit in her, though it seldom showed; as yet she valued her liberty more than any love offered her, and she resented the authority he assumed too soon— resented it all the more warmly, because of the effort she was making to reinstate her hero, who would insist on being a very faulty and ungrateful man. She rose straight out of her chair, saying with a look and tone which rather startled her hearer, and convinced him that she was no longer a tender-hearted child, but a woman with a will of her own, and a spirit as proud and fiery as any of her race—

"My heart is my own, to dispose of as I please. Don't shut yourself out of it by presuming too much; for you have no claim on me but that of cousinship, and you never will have unless you earn it. Remember that, and neither threaten nor defy me any more."

For a minute it was doubtful whether Charlie would answer this flash with another, and a general explosion ensue; or wisely quench the flame with the mild answer which turneth away wrath. He chose the latter course, and made it very effective by throwing himself down before his offended goddess, as he had often done in jest; this time it was not acting, but serious earnest, and there was real passion in his voice, as he caught Rose's dress in both hands, saying eagerly—

"No, no! don't shut your heart against me, or I shall turn desperate. I'm not half good enough for such a saint as you, but you can do what you will with me. I only need a motive to make a man of me, and where can I find a stronger one than in trying to keep your love?"

"It is not yours yet," began Rose, much moved, though all the while she felt as if she was on a stage, and had a part to play for Charlie had made life so like a melodrama that it was hard for him to be quite simple even when most sincere.

"Let me earn it, then. Show me how, and I'll do anything: for you are my good angel, Rose; and, if you cast me off, I feel as if I shouldn't care how soon there was an end of me," cried Charlie, getting tragic in his earnestness, and putting both arms round her, as if his only safety lay in clinging to this beloved fellow-creature.

Behind footlights it would have been irresistible; but somehow it did not touch the one spectator, though she had neither time nor skill to discover why. For all their ardour the words did not ring quite true: despite the grace of the attitude, she would have liked him better manfully erect upon his feet; and, though the gesture was full of tenderness, a subtle instinct made her shrink away, as she said with a composure that surprised herself, even more than it did him—

"Please don't. No, I will promise nothing yet; for I must respect the man I love."

That brought Charlie to his feet, pale with something deeper than anger; for the recoil told him more plainly than the words how much he had fallen in her regard since yesterday. The memory of the happy moment when she gave the rose with that new softness in her eyes, the shy colour, the sweet "for my sake," came back with sudden vividness, contrasting sharply with the now averted face, the hand outstretched to put him back, the shrinking figure: and in that instant's silence poor Charlie realized what he had lost; for a girl's first thought of love is as delicate a thing as the rosy morning-glory, that a breath of air can shatter. Only a hint of evil, only an hour's debasement for him, a moment's glimpse for her of the coarser

pleasures men know, and the innocent heart, just opening to
bless and to be blessed, closed again like a sensitive plant, and
shut him out perhaps for ever.

The consciousness of this turned him pale with fear: for his
love was deeper than she knew; and he proved this when he
said in a tone so full of mingled pain and patience that it touched
her to the heart—

"You *shall* respect me if I can make you; and when I've
earned it may I hope for something more?"

She looked up then, saw in his face the noble shame, the
humble sort of courage, that shows repentance to be genuine,
and gives promise of success, and, with a hopeful smile that was
a cordial to him, answered heartily—

"You may."

"Bless you for that! I'll make no promises, I'll ask for none:
only trust me, Rose; and, while you treat me like a cousin,
remember that no matter how many lovers you may have,
you'll never be to any of them as dear as you are to me."

A traitorous break in his voice warned Charlie to stop there:
and, with no other good-bye, he very wisely went away, leaving
Rose to put the neglected flowers into water with remorseful
care, and lay away the bracelet, saying to herself—

"I'll never wear it till I feel as I did before; then he shall
put it on, and I'll say 'Yes.' "

11

Small Temptations

"O ROSE, I've got something *so* exciting to tell you!" cried Kitty Van Tassel, skipping into the carriage next morning when her friend called for her to go shopping.

Kitty always did have some "perfectly thrilling" communication to make, and Rose had learned to take them quietly: but the next demonstration was a new one; for, regardless alike of curious observers outside and disordered hats within, Kitty caught Rose round the neck, exclaiming in a rapturous whisper—

"My dearest creature, I'm engaged!"

"I'm so glad! Of course it is Steve?"

"Dear fellow, he did it last night in the nicest way, and mamma is *so* delighted. Now what *shall* I be married in?" and Kitty composed herself with a face full of the deepest anxiety.

"How can you talk of that so soon? Why, Kit, you unromantic girl, you ought to be thinking of your lover and not your clothes," said Rose, amused, yet rather scandalized at such want of sentiment.

"I *am* thinking of my lover; for he says he will *not* have a long engagement, so I *must* begin to think about the most important things at once, mustn't I?"

"Ah, he wants to be sure of you; for you are such a slippery creature he is afraid you'll treat him as you did poor Jackson and the rest," interrupted Rose, shaking her finger at her prospective cousin, who had tried this pastime twice before, and was rather proud than otherwise of her brief engagements.

"You needn't scold, for I know I'm right; and, when you've been in society as long as I have, you'll find that the only way to

135

really know a man is to be engaged to him. While they want you, they are all devotion; but when they think they've got you, then you find out what wretches they are," answered Kitty, with an air of worldly wisdom which contrasted oddly with her youthful face and giddy manners.

"A sad prospect for poor Steve, unless I give him a hint to look well to his ways."

"O my dear child, I'm sure of him; for my experience has made me very sharp, and I'm convinced I can manage him without a bit of trouble. We've known each other for ages" (Steve was twenty and Kitty eighteen) "and always been the best of friends. Besides he is quite my ideal man: I never *could* bear big hands and feet, and his are simply adorable. Then he's the best dancer I know, and dresses in perfect taste. I really do believe I fell in love with his pocket-handkerchiefs first; they were so enchanting I couldn't resist," laughed Kitty, pulling a large one out of her pocket, and burying her little nose in the folds, which shed a delicious fragrance upon the air.

"Now that looks promising, and I begin to think you *have* got a little sentiment after all," said Rose, well pleased; for the merry brown eyes had softened suddenly, and a quick colour came up in Kitty's cheek, as she answered, still half hiding her face in the beloved handkerchief—

"Of course I have, lots of it; only I'm ashamed to show it to most people, because it's the style to take everything in the most nonchalant way. My gracious, Rose, you'd have thought me a romantic goose last night while Steve proposed in the back parlour: for I actually cried; he was so dreadfully in earnest when I pretended that I didn't care for him, and so very dear and nice when I told the truth. I didn't know he had it in him; but he came out delightfully, and never cared a particle, though I dropped tears all over his lovely shirt-front. Wasn't that good of him? for you know he hates his things to be mussed.'

"He's a true Campbell, and has got a good warm heart of his own under those fine fronts of his. Aunt Jane doesn't believe in sentiment, so he has been trained never to show any: but it is there, and you must encourage him to let it out; not foolishly, but in a way to make him more manly and serious."

"I will if I can; for, though I wouldn't own this to everybody, I like it in him very much, and feel as if Steve and I should get on beautifully. Here we are; now be sure not to breathe a word if we meet anyone; I want it to be a profound secret for a week at least," added Kitty, whisking the handkerchief out of sight, as the carriage stopped before the fashionable store they were about to visit.

Rose promised with a smile; for Kitty's face betrayed her without words, so full was it of the happiness which few eyes fail to understand wherever they see it.

"Just a glance at the silks. You ask my opinion about white ones, and I'll look at the colours. Mamma says satin; but that is out now, and I've set my heart on the heaviest corded thing I can find," whispered Kitty, as they went rustling by the long counters strewn with all that could delight the feminine eye, and tempt the feminine pocket.

"Isn't that opal the loveliest thing you ever saw? I'm afraid I'm too dark to wear it, but it would just suit you. You'll need a variety you know," added Kitty in a significant aside, as Rose stood among the white silks, while her companion affected great interest in the delicate hues laid before her.

"But I have a variety now, and don't need a new dress of any sort."

"No matter, get it; else it will be gone: you've worn all yours several times already, and *must* have a new one whether you need it or not. Dear me! if I had as much pocket-money as you have, I'd come out in a fresh toilet at every party I went to," answered Kitty, casting an envious eye upon the rainbow piles before her.

The quick-witted shopman saw that a wedding was afoot; for when two pretty girls whisper, smile, and blush over their shopping, clerks scent bridal finery, and a transient gleam of interest brightens their imperturbable countenances, and lends a brief energy to languid voices weary with crying "Cash!" Gathering both silks with practised turn of the hand, he held them up for inspection, detecting at a glance which was the bride-elect and which the friend; for Kitty fell back to study the effect of the silvery white folds with an absorbing interest impossible to mistake, while Rose sat looking at the opal as if she scarcely heard a bland voice saying, with the rustle of silk so dear to girlish ears—

"A superb thing; just opened; all the rage in Paris; very rare shade; trying to most, as the lady says, but quite perfect for a blonde."

E*

Rose was not listening to those words, but to others which
Aunt Clara had lately uttered; laughed at then, but thought over
more than once since.

"I'm tired of hearing people wonder why Miss Campbell does
not dress more. Simplicity is all very well for schoolgirls and
women who can't afford anything better, but *you* can, and you
really ought. Your things are pretty enough in their way, and
I rather like you to have a style of your own; but it looks odd
and people will think you are mean if you don't make more show.
Besides, you don't do justice to your beauty, which would be
both peculiar and striking, if you'd devote your mind to getting
up ravishing costumes."

Much more to the same effect did her aunt say, discussing the
subject quite artistically, and unconsciously appealing to several
of Rose's ruling passions. One was a love for the delicate fabrics,
colours, and ornaments which refined tastes enjoy, and whose
costliness keeps them from ever growing common; another, her
strong desire to please the eyes of those she cared for, and gratify
their wishes in the smallest matter if she could. And last, but not
least, the natural desire of a young and pretty woman to enhance
the beauty which she so soon discovers to be her most potent
charm for the other sex, her passport to a high place among her
maiden peers.

She had thought seriously of surprising and delighting everyone, by appearing in a costume which should do justice to the
loveliness which was so modest that it was apt to forget itself in
admiring others—what girls call a "ravishing" dress, such as
she could imagine and easily procure by the magic of the For-
tunatus' purse in her pocket. She had planned it all: the shimmer
of pale silk through lace like woven frostwork, ornaments of
some classic pattern, and all the dainty accessories as perfect as
time, taste, and money could make them.

She knew that Uncle Alec's healthful training had given her
a figure that could venture on any fashion, and Nature blessed
her with a complexion that defied all hues. So it was little wonder
that she felt a strong desire to use these gifts, not for the pleasure
of display, but to seem fair in the eyes that seldom looked at her
without a tender sort of admiration, all the more winning when
no words marred the involuntary homage women love.

These thoughts were busy in Rose's mind, as she sat looking
at the lovely silk, and wondering what Charlie would say if she

should some night burst upon him in a pale, rosy cloud, like the Aurora to whom he often likened her. She knew it would please him very much, and she longed to do all she honestly could to gratify the poor fellow; for her tender heart already felt some remorseful pangs, remembering how severe she had been the night before. She could not revoke her words, because she meant them every one; but she might be kind, and show that she did not wholly shut him out from her regard, by asking him to go with her to Kitty's ball, and gratify his artistic taste by a lovely costume. A very girlish but kindly plan; for that ball was to be the last of her frivolities, so she wanted it to be a pleasant one, and felt that "being friends" with Charlie would add much to her enjoyment. This idea made her fingers tighten on the gleaming fabric so temptingly upheld, and she was about to take it when, "If ye please, sir, would ye kindly tell me where I'd be finding the flannel place?" said a voice behind her; and, glancing up, she saw a meek little Irishwoman looking quite lost and out of place among the luxuries around her.

"Downstairs, turn to the left," was the clerk's hasty reply, with a vague wave of the hand which left the inquirer more in the dark than ever.

Rose saw the woman's perplexity, and said kindly, "I'll show you: this way."

"I'm ashamed to be throublin' ye, miss; but it's strange I am in it, and wouldn't be comin' here at all, at all, barrin' they tould me I'd get the bit I'm wantin' chaper in this big shop than the little ones more becomin' the like o' me," explained the little woman humbly.

Rose looked again, as she led the way through a well-dressed crowd of busy shoppers: and something in the anxious, tired face under the old woollen hood; the bare, purple hands, holding fast a meagre wallet and a faded scrap of the dotted flannel little children's frocks are so often made of—touched the generous heart, that never could see want without an impulse to relieve it. She had meant only to point the way; but, following a new impulse, she went on, listening to the poor soul's motherly prattle about "me baby," and the "throuble" it was to "find clothes for the growin' childer, when me man is out av work, and the bit and sup inconvaynient these hard times," as they descended to that darksome lower world, where necessities take refuge when luxuries crowd them out from the gayer place above,

The presence of a lady made Mrs. Sullivan's shopping very easy now; and her one poor "bit" of flannel grew miraculously into yards of several colours, since the shabby purse was no lighter when she went away, wiping her eyes on the corner of a big, brown bundle. A very little thing and no one saw it but a wooden-faced clerk, who never told; yet it did Rose good and sent her up into the light again with a sober face, thinking self-reproachfully—

"What right have I to more gay gowns, when some poor babies have none; or to spend time making myself fine, while there is so much bitter want in the world?"

Nevertheless the pretty things were just as tempting as ever, and she yearned for the opal silk with a renewed yearning when she got back. I am not sure that it would not have been bought in spite of her better self, if a good angel in the likeness of a stout lady with silvery curls about the benevolent face, enshrined in a plain bonnet, had not accosted her as she joined Kitty, still brooding over the wedding gowns.

"I waited a moment for you, my dear, because I'm in haste, and very glad to save myself a journey or a note," began the newcomer in a low tone, as Rose shook hands with the most affectionate respect. "You know the great box factory was burned a day or two ago, and over a hundred girls thrown out of work. Some were hurt and are in the hospital, many have no homes to go to, and nearly all need temporary help of some sort. We've had so many calls this winter I hardly know which way to turn; for the want is pressing, and I've had my fingers in so many purses I'm almost ashamed to ask again. Any little con-tribution—ah, thank you; I was sure you wouldn't fail me, my good child," and Mrs. Gardener warmly pressed the hand that went so quickly into the little portemonnaie, and came out so generously filled.

"Let me know how else I can help, and thank you very much for allowing me to have a share in your good works," said Rose, forgetting all about gay gowns, as she watched the black bonnet go briskly away, with an approving smile on the fine old face inside it.

"You extravagant thing! how could you give so much?" whispered Kitty, whose curious eye had seen three figures on the single bill which had so rapidly changed hands.

"I believe if Mrs. Gardener asked me for my head I should

give it to her," answered Rose lightly; then turning to the silks she asked, "Which have you decided upon; the yellow white or the blue, the corded or the striped?"

"I've decided nothing, except that *you* are to have the pink, and wear it at my—ahem! ball," said Kitty, who *had* made up her mind, but could not give her orders till mamma had been consulted.

"No, I can't afford it just yet. I never overstep my allowance, and I shall have to if I get any more finery. Come, we ought not to waste time here, if you have all the patterns you want," and Rose walked quickly away, glad that it was out of her power to break through two resolutions which hitherto had been faithfully kept—one to dress simply for example's sake, the other not to be extravagant for charity's sake.

As Rosamond had her day of misfortunes, so this seemed to be one of small temptations to Rose. After she had set Kitty down at home and been to see her new houses, she drove about doing various errands for the aunts; and, while waiting in the carriage for the execution of an order, young Pemberton came by.

As Steve said, this gentleman had been "hard hit," and still hovered moth-like about the forbidden light. Being the most eligible *parti* of the season, his regard was considered a distinction to be proud of; and Rose had been well scolded by Aunt Clara for refusing so honourable a mate. The girl liked him; and he was the suitor of whom she had spoken so respectfully to Dr. Alec, because he had no need of the heiress and had sincerely loved the woman. He had been away, and she hoped had got over his disappointment as happily as the rest; but now when he saw her, and came hurrying up so hungry for a word, she felt that he had not forgotten, and was too kind to chill him with the bow which plainly says, "Don't stop."

A personable youth was Pemberton, and had brought with him from the wilds of Canada a sable-lined overcoat, which was the envy of every masculine and the admiration of every feminine friend he had; and, as he stood at her carriage window, Rose knew that this luxurious garment and its stalwart wearer were objects of interest to the passers-by. It chanced that the tide of shoppers flowed in that direction; and, as she chatted, familiar faces often passed with glances, smiles, and nods of varying curiosity, significance, and wonder.

She could not help feeling a certain satisfaction in giving him a moment's pleasure, since she could do no more; but it was not that amiable desire alone which made her ignore the neat white parcels which the druggist's boy deposited on the front seat, and kept her lingering a little longer to enjoy one of the small triumphs which girls often risk more than a cold in the head to display. The sight of several snow-flakes on the broad shoulders which partially obstructed her view, as well as the rapidly increasing animation of Pemberton's chat, reminded her that it was high time to go.

"I mustn't keep you: it is beginning to storm," she said, taking up her muff, much to old Jacob's satisfaction; for small talk is not exciting to a hungry man whose nose feels like an icicle.

"Is it? I thought the sun was shining." And the absorbed gentleman turned to the outer world with visible reluctance, for it looked very warm and cosy in the red-lined carriage.

"Wise people say we must carry our sunshine with us," answered Rose, taking refuge in commonplaces, for the face at the window grew pensive suddenly, as he answered, with a longing look—

"I wish I could:" then, smiling gratefully, he added, "Thank you for giving me a little of yours."

"You are very welcome." And Rose offered him her hand, while her eyes mutely asked pardon for withholding her leave to keep it.

He pressed it silently, and, shouldering the umbrella which he forgot to open, turned away, with an "up-again-and-take-another" expression, which caused the soft eyes to follow him admiringly.

"I ought not to have kept him a minute longer than I could help: for it wasn't all pity; it was my foolish wish to show off and do as I liked for a minute, to pay for being good about the gown. Oh me! how weak and silly I am in spite of all my trying!" And Miss Campbell fell into a remorseful reverie, which lasted till she got home.

"Now, young man, what brought you out in this driving storm?" asked Rose, as Jamie came stamping in that same afternoon.

"Mamma sent you a new book—thought you'd like it: *I* don't mind your old storms!" replied the boy, wrestling his way out of his coat, and presenting a face as round and red and shiny as a well-polished Baldwin apple.

"Much obliged: it is just the day to enjoy it, and I was longing for something nice to read," said Rose, as Jamie sat down upon the lower stair for a protracted struggle with his rubber boots.

"Here you are, then—no—yes—I do believe I've forgotten it, after all!" cried Jamie, slapping his pockets one after the other, with a dismayed expression of countenance.

"Never mind: I'll hunt up something else. Let me help with those: your hands are so cold." And Rose good-naturedly gave a tug at the boots, while Jamie clutched the banisters; murmuring somewhat incoherently, as his legs flew up and down—

"I'll go back if you want me to. I'm so sorry! It's very good of you, I'm sure. Getting these horrid things on made me forget. Mother would make me wear 'em, though I told her they'd stick like—like gumdrops," he added, inspired by recollections of certain dire disappointments when the above-mentioned sweetmeat melted in his pockets, and refused to come out.

"Now what shall we do?" asked Rose, when he was finally extricated. "Since I've nothing to read, I may as well play."

"I'll teach you to pitch and toss. You catch very well for a girl, but you can't throw worth a cent," replied Jamie, gambading down the hall in his slippers, and producing a ball from some of the mysterious receptacles in which boys have the art of storing rubbish enough to fill a peck measure.

Of course Rose agreed, and cheerfully risked getting her eyes blackened and her fingers bruised, till her young preceptor gratefully observed that "it was no fun playing where you had to look out for windows and jars and things; so I'd like that jolly book about Captain Nemo and the 'Nautilus,' please."

Being gratified, he spread himself upon the couch, crossed his legs in the air and without another word dived "Twenty Thousand Leagues Under the Sea," where he remained for two mortal hours, to the general satisfaction of his relatives.

Bereft both of her unexpected playfellow and the much-desired book, Rose went into the parlour, there to discover a French novel, which Kitty had taken from a library and left in the carriage among the bundles. Settling herself in her favourite lounging-chair, she read as diligently as Jamie, while the wind howled and snow fell fast without.

For an hour, nothing disturbed the cosy quiet of the house; for Aunt Plenty was napping upstairs, and Dr. Alec writing in his own sanctum; at least, Rose thought so, till his step made her hastily drop the book, and look up with very much the expression she used to wear when caught in mischief years ago.

"Did I startle you? Have a screen: you are burning your face before this hot fire." And Dr. Alec pulled one forward.

"Thank you, uncle; I didn't feel it." And the colour seemed to deepen in spite of the screen, while the uneasy eyes fell upon the book in her lap.

"Have you got the 'Quarterly' there? I want to glance at an article in it, if you can spare it for a moment," he said, leaning towards her with an inquiring glance.

"No, sir: I am reading—" And, without mentioning the name, Rose put the book into his hand.

The instant his eye fell on the title, he understood the look she wore, and knew what "mischief" she had been in. He knit his brows: then smiled, because it was impossible to help it; Rose looked so conscience-stricken in spite of her twenty years.

"How do you find it?—interesting?"

"Oh, very! I felt as if I was in another world, and forgot all about this."

"Not a very good world, I fancy, if you were afraid or ashamed to be found in it. Where did this come from?" asked Dr. Alec, surveying the book with great disfavour.

Rose told him, and added slowly—

"I particularly wanted to read it, and fancied I might, because you did when it was so much talked about the winter we were in Rome."

"I did read it to see if it was fit for you."

"And decided that it was not, I suppose; since you never gave it to me?"

"Yes."

"Then I won't finish it. But, uncle, I don't see why I should not," added Rose, wistfully; for she had reached the heart of the romance and found it wonderfully fascinating.

"You may not *see*, but don't you *feel* why not?" asked Dr. Alec, gravely.

Rose leaned her flushed cheek on her hand and thought a minute; then looked up, and answered honestly—

"Yes, I do: but can't explain it; except that I know something *must* be wrong, because I blushed and started when you came in."

"Exactly," and the doctor gave an emphatic nod, as if the symptoms pleased him.

"But I really don't see any harm in the book so far. It is by a famous author, wonderfully well written as you know, and the characters so life-like that I feel as if I should really meet them somewhere."

"I hope not!" ejaculated the doctor, shutting the book quickly, as if to keep the objectionable beings from escaping.

Rose laughed, but persisted in her defence; for she did want to finish the absorbing story, yet would not without leave.

"I have read French novels before, and you gave them to me. Not many to be sure, but the best; so I think I know what is good, and shouldn't like this if it was harmful."

Her uncle's answer was to reopen the volume and turn the leaves an instant as if to find a particular place; then he put it into her hand, saying quietly—

"Read a page or two aloud, translating as you go. You used to like that: try it again."

Rose obeyed, and went glibly down a page, doing her best to give the sense in her purest English. Presently she went more slowly, then skipped a sentence here and there, and finally stopped short, looking as if she needed a screen again.

"What's the matter?" asked her uncle, who had been watching her with a serious eye.

"Some phrases are untranslatable, and it only spoils them to try. They are not amiss in French, but sound coarse and bad in our blunt English," she said a little pettishly; for she felt annoyed by her failure to prove the contested point.

"Ah, my dear! if the fine phrases won't bear putting into honest English, the thoughts they express won't bear putting into your innocent mind. That chapter is the key to the whole book; and if you had been led up, or rather down, to it artfully and artistically, you might have read it to yourself without seeing how bad it is. All the worse for the undeniable talent which hides the evil so subtly and makes the danger so delightful."

He paused a moment, then added with an anxious glance at the book, over which she was still bending—

"Finish it if you choose: only remember, my girl, that one may read at forty what is unsafe at twenty, and that we never can be too careful what food we give that precious yet perilous thing called imagination."

And taking his "Review" he went away to look over a learned article which interested him much less than the workings of a young mind near by.

Another long silence, broken only by an occasional excited bounce from Jamie, when the sociable cuttle-fish looked in at the windows, or the "Nautilus" scuttled a ship or two in its terrific course. A bell rang, and the doctor popped his head out to see if he was wanted. It was only a message for Aunt Plenty, and he was about to pop in again when his eye was caught by a square parcel on the slab.

"What's this?" he asked, taking it up.

"Rose wants me to leave it at Kitty Van's when I go. I forgot to bring her book from mamma; so I shall go and get it as soon as ever I've done this," replied Jamie, from his nest.

As the volume in his hands was a corpulent one, and Jamie only a third of the way through, Dr. Alec thought Rose's prospect rather doubtful; and, slipping the parcel into his pocket, he walked away, saying with a satisfied air—

"Virtue doesn't always get rewarded; but it shall be this time, if I can do it."

More than half an hour afterwards, Rose woke from a little nap, and found the various old favourites, with which she had tried to solace herself, replaced by the simple, wholesome story promised by Aunt Jessie.

"Good boy! I'll go and thank him," she said, half-aloud; jumping up, wide awake and much pleased.

But she did not go; for, just then, she espied her uncle standing on the rug warming his hands with a generally fresh and breezy look about him, which suggested a recent struggle with the elements.

"How did this come?" she asked suspiciously.

"A man brought it."

"This man? O uncle! why did you take so much trouble just to gratify a wish of mine?" she cried, taking both the cold hands in hers, with a tenderly reproachful glance from the storm without to the ruddy face above her.

"Because, having taken away your French bonbons, with the poisonous colour on them, I wanted to get you something better. Here it is, all pure sugar; the sort that sweetens the heart as well as the tongue, and leaves no bad taste behind."

"How good you are to me! I don't deserve it; for I didn't resist temptation, though I tried. Uncle, after I'd put the book away, I thought I *must* just see how it ended, and I'm afraid I should have read it all if it had not been gone," said Rose, laying her face down on the hands she held, as humbly as a repentant child.

But Uncle Alec lifted up the bent head, and looking into the eyes that met his frankly, though either held a tear, he said, with the energy that always made his words remembered—

"My little girl, I would face a dozen storms far worse than this to keep your soul as stainless as snow; for it is the small temptations which undermine integrity, unless we watch and pray, and never think them too trivial to be resisted."

Some people would consider Dr. Alec an over-careful man: but Rose felt that he was right; and, when she said her prayers that night, added a meek petition to be kept from yielding to three of the small temptations which beset a rich, pretty, and romantic girl—extravagance, coquetry, and novel-reading.

12

At Kitty's Ball

Rose had had no new gown to wear on this festive occasion, and gave one little sigh of regret as she put on the pale blue silk, refreshed with clouds of *gaze de Chambéry*. But a smile followed, very bright and sweet, as she added the clusters of forget-me-not which Charlie had conjured up through the agency of an old German florist: for one part of her plan *had* been carried out, and Prince was invited to be her escort, much to his delight; though he wisely made no protestations of any sort, and showed his gratitude by being a model gentleman. This pleased Rose; for the late humiliation and a very sincere desire to atone for it, gave him an air of pensive dignity which was very effective.

Aunt Clara could not go; for a certain new cosmetic, privately used to improve the once fine complexion, which had been her pride till late hours impaired it, had brought out an unsightly eruption, reducing her to the depths of woe, and leaving her no solace for her disappointment but the sight of the elegant velvet dress spread forth upon her bed in melancholy state.

So Aunt Jessie was chaperon, to Rose's great satisfaction, and looked as "pretty as a pink," Archie thought, in her matronly pearl-coloured gown, with a dainty trifle of rich lace on her still abundant hair. He was very proud of his little mamma, and as devoted as a lover, "to keep his hand in against Phebe's return," she said laughingly, when he brought her a nosegay of blush-roses to light up her quiet costume.

A happier mother did not live than Mrs. Jessie, as she sat contentedly beside Sister Jane (who graced the frivolous scene in a serious black gown with a diadem of purple asters nodding

149

above her severe brow), both watching their boys with the
maternal conviction that no other parent could show such
remarkable specimens as these. Each had done her best according to her light; and years of faithful care were now beginning
to bear fruit in the promise of goodly men, so dear to the hearts
of true mothers.

Mrs. Jessie watched her three tall sons with something like
wonder; for Archie was a fine fellow, grave and rather stately,
but full of the cordial courtesy and respect we see so little of
nowadays, and which is the sure sign of good home-training.
"The cadets," as Will and Geordie called themselves, were
there as gorgeous as you please; and the agonies they suffered
that night with tight boots and stiff collars no pen can fitly tell.

But only to one another did they confide these sufferings, in
the rare moments of repose when they could stand on one aching
foot with heads comfortably sunken inside the excruciating
collars, which rasped their ears and made the lobes thereof a
pleasing scarlet. Brief were these moments, however; and the
Spartan boys danced on with smiling faces, undaunted by the
hidden anguish which preyed upon them "fore and aft," as Will
expressed it.

Mrs. Jane's pair were an odd contrast, and even the stern
disciplinarian herself could not help smiling as she watched
them. Steve was superb, and might have been married on the
spot, so superfine was his broadcloth, glossy his linen, and
perfect the fit of his gloves; while pride and happiness so fermented in his youthful bosom, that there would have been
danger of spontaneous combustion if dancing had not proved a
safety-valve; for his strong sense of the proprieties would not
permit him to vent his emotions in any other way.

Kitty felt no such restraint, and looked like a blissful little
gypsy, with her brunette prettiness set off by a dashing costume
of cardinal and cream colour, and every hair on her head curled
in a Merry Pecksniffian crop; for youth was her strong point,
and she much enjoyed the fact that she had been engaged three
times before she was nineteen.

To see her and Steve spin round the room was a sight to
bring a smile to the lips of the crustiest bachelor or saddest
spinster; for happy lovers are always a pleasing spectacle, and
two such merry little grigs as these are seldom seen.

Mac, meantime, with glasses astride of his nose, surveyed his brother's performances "on the light fantastic" very much as a benevolent Newfoundland would the gambols of a toy terrier, receiving with thanks the hasty hints for his guidance which Steve breathed into his ear as he passed, and forgetting all about them the next minute. When not thus engaged, Mac stood about with his thumbs in his vest pockets, regarding the lively crowd like a meditative philosopher of a cheerful aspect, often smiling to himself at some whimsical fancy of his own, knitting his brows as some bit of ill-natured gossip met his ear, or staring with undisguised admiration as a beautiful face or figure caught his eye.

"I hope that girl knows what a treasure she has got. But I doubt if she ever fully appreciates it," said Mrs. Jane, bringing her spectacles to bear upon Kitty, as she whisked by, causing quite a gale with her flying skirts.

"I think she will; for Steve has been so well brought up, she cannot but see and feel the worth of what she has never had; and being so young she will profit by it," answered Mrs. Jessie, softly; thinking of the days when she and her Jem danced together, just betrothed.

"I've done my duty by both the boys, and done it *thoroughly*: or their father would have spoilt them; for he's no more idea of discipline than a child," and Aunt Jane gave her own palm a smart rap with her closed fan, emphasizing the word "thoroughly" in a most suggestive manner.

"I've often wished I had your firmness, Jane: but, after all, I'm not sure that I don't like my own way best, at least with my boys; for plenty of love, and plenty of patience, seems to have succeeded pretty well;" and Aunt Jessie lifted the nosegay from her lap, feeling as if that unfailing love and patience were already blooming into her life, as beautifully as the sweet-breathed roses given by her boy refreshed and brightened these long hours of patient waiting in a corner.

"I don't deny that you've done well, Jessie; but you've been let alone, and had no one to hold your hand or interfere. If my Mac had gone to sea as your Jem did, I never should have been as severe as I am. Men are so perverse and short-sighted, they don't trouble about the future as long as things are quiet and comfortable in the present," continued Mrs. Jane, quite forgetting that the short-sighted partner of the firm, physically speaking at least, was herself.

"Ah, yes! we mothers love to foresee and foretell our children's lives even before they are born, and are very apt to be disappointed if they do not turn out as we planned. I know I am: yet I really have no cause to complain, and am learning to see that all we can do is to give the dear boys good principles, and the best training we may, then leave them to finish what we have begun;" and Mrs. Jessie's eye wandered away to Archie, dancing with Rose, quite unconscious what a pretty little castle in the air tumbled down when he fell in love with Phebe.

"Right, quite right: on that point we agree exactly. I have spared nothing to give my boys good principles and good habits, and I am willing to trust them anywhere. Nine times did I whip Steve to cure him of fibbing, and over and over again did Mac go without his dinner rather than wash his hands. But I whipped and starved them both into obedience, and *now* I have my reward," concluded the "stern parent," with a proud wave of the fan, which looked very like a ferrule, being as big, hard, and uncompromising as such an article could be.

Mrs. Jessie gave a mild murmur of assent, but could not help thinking, with a smile, that, in spite of their early tribulations, the sins for which the boys suffered had got a little mixed in their results; for fibbing Steve was now the tidy one, and careless Mac the truth-teller. But such small contradictions will happen in the best-regulated families, and all perplexed parents can do is to keep up a steadfast preaching and practising, in the hope that it will bear fruit sometime; for according to the old proverb—

> " 'Children pick up words as pigeons pease,
>   To utter them again as God shall please.' "

"I hope they won't dance the child to death among them; for each one seems bound to have his turn, even your sober Mac," said Mrs. Jessie, a few minutes later, as she saw Archie hand Rose over to his cousin, who carried her off with an air of triumph from several other claimants.

"She's very good to him, and her influence is excellent; for he is of an age now when a young woman's opinion has more weight than an old one's. Though he is always good to his mother, and I feel as if I should take great comfort in him. He's one of the sort who will not marry till late, if ever, being fond of books and a quiet life," responded Mrs. Jane, remembering how often her son had expressed his belief that philosophers should not marry, and brought up Plato as an example of the serene wisdom only to be attained by a single man, while her husband sided with Socrates, for whom he felt a profound sympathy, though he didn't dare to own it.

"Well, I don't know about that. Since my Archie surprised me by losing his heart as he did, I'm prepared for anything, and advise you to do likewise. I really shouldn't wonder if Mac did something remarkable in that line, though he shows no signs of it yet, I confess," answered Mrs. Jessie, laughing.

"It won't be in that direction, you may be sure; for *her* fate is sealed. Dear me, how sad it is to see a superior girl, like that, about to throw herself away on a handsome scapegrace. I won't mention names, but you understand me;" and Mrs. Jane shook her head, as if she *could* mention the name of one superior girl who had thrown herself away, and now saw the folly of it.

"I'm very anxious, of course, and so is Alec: but it may be the saving of one party, and the happiness of the other; for some women love to give more than they receive," said Mrs. Jessie, privately wondering, for the thousandth time, why brother Mac ever married the learned Miss Humphries.

"You'll see that it won't prosper; and I shall always maintain that a wife cannot entirely undo a mother's work. Rose will have her hands full if she tries to set all Clara's mistakes right," answered Aunt Jane, grimly; then began to fan violently as their hostess approached to have a dish of chat about "our dear young people."

Rose was in a merry mood that night, and found Mac quite ready for fun, which was fortunate, since her first remark set them off on a droll subject.

"O Mac! Annabel has just confided to me that she is engaged to Fun See! Think of her going to housekeeping in Canton some day, and having to order rats, puppies, and birds'-nest soup for dinner," whispered Rose, too much amused to keep the news to herself.

"By Confucius! isn't that a sweet prospect?" and Mac burst out laughing, to the great surprise of his neighbours, who wondered what there was amusing about the Chinese sage. "It is rather alarming, though, to have these infants going on at this rate. Seems to be catching; a new sort of scarlet-fever, to judge by Annabel's cheeks and Kitty's gown," he added, regarding the aforesaid ladies with eyes still twinkling with merriment.

"Don't be ungallant, but go and do likewise; for it is all the fashion. I heard Mrs. Van tell old Mrs. Joy that it was going to be a marrying year; so you'll be sure to catch it," answered Rose, reefing her skirts; for, with all his training, Mac still found it difficult to keep his long legs out of the man-traps.

"It doesn't look like a painful disease; but I must be careful, for I've no time to be ill now. What are the symptoms?" asked Mac, trying to combine business with pleasure, and improve his mind while doing his duty.

"If you ever come back I'll tell you," laughed Rose, as he danced away into the wrong corner, bumped smartly against another gentleman, and returned as soberly as if that was the proper figure.

"Well, tell me 'how not to do it,'" he said, subsiding for a moment's talk when Rose had floated to and fro in her turn.

"Oh! you see some young girl who strikes you as particularly charming—whether she really is or not doesn't matter a bit— and you begin to think about her a great deal, to want to see her, and to get generally sentimental and absurd," began Rose, finding it difficult to give a diagnosis of the most mysterious disease under the sun.

"Don't think it sounds enticing. Can't I find an antidote somewhere; for if it is in the air this year I'm sure to get it, and it may be fatal," said Mac, who felt pretty lively and liked to make Rose merry; for he suspected that she had a little trouble from a hint Dr. Alec had given him.

"I hope you will catch it, because you'll be so funny."

"Will you take care of me as you did before or have you got your hands full?"

"I'll help; but really with Archie and Steve and—Charlie, I shall have enough to do. You'd better take it lightly the first time, and so won't need much care."

"Very well, how shall I begin? Enlighten my ignorance and start me right, I beg."

"Go about and see people; make yourself agreeable, and not sit in corners observing other people as if they were puppets dancing for your amusement. I heard Mrs. Van once say that propinquity works wonders; and she ought to know, having married off two daughters, and just engaged a third to 'a most charming young man.' "

"Good lack! the cure sounds worse than the disease. Propinquity, hey? Why, I may be in danger this identical moment, and can't flee for my life," said Mac, gently catching her round the waist for a general waltz.

"Don't be alarmed, but mind your steps; for Charlie is looking at us, and I want you to do your best. That's perfect: take me quite round; for I love to waltz, and seldom get a good turn except with you boys," said Rose, smiling up at him approvingly, as his strong arm guided her among the revolving couples, and his feet kept time without a fault.

"This certainly is a great improvement on the chair business, to which I have devoted myself with such energy that I've broken the backs of two partners and dislocated the arm of the old rocker. I took an occasional turn with that heavy party, thinking it good practice in case I ever happen to dance with stout ladies," and Mac nodded towards Annabel, pounding gaily away with Mr. Tokio, whose yellow countenance beamed as his beady eyes rested on his plump *fiancée*.

Pausing in the midst of her merriment at the image of Mac and the old rocking-chair, Rose said reprovingly—

"Though a heathen Chinee, Fun puts you to shame; for *he* did not ask foolish questions, but went a-wooing like a sensible little man; and I've no doubt Annabel will be very happy."

"Choose me a suitable divinity, and I will try to adore. Can I do more than that to retrieve my character?" answered Mac, safely landing his partner, and plying the fan according to instructions.

"How would Emma do?" inquired Rose, whose sense of the ludicrous was strong, and who could not resist the temptation of horrifying Mac by the suggestion.

"Never! It sets my teeth on edge to look at her tonight. I suppose that dress is 'a sweet thing just out;' but, upon my word, she reminds me of nothing but a harlequin ice," and Mac turned his back on her with a shudder; for he was sensitive to discords of all kinds.

"She certainly does; and that mixture of chocolate, pea green, and pink is simply detestable, though many people would consider it decidedly 'chic,' to use her favourite word. I suppose you will dress your wife like a Spartan matron of the time of

Lycurgus," added Rose, much tickled by his new conceit.

"I'll wait till I get her before I decide. But one thing I'm sure of—she shall *not* dress like a Greek dancer of the time of Pericles," answered Mac, regarding with great disfavour a young lady who, having a statuesque figure, affected drapery of the scanty and clinging description.

"Then it is of no use to suggest that classic creature; so, as you reject my first attempts, I won't go on, but look about me quietly, and you had better do the same. Seriously, Mac, more gaiety and less study would do you good; for you will grow old before your time, if you shut yourself up and pore over books so much."

"I don't believe there is a younger or a jollier feeling fellow in the room than I am, though I may not conduct myself like a dancing dervish. But I own you may be right about the books; for there are many sorts of intemperance, and a library is as irresistible to me as a bar-room to a toper. I shall have to sign a pledge, and cork up the only bottle that tempts me—my inkstand.

"I'll tell you how to make it easier to abstain. Stop studying, and write a novel into which you can put all your wise things, and so clear your brains for a new start by and by. Do: I should *so* like to read it," cried Rose, delighted with the project; for she was sure Mac could do anything he liked in that line.

"First live, then write. How can I go to romancing till I know what romance means?" he asked soberly, feeling that so far he had had very little in his life.

"Then you must find out, and nothing will help you more than to love someone very much. Do as I've advised, and be a modern Diogenes going about with spectacles, instead of a lantern, in search, not of an honest man, but a perfect woman. I do hope you will be successful," and Rose made her curtsy as the dance ended.

"I don't expect perfection, but I *should* like one as good as they ever make them nowadays. If you are looking for the honest man, I wish you success in return," said Mac, relinquishing her fan with a glance of such sympathetic significance that a quick flush of feeling rose to the girl's face, as she answered very low—

"If honesty was all I wanted, I certainly have found it in you."

Then she went away with Charlie, who was waiting for his

turn, and Mac roamed about, wondering if anywhere in all that crowd his future wife was hidden, saying to himself, as he glanced from face to face, quite unresponsive to the various allurements displayed—

> "What care I how fair she be,
> If she be not fair for me?"

Just before supper, several young ladies met in the dressing-room to repair damages; and, being friends, they fell into discourse, as they smoothed their locks, and had their tattered furbelows sewed or pinned up by the neat-handed Phillis in waiting.

When each had asked the other, "How do I look tonight, dear?" and been answered with reciprocal enthusiasm, "Perfectly lovely, darling!" Kitty said to Rose, who was helping her to restore order out of the chaos to which much exercise had reduced her curls—

"By the way, young Randal is dying to be presented to you. May I after supper?"

"No, thank you," answered Rose, very decidedly.

"Well, I'm sure I don't see why not," began Kitty, looking displeased, but not surprised.

"I think you do else why didn't you present him when he asked? You seldom stop to think of etiquette: why did you now?"

"I didn't like to do it till I had—you are so particular—I thought you'd say 'No;' but I couldn't tell him so," stammered Kitty, feeling that she had better have settled the matter herself; for Rose *was* very particular, and had especial reason to dislike this person, because he was not only a dissipated young reprobate himself, but seemed possessed of Satan to lead others astray likewise.

"I don't wish to be rude, dear; but I really must decline; for I cannot know such people, even though I meet them here," said Rose, remembering Charlie's revelations on New Year's night, and hardening her heart against the man who had been his undoing on that as well as on other occasions, she had reason to believe.

"I couldn't help it! Old Mr. Randal and papa are friends; and, though I spoke of it, brother Alf wouldn't hear of passing that bad boy over," explained Kitty, eagerly.

"Yet Alf forbade your driving or skating with him; for he knows better than we how unfit he is to come among us."

"I'd drop him tomorrow if I could; but I must be civil in my own house. His mother brought him, and he won't dare to behave here as he does at their bachelor parties."

"She ought not to have brought him till he had shown some desire to mend his ways. It is none of my business, I know; but I do wish people wouldn't be so inconsistent, letting boys go to destruction, and then expecting us girls to receive them like decent people." Rose spoke in an energetic whisper, but Annabel heard her, and exclaimed, as she turned round with a powder-puff in her hand—

"My goodness, Rose! what is all that about going to destruction?"

"She is being strong-minded; and I don't very much blame her in this case. But it leaves me in a dreadful scrape," said Kitty, supporting her spirits with a sniff of aromatic vinegar.

"I appeal to you, since you heard me, and there's no one here but ourselves: do you consider young Randal a nice person to know?" and Rose turned to Annabel and Emma with an anxious eye; for she did not find it easy to abide by her principles when so doing annoyed friends.

"No, indeed: he's perfectly horrid! Papa says he and Gorham are the wildest young men he knows, and enough to spoil the whole set. I'm so glad I've got no brothers," responded Annabel, placidly powdering her pink arms, quite undeterred by the memory of sundry white streaks left on sundry coat-sleeves.

"*I* think that sort of scrupulousness is very ill-bred, if you'll excuse my saying so, Rose. *We* are not supposed to know anything about fastness, and wildness, and so on; but to treat every man alike, and not be fussy and prudish," said Emma, settling her many-coloured streamers with the superior air of a woman of the world, aged twenty.

"Ah! but we do know; and, if our silence and civility have no effect, we ought to try something else, and not encourage wickedness of any kind. We needn't scold and preach, but we *can* refuse to know such people; and that will do some good, for they don't like to be shunned and shut out from respectable society. Uncle Alec told me not to know that man, and I won't." Rose spoke with unusual warmth, forgetting that she could not tell the real reason for her strong prejudice against "that man."

"Well, *I* know him: *I* think him very jolly, and I'm engaged to dance the German with him after supper. He leads quite as well as your cousin Charlie, and is quite as fascinating, some people think," returned Emma, tossing her head disdainfully; for Prince Charming did not worship at her shrine, and it piqued her vanity.

In spite of her quandary, Rose could not help smiling as she recalled Mac's comparison; for Emma turned so red with spiteful chagrin, she seemed to have added strawberry-ice to the other varieties composing the Harlequin.

"Each must judge for herself. I shall follow Aunt Jessie's advice and try to keep my atmosphere as pure as I can; for she says every woman has her own little circle, and in it can use her influence for good, if she will. I do will heartily; and I'll prove that I'm neither proud nor fussy by receiving, here or at home, any respectable man you like to present to me no matter how poor or plain or insignificant he may be."

With which declaration Rose ended her protest, and the four damsels streamed downstairs together like a wandering rainbow. But Kitty laid to heart what she had said; Annabel took credit to herself for siding with her; and Emma owned that *she* was not trying to keep her atmosphere pure when she came to dance with the objectionable Randal. So Rose's "little circle" was the better for the influence she tried to exert, although she never knew it.

All supper-time, Charlie kept near her and she was quite content with him; for he drank only coffee, and she saw him shake his head with a frown when young Van beckoned him towards an anteroom, from whence the sound of popping corks had issued with increasing frequency as the evening wore on.

"Dear fellow, he does try," thought Rose, longing to show how she admired his self-denial; but she could only say, as they left the supper-room with the aunts, who were going early—

"If I had not promised uncle to get home as soon after midnight as possible, I'd stay and dance the German with you; for you deserve a reward tonight."

"A thousand thanks! but I am going when you do," answered Charlie, understanding both her look and words, and very grateful for them.

"Really?" cried Rose, delighted.

"Really. I'll be in the hall when you come down." And Charlie thought the Fra Angelico angel was not half so bright and beautiful as the one who looked back at him out of a pale-blue cloud, as Rose went upstairs as if on wings.

When she came down again, Charlie was not in the hall, however; and, after waiting a few minutes, Mac offered to go and find him, for Aunt Jane was still hunting a lost rubber above.

"Please say I'm ready, but he needn't come if he doesn't want to," said Rose, not wishing to demand too much of her promising penitent.

"If he has gone into that bar-room, I'll have him out, no matter who is there!" growled Mac to himself, as he made his way to the small apartment whither the gentlemen retired for a little private refreshment when the spirit moved, as it often did.

The door was ajar, and Charlie seemed to have just entered; for Mac heard a familiar voice call out, in a jovial tone—

"Come, Prince! you're just in time to help us drink Steve's health with all the honours."

"Can't stop; only ran in to say good-night, Van. Had a capital time; but I'm on duty, and must go."

"That's a new dodge. Take a stirrup-cup anyway, and come back in time for a merry-go-rounder when you've disposed of the ladies," answered the young host, diving into the wine-cooler for another bottle.

"Charlie's going in for sanctity, and it doesn't seem to agree with him," laughed one of the two other young men, who occupied several chairs apiece, resting their soles in every sense of the word.

"Apron-strings are coming into fashion—the bluer the better: hey, Prince?" added the other, trying to be witty, with the usual success.

"You'd better go home early yourself, Barrow, or that tongue of yours will get you into trouble," retorted Charlie, conscious that he ought to take his own advice, yet lingering, nervously putting on his gloves while the glasses were being filled.

"Now, brother-in-law, fire away! Here you are Prince." And Steve handed a glass across the table to his cousin, feeling too much elated with various pleasurable emotions to think what he was doing; for the boys all knew Charlie's weakness, and usually tried to defend him from it.

Before the glass could be taken, however, Mac entered in a great hurry, delivering his message in an abbreviated and rather peremptory form—

"Rose is waiting for you. Hurry up!"

"All right. Good-night, old fellows!" And Charlie was off, as if the name had power to stop him in the very act of breaking the promise made to himself.

"Come, Solon, take a social drop, and give us an epithalamium in your best Greek. Here's to you!" And Steve was lifting the wine to his own lips, when Mac knocked the glass out of his hand, with a flash of the eye that caused his brother to stare at him, with his mouth open, in an imbecile sort of way, which seemed to excite Mac still more; for, turning to his young host, he said, in a low voice, and with a look that made the gentlemen on the chairs sit up suddenly—

"I beg pardon, Van, for making a mess; but I can't stand by and see my own brother tempt another man beyond his strength, or make a brute of himself. That's plain English: but I can't help speaking out; for I know not one of you would willingly hurt Charlie, and you will if you don't let him alone."

"What do you pitch into me for? I've done nothing. A fellow must be civil in his own house, mustn't he?" asked Van, good-humouredly, as he faced about, corkscrew in hand.

"Yes, but it is not civil to urge or joke a guest into doing what you know and he knows is bad for him. That's only a glass of wine to you, but it is perdition to Charlie; and, if Steve knew what he was about, he'd cut his right hand off before he'd offer it."

"Do you mean to say I'm tipsy?" demanded Steve, ruffling up like a little game-cock; for, though he saw now what he had done and was ashamed of it, he hated to have Mac air his peculiar notions before other people.

"With excitement, not champagne, I hope; for I wouldn't own you if you were," answered Mac, in whom indignation was effervescing like the wine in the forgotten bottle; for the men were all young, friends of Steve's and admirers of Charlie's. "Look here, boys," he went on more quietly: "I know I ought not to explode in this violent sort of way, but upon my life I couldn't help it, when I heard what you were saying and saw what Steve was doing. Since I *have* begun I may as well finish, and tell you straight out that Prince can't stand this sort of thing.

F

He is trying to flee temptation, and whoever leads him into it does a cowardly and sinful act; for the loss of one's own self-respect is bad enough, without losing the more precious things that make life worth having. Don't tell him I've said this, but lend a hand if you can, and never have to reproach yourselves with the knowledge that you helped to ruin a fellow-creature, soul and body."

It was well for the success of Mac's first crusade, that his hearers were gentlemen and sober: so his outburst was not received with jeers or laughter, but listened to in silence, while the expression of the faces changed from one of surprise to regret and respect; for earnestness is always effective, and championship of this sort seldom fails to touch hearts as yet unspoiled. As he paused with an eloquent little quiver in his eager voice, Van corked the bottle at a blow, threw down the corkscrew, and offered Mac his hand, saying heartily, in spite of his slang—

"You are a first-class old brick! I'll lend a hand for one, and do my best to back up Charlie; for he's the finest fellow I know, and shan't go to the devil like poor Randal if *I* can help it."

Murmurs of applause from the others seemed to express a general assent to this vigorous statement; and, giving the hand a grateful shake, Mac retreated to the door, anxious to be off now that he had freed his mind with such unusual impetuosity.

"Count on me for anything I can do in return for this, Van. I'm sorry to be such a marplot, but you can take it out in quizzing me after I'm gone. I'm fair game, and Steve can set you going."

With that, Mac departed as abruptly as he came, feeling that he *had* "made a mess" of it; but comforting himself with the thought that perhaps he had secured help for Charlie at his own expense, and thinking with a droll smile as he went back to his mother—

"My romance begins by looking after other girls' lovers instead of finding a sweetheart for myself; but I can't tell Rose, so *she* won't laugh at me."

13

Both Sides

STEVE'S ENGAGEMENT made a great stir in the family: a pleasant one this time; for nobody objected, everything seemed felicitous, and the course of true love ran very smoothly for the young couple, who promised to remove the only obstacle to their union by growing old and wise as soon as possible. If he had not been so genuinely happy, the little lover's airs would have been unbearable; for he patronized all mankind in general, his brother and elder cousins in particular.

"Now that is the way to manage matters," he declared, standing before the fire in Aunt Clara's billiard room a day or two after the ball, with his hands behind his back—"no nonsense, no delay, no domestic rows or tragic separations. Just choose with taste and judgment, make yourself agreeable through thick and thin; and, when it is perfectly evident that the dear creature adores the ground you walk on, say the word like a man, and there you are."

"All very easy to do that with a girl like Kitty, who has no confounded notions to spoil her and trip you up every time you don't exactly toe the mark," muttered Charlie, knocking the balls about as if it were a relief to hit something; for he was in a gloriously bad humour that evening, because time hung heavy on his hands since he had forsworn the company he could not keep without danger to himself.

"You should humour those little notions; for all women have them and it needs tact to steer clear of them. Kitty's got dozens; but I treat them with respect, have my own way when I can, give in without growling when I can't, and we get on like a couple of—"

"Spoons," put in Charlie, who felt that he had *not* steered clear, and so suffered shipwreck in sight of land.

Steve meant to have said "doves," but his cousin's levity caused him to add with calm dignity, "reasonable beings," and then revenged himself by making a good shot which won him the game.

"You always were a lucky little dog, Steve. I don't begrudge you a particle of your happiness but it does seem as if things weren't quite fair sometimes," said Archie, suppressing an envious sigh; for, though he seldom complained, it was impossible to contrast his own and his cousin's prospects with perfect equanimity.

> " 'His worth shines forth the brightest who in hope
>   Always confides: the abject soul despairs,' "

observed Mac, quoting Euripides in a conversational tone, as he lay upon a divan reposing after a hard day's work.

"Thank you," said Archie, brightening a little; for a hopeful word from any source was very comfortable.

"That's your favourite Rip, isn't it? He was a wise old boy, but you could find advice as good as that nearer home," put in Steve, who just then felt equal to slapping Plato on the shoulder; so elated was he at being engaged "first of all the lot," as he gracefully expressed it.

"Don't halloo till you are out of the wood, Dandy: Mrs. Kit has jilted two men, and may a third; so you'd better not brag of your wisdom too soon; for she may make a fool of you yet," said Charlie, cynically, his views of life being very gloomy about this time.

"No, she won't, Steve, if you do your part honestly. There's the making of a good little woman in Kitty, and she has proved it by taking you instead of those other fellows. You are not a Solomon, but you're not spoilt yet; and she had the sense to see it," said Mac, encouragingly from his corner; for he and his brother were better friends than ever since the little scene at the Van Tassels.

"Hear! hear!" cried Steve, looking more than ever like a cheerful young cockerel trying to crow, as he stood upon the hearth-rug with his hands under his coat-tails, rising and falling alternately upon the toes and heels of his neat little boots.

"Come, you've given them each a pat on the head: haven't

you got one for me? I need it enough; for if ever there was a
poor devil born under an evil star, it is C. C. Campbell,"
exclaimed Charlie, leaning his chin on his cue with a discontented expression of countenance; for trying to be good is
often very hard work till one gets used to it.

"Oh, yes! I can accommodate you;" and, as if his words
suggested the selection, Mac, still lying flat upon his back,
repeated one of his favourite bits from Beaumont and Fletcher;
for he had a wonderful memory, and could reel off poetry by the
hour together.

> " 'Man is his own star: and the soul that can
> Render an honest and a perfect man
> Commands all light, all influence, all fate
> Nothing to him falls early or too late.
> Our acts our angels are; or good or ill,
> Our fatal shadows that walk by us still.' "

"Confoundedly bad angels they are too," muttered Charlie,
ruefully; remembering the one that undid him.

His cousins never knew exactly what occurred on New
Year's night, but suspected that something was amiss; for
Charlie had the blues, and Rose, though as kind as ever,
expressed no surprise at his long absences. They had all observed and wondered at this state of things, yet discreetly made
no remark, till Steve, who was as inquisitive as a magpie, seized
this opportunity to say in a friendly tone, which showed that he
bore no malice for the dark prophecy regarding his Kitty's
faithfulness—

"What's the trouble, Prince? You are so seldom in a bad
humour that we don't know what to make of it, and all feel out
of spirits when you have the blues. Had a tiff with Rose?"

"Never you mind, little boy; but this I will say—the better
women are, the more unreasonable they are. They don't require
us to be saints like themselves, which is lucky; but they do expect
us to render 'an honest and a perfect man' sometimes, and that
is asking rather too much in a fallen world like this," said
Charlie, glad to get a little sympathy, though he had no intention of confessing his transgressions.

"No, it isn't," said Mac, decidedly.

"Much you know about it," began Charlie, ill pleased to be
so flatly contradicted.

"Well, I know this much," added Mac, suddenly sitting up with his hair in a highly dishevelled condition. "It is very unreasonable in us to ask women to be saints, and then expect them to feel honoured when we offer them our damaged hearts, or, at best, ones not half as good as theirs. If they weren't blinded by love, they'd see what a mean advantage we take of them, and not make such bad bargains."

"Upon my word, the philosopher is coming out strong upon the subject! We shall have him preaching 'Women's Rights' directly," cried Steve, much amazed at this outburst.

"I've begun you see, and much good may it do you," answered Mac, laying himself placidly down again.

"Well, but look here, man: you are arguing on the wrong side," put in Archie, quite agreeing with him, but feeling that he must stand by his order at all costs.

"Never mind sides, uphold the right wherever you find it. You needn't stare, Steve: I told you I was going to look into this matter, and I am. You think I'm wrapt up in books: but I see a great deal more of what is going on round me than you imagine; and I'm getting on in this new branch, let me tell you; quite as fast as is good for me, I dare say."

"Going in for perfection, are you?" asked Charlie, both amused and interested; for he respected Mac more than he owned even to himself, and though he had never alluded to the timely warning, neither forgot.

"Yes, I think of it."

"How will you begin?"

"Do my best all round: keep good company, read good books, love good things, and cultivate soul and body as faithfully and wisely as I can."

"And you expect to succeed, do you?"

"Please God, I will."

The quiet energy of Mac's last words produced a momentary silence. Charlie thoughtfully studied the carpet; Archie, who had been absently poking the fire, looked over at Mac as if he thanked him again, and Steve, forgetting his self-conceit, began to wonder if it was not possible to improve himself a little for Kitty's sake. Only a minute; for young men do not give much time to thoughts of this kind, even when love stirs up the noblest impulses within them. To act rather than to talk is more natural to most of them, as Charlie's next question showed; for, having the matter much at heart, he ventured to ask in an off-hand way, as he laughed and twirled his cue—

"Do you intend to reach the highest point of perfection before you address one of the fair saints, or shall you ask her to lend a hand somewhere short of that?"

"As it takes a long lifetime to do what I plan, I think I shall ask some good woman 'to lend a hand' when I've got anything worth offering her. Not a saint, for I never shall be one myself, but a gentle creature who will help me, as I shall try to help her; so that we can go on together, and finish our work hereafter, if we haven't time to do it here."

If Mac had been a lover, he would not have discussed the subject in this simple and sincere fashion, though he might have felt it far more deeply; but being quite heart-free he frankly showed his interest, and, curiously enough, out of his wise young head unconsciously gave the three lovers before him counsel which they valued, because he practised what he preached.

"Well, I hope you'll find her!" said Charlie, heartily, as he went back to his game.

"I think I shall," and, while the others played, Mac lay staring at the window-curtain, as contentedly as if, through it, he beheld "a dream of fair women," from which to choose his future mate.

A few days after this talk in the billiard room, Kitty went to call upon Rose; for, as she was about to enter the family, she felt it her duty to become acquainted with all its branches. This branch, however, she cultivated more assiduously than any other, and was continually running in to confer with "Cousin Rose," whom she considered the wisest, dearest, kindest girl ever created. And Rose, finding that, in spite of her flighty head, Kitty had a good heart of her own, did her best to encourage all the new hopes and aspirations springing up in it under the warmth of the first genuine affection she had ever known.

"My dear, I want to have some serious conversation with you upon a subject in which I take an interest for the first time in my life," began Miss Kitty, seating herself and pulling off her gloves, as if the subject was one which needed a firm grasp.

"Tell away, and don't mind if I go on working, as I want to finish this job today," answered Rose, with a long-handled paint-brush in her hand, and a great pair of shears at her side.

"You are always so busy! What is it now? Let me help: I can

talk faster when I'm doing something," which seemed hardly possible; for Kitty's tongue went like a mill-clapper at all hours.

"Making picture-books for my sick babies at the hospital. Pretty work, isn't it? You cut out, and I'll paste them on these squares of gay cambric: then we just tie up a few pages with a ribbon; and there is a nice, light, durable book for the poor dears to look at as they lie in their little beds."

"A capital idea. Do you go there often? How ever do you find the time for such things?" asked Kitty, busily cutting from a big sheet the touching picture of a parent bird with a red head and a blue tail, offering what looked like a small boa-constrictor to one of its nestlings; a fat young squab with a green head, yellow body, and no tail at all.

"I have plenty of time now I don't go out so much; for a party uses up two days generally—one to prepare for it, and one to get over it, you know."

"People think it is so odd of you to give up society all of a sudden. They say you have 'turned pious,' and it is owing to your peculiar bringing up. I always take your part, and say it is a pity other girls haven't as sensible an education; for I don't know one who is as satisfactory on the whole as you are."

"Much obliged. You may also tell people I gave up gaiety because I valued health more. But I haven't forsworn everything of the kind, Kit. I go to concerts and lectures, and all sorts of early things, and have nice times at home, as you know. I like fun as well as ever: but I'm getting on, you see, and must be preparing a little for the serious part of life; one never knows when it may come," said Rose, thoughtfully, as she pasted a squirrel upside-down on the pink cotton page before her.

"That reminds me of what I wanted to say. If you'll believe me, my dear, Steve has got that very idea into his head! Did you or Mac put it there?" asked Kitty, industriously clashing her shears.

"No, I've given up lecturing the boys lately: they are so big now they don't like it, and I fancy I'd got into a way that was rather tiresome."

"Well, then, *he* is 'turning pious' too. And what is very singular, I like it. Now don't smile: I really do; and I want to be getting ready for the 'serious part of life,' as you call it. That is, I want to grow better as fast as I can; for Steve says he isn't half good enough for me. Just think of that!"

Kitty looked so surprised and pleased and proud, that Rose felt no desire to laugh at her sudden fancy for sobriety, but said in her most sympathetic tone—

"I'm very glad to hear it; for it shows that he loves you in the right way."

"Is there more than one way?"

"Yes, I fancy so; because some people improve so much after they fall in love, and others do not at all. Have you never observed that?"

"I never learned how to observe. Of course, I know that some matches turn out well and some don't, but I never thought much about it."

"Well, I have; for I was rather interested in the subject lately, and had a talk with Aunt Jessie and uncle about it."

"Gracious! you don't talk to them about such things, do you?"

"Yes, indeed; I ask any question I like, and always get a good answer. It is such a nice way to learn, Kitty; for you don't have to poke over books, but as things come along you talk about them, and remember; and when they are spoken of afterwards you understand and are interested, though you don't say a word," explained Rose.

"It must be nice; but I haven't anyone to do so for me. Papa is too busy, and mamma always says when I ask questions, 'Don't trouble your head with such things, child;' so I don't. What did you learn about matches turning out well? I'm interested in that because I want mine to be quite perfect in all respects."

"After thinking it over, I came to the conclusion that uncle *was* right, and it is *not* always safe to marry a person just because you love him," began Rose, trying to enlighten Kitty without betraying herself.

"Of course not: if they haven't money or are bad. But otherwise I don't see what more is needed," said Kitty, wonderingly.

"One should stop and see if it is a wise love, likely to help both parties, and wear well; for you know it ought to last all one's lifetime, and it is very sad if it doesn't."

"I declare it quite scares me to think of it; for I don't usually go beyond my wedding-day in making plans. I remember, though, that when I was engaged the first time (you don't know the man: it was just after you went away, and I was only sixteen), some one very ill-naturedly said I should 'marry in haste

F*

and repent at leisure;' and that made me try to imagine how it would seem to go on year after year with Gustavus (who had a dreadful temper, by the way), and it worried me so to think of it that I broke the engagement, and was so glad ever afterwards."

"You were a wise girl; and I hope you'll do it again, if you find, after a time, that you and Steve do not truly trust and respect as well as love one another. If you don't, you'll be miserable when it is too late, as so many people are who do marry in haste and have a lifetime to repent in. Aunt Jessie says so, and she knows."

"Don't be solemn, Rose. It fidgets me to think about lifetimes, and respecting, and all those responsible things. I'm not used to it, and I don't know how to do it."

"But you *must* think, and you must learn how before you take the responsibility upon yourself. That is what your life is for; and you mustn't spoil it by doing a very solemn thing without seeing if you are ready for it."

"Do you think about all this?" asked Kitty, shrugging up her shoulders as if responsibility of any sort did not sit comfortably on them.

"One has to sometimes, you know. But is that all you wanted to tell me?" added Rose anxious to turn the conversation from herself.

"Oh, dear, no! The most serious thing of all is this. Steve is putting himself in order generally, and so I want to do my part; and I must begin right away before my thoughts get distracted with clothes, and all sorts of dear, delightful, frivolous things that I can't help liking. Now I wish you'd tell me where to begin. Shouldn't I improve my mind by reading something solid?" and Kitty looked over at the well-filled book-case, as if to see if it contained anything large and dry enough to be considered "solid."

"It would be an excellent plan, and we'll look up something. What do you feel as if you needed most?"

"A little of everything I should say; for when I look into my mind there really doesn't seem to be much there but odds and ends, and yet I'm sure I've read a great deal more than some girls do. I suppose novels don't count, though, and are of no use; for, goodness knows, the people and things they describe aren't a bit like the real ones."

"Some novels are very useful and do as much good as sermons, I've heard uncle say; because they not only describe truly, but teach so pleasantly that people like to learn in that way," said Rose, who knew the sort of books Kitty had read, and did not wonder that she felt rather astray when she tried to guide herself by their teaching.

"You pick me out some of the right kind, and I'll apply my mind to them. Then I ought to have some 'serious views' and 'methods' and 'principles;' Steve said 'principles,' good firm ones, you know," and Kitty gave a little pull at the bit of cambric she was cutting, as housewives pull cotton or calico then they want "a good firm article."

Rose could not help laughing now, though much pleased; for Kitty was so prettily in earnest, and yet so perfectly ignorant how to begin on the self-improvement she very much needed, that it was pathetic as well as comical to see and hear her.

"You certainly want some of those, and must begin at once to get them: but Aunt Jessie can help you there better than I can; or Aunt Jane, for she has very 'firm' ones, I assure you," said Rose, sobering down as quickly as possible.

"Mercy on us! I should never dare to say a word about it to Mrs. Mac: for I'm dreadfully afraid of her, she is so stern; and how I'm ever to get on when she is my mother-in-law I don't know!" cried Kitty, clasping her hands in dismay at the idea.

"She isn't half as stern as she looks; and if you go to her without fear, you've no idea how sensible and helpful she is. I used to be frighted out of my wits with her, but now I'm not a bit, and we get on nicely: indeed I'm fond of her, she is so reliable and upright in all things."

"She certainly is the straightest woman I ever saw, and the most precise. I never shall forget how scared I was when Steve took me up to see her that first time. I put on all my plainest things, did my hair in a meek knob, and tried to act like a sober, sedate young woman. Steve would laugh at me, and say I looked like a pretty nun, so I couldn't be as proper as I wished. Mrs. Mac was very kind, of course; but her eye was so sharp I felt as if she saw right through me, and knew that I'd pinned on my bonnet-strings, lost a button off my boot, and didn't brush my hair for ten minutes every night," said Kitty in an awe-stricken tone.

"She likes you, though, and so does uncle, and he's set his

heart on having you live with them by and by; so don't mind her eyes but look straight up at her, and you'll see how kind they can grow."

"Mac likes me too, and that did please me; for he doesn't like girls generally. Steve told me he said I had the 'making of a capital little woman in me.' Wasn't it nice of him? Steve was *so* proud, though he does laugh at Mac sometimes."

"Don't disappoint them, dear. Encourage Steve in all the good things he likes or wants, make friends with Mac, love Aunt Jane, and be a daughter to uncle, and you'll find yourself a very happy girl."

"I truly will, and thank you very much for not making fun of me. I know I'm a little goose; but lately I've felt as if I might come to something if I had the right sort of help. I'll go up and see Aunt Jessie tomorrow; I'm not a bit afraid of her: and then if you'll just quietly find out from Uncle Doctor what I must read, I'll work as hard as I can. Don't tell anyone please; they'll think it odd and affected, and I can't bear to be laughed at, though I dare say it is good discipline."

Rose promised, and both worked in silence for a moment; then Kitty asked rather timidly—

"Are you and Charlie trying this plan too? Since you've left off going out so much, he keeps away also; and we don't know what to make of it."

"He has had what he calls an 'artistic fit' lately, set up a studio, and is doing some crayon sketches of us all. If he'd only finish his things, they would be excellent; but he likes to try a great variety at once. I'll take you in sometime, and perhaps he will do a portrait of you for Steve. He likes girls' faces, and gets the likenesses wonderfully well."

"People say you are engaged: but I contradict it; because, of course, *I* should know if you were."

"We are not."

"I'm glad of it; for really, Rose, I'm afraid Charlie hasn't got 'firm principles,' though he is a fascinating fellow and one can't scold him. You don't mind my saying so, do you, dear?" added Kitty; for Rose did not answer at once.

"Not in the least: for you are one of us now, and I can speak frankly, and I will; for I think in one way you *can* help Steve very much. You are right about Charlie, both as to the principles and the fascination: Steve admires him exceedingly, and

always from a boy liked to imitate his pleasant ways. Some of
them are very harmless and do Steve good, but some are not.
I needn't talk about it, only you must show your boy that you
depend on him to keep out of harm, and help him do it."

"I will, I will! and then perhaps, when he is a perfect model,
Charlie will imitate him. I really begin to feel as if I had a great
deal to do," and Kitty looked as if she was beginning to like
it also.

"We all have; and the sooner we go to work the better for
us and those we love. You wouldn't think now that Phebe was
doing anything for Archie, but she is; and writes such splendid
letters, they stir him up wonderfully, and make us all love
and admire her more than ever."

"How is she getting on?" asked Kitty, who, though she called
herself a "little goose," had tact enough to see that Rose did not
care to talk about Charlie.

"Nicely; for you know she used to sing in our choir, so that
was a good recommendation for another. She got a fine place
in the new church at L——; and that gives her a comfortable
salary, though she has something put away. She was always a
saving creature and kept her wages carefully; uncle invested
them, and she begins to feel quite independent already. No fear
but my Phebe will get on: she has such energy, and manages so
well. I sometimes wish I could run away and work with her.

"Ah, my dear! we rich girls have our trials as well as poor
ones, though we don't get as much pity as they do," sighed
Kitty. "Nobody knows what I suffer sometimes from worries
that I can't talk about, and I shouldn't get much sympathy if I
did; just because I live in a big house, wear good gowns, and
have lots of lovers. Annabel used to say she envied me above all
created beings; but she doesn't now, and is perfectly absorbed
in her dear little Chinaman. Do you see how she ever could like
him?"

So they began to gossip, and the sober talk was over for that
time; but when Kitty departed, after criticizing all her dear
friends and their respective sweethearts, she had a helpful little
book in her muff, a resolute expression on her bright face, and
so many excellent plans for self-improvement in her busy brain,
that she and Steve bid fair to turn out the model couple of the
century.

14

Aunt Clara's Plan

BEING SERIOUSLY ALARMED by the fear of losing the desire
of his heart, Charlie had gone resolutely to work, and, like
many another young reformer, he rather overdid the matter; for,
in trying to keep out of the way of temptation, he denied himself
much innocent enjoyment. The artistic fit was a good excuse for
the seclusion which he fancied would be a proper penance; and
he sat listlessly plying crayon or paint-brush, with daily wild
rides on black Brutus, which seemed to do him good; for danger
of that sort was his delight.

People were used to his whims, and made light of what they
considered a new one; but, when it lasted week after week and
all attempts to draw him out were vain, his jolly comrades gave
him up, and the family began to say approvingly—"Now he
really *is* going to settle down and do something." Fortunately,
his mother let him alone; for though Dr. Alec had not 'thun-
dered in her ear," as he threatened, he *had* talked with her in a
way which first made her very angry, then anxious, and, lastly,
quite submissive; for her heart was set on her boy's winning
Rose, and she would have had him put on sackcloth and ashes if
that would have secured the prize. She made light of the cause of
Rose's displeasure, considering her extremely foolish and strait-
laced; "for all young men of any spirit had their little vices, and
came out well enough when the wild oats were sowed." So she
indulged Charlie in his new vagary, as she had in all his others,
and treated him like an ill-used being, which was neither an
inspiring nor helpful course on her part. Poor soul! she saw
her mistake by and by, and when too late repented of it bitterly.

Rose wanted to be kind, and tried in various ways to help her cousin, feeling very sure she should succeed as many another hopeful woman has done, quite unconscious how much stronger an undisciplined will is than the truest love; and what a difficult task the wisest find it to undo the mistakes of a bad education. But it was a hard thing to do: for, at the least hint of commendation or encouragement, he looked so hopeful that she was afraid of seeming to promise too much, and, of all things, she desired to escape the accusation of having trifled with him.

So life was not very comfortable to either just then; and, while Charlie was "mortifying soul and body" to please her, she was studying how to serve him best. Aunt Jessie helped her very much, and no one guessed, when they saw pretty Miss Campbell going up and down the hill with such a serious face, that she was intent on anything except taking, with praiseworthy regularity, the constitutionals which gave her such a charming colour.

Matters were in this state, when one day a note came to Rose from Mrs. Clara.

"MY SWEET CHILD,—Do take pity on my poor boy, and cheer him up with a sight of you; for he is so *triste* it breaks my heart to see him. He has a new plan in his head, which strikes me as an excellent one, if you will only favour it. Let him come and take you for a drive this fine afternoon, and talk things over. It will do him a world of good and deeply oblige

Your ever loving

AUNT CLARA."

Rose read the note twice, and stood a moment pondering, with her eyes absently fixed on the little bay before her window. The sight of several black figures moving briskly to and fro across its frozen surface seemed to suggest a mode of escape from the drive she dreaded in more ways than one. "That will be safer and pleasanter," she said, and going to her desk wrote her answer.

"DEAR AUNTY,—I'm afraid of Brutus; but, if Charlie will go skating with me, I should enjoy it very much, and it would do us both good. I can listen to the new plan with an undivided mind there; so give him my love, please, and say I shall expect him at three.

Affectionately,

ROSE."

Punctually at three, Charlie appeared with his skates over his arm, and a very contented face, which brightened wonderfully as Rose came downstairs in a seal-skin suit and scarlet skirt so like the one she wore years ago that he involuntarily exclaimed as he took her skates—

"You look so like little Rose I hardly know you, and it seems so like old times I feel sixteen again."

"That is just the way one ought to feel such a day as this. Now let us be off and have a good spin before anyone comes. There are only a few children there now; but it is Saturday, you know, and everybody will be out before long," answered Rose, carefully putting on her mittens as she talked: for her heart was not as light as the one little Rose carried under the brown jacket; and the boy of sixteen never looked at her with the love and longing she read in the eyes of the young man before her.

Away they went, and were soon almost as merry and warm as the children round them; for the ice was in good condition, the February sunshine brilliant, and the keen wind set their blood a-tingle with a healthful glow.

"Now tell me the plan your mother spoke of," began Rose, as they went gliding across the wide expanse before them; for Charlie seemed to have forgotten everything but the bliss of having her all to himself for a little while.

"Plan? Oh, yes! it is simply this. I'm going out to father next month."

"Really?" and Rose looked both surprised and incredulous; for this plan was not a new one.

"Really. You don't believe it, but I am; and mother means to go with me. We've had another letter from the governor, and he says if she can't part from her big baby to come along too, and all be happy together. What do you think of that?" he asked, eyeing her intently; for they were face to face, as she went backwards and he held both her hands to steer and steady her.

"I like it immensely, and I do believe it now: only it rather takes my breath away to think of aunty's going, when she never would hear of it before."

"She doesn't like the plan very well now, and consents to go only on one condition."

"What is that?" asked Rose, trying to free her hands; for a look at Charlie made her suspect what was coming.

"That you go with us;" and, holding the hands fast, he added rapidly, "Let me finish before you speak. I don't mean that any-thing is to be changed till you are ready; but if *you* go I'm willing to give up everything else, and live anywhere as long as you like. Why shouldn't you come to us for a year or two? We've never had our share. Father would be delighted, mother contented, and I the happiest man alive."

"Who made this plan?" asked Rose, as soon as she got the breath which certainly *had* been rather taken away by this entirely new and by no means agreeable scheme.

"Mother suggested it: I shouldn't have dared to even dream of such richness. I'd made up my mind to go alone; and when I told her she was in despair, till this superb idea came into her head. After that, of course it was easy enough for me to stick to the resolution I'd made."

"Why did *you* decide to go, Charlie?" and Rose looked up into the eyes that were fixed beseechingly on hers.

They wavered and glanced aside; then met hers honestly, yet full of a humility which made her own fall as he answered very low—

"Because I don't *dare* to stay."

"Is it so hard?" she said pitifully.

"Very hard. I haven't the moral courage to own up and face ridicule, and it seems so mean to hide for fear of breaking my word. I *will* keep it this time, Rose, if I go to the ends of the earth to do it."

"It is not cowardly to flee temptation; and nobody whose opinion is worth having will ridicule any brave attempt to conquer one's self. Don't mind it, Charlie, but stand fast; and I am sure you will succeed."

"You don't know what it is, and I can't tell you; for till I tried to give it up I never guessed what a grip it had on me. I thought it was only a habit, easy to drop when I liked: but it is stronger than I; and sometimes I feel as if possessed of a devil that *will* get the better of me, try as I may."

He dropped her hands abruptly as he said that, with the energy of despair; and, as if afraid of saying too much, he left her for a minute, striking away at full speed, as if in truth he would "go to the ends of the earth" to escape the enemy within himself.

Rose stood still, appalled by this sudden knowledge of how much greater the evil was than she had dreamed. What ought

she to do? Go with her cousin, and by so doing tacitly pledge
herself as his companion on that longer journey for which he was
as yet so poorly equipped? Both heart and conscience protested
against this so strongly that she put the thought away. But
compassion pleaded for him tenderly; and the spirit of self-
sacrifice, which makes women love to give more than they
receive, caused her to feel as if in a measure this man's fate lay
in her hands, to be decided for good or ill through her. How
should she be true both to him and to herself?

Before this question could be answered, he was back again,
looking as if he had left his care behind him; for his moods
varied like the wind. Her attitude, as she stood motionless and
alone with downcast face, was so unlike the cheerful creature
who came to meet him an hour ago, it filled him with self-
reproach; and, coming up, he drew one hand through his arm,
saying, as she involuntarily followed him—

"You must not stand still. Forget my heroics, and answer my
question. Will you go with us, Rose?"

"Not now: that is asking too much, Charlie, and I will promise
nothing, because I cannot do it honestly," she answered, so
firmly that he knew appeal was useless.

"Am I to go alone, then, leaving all I care for behind me?"

"No, take your mother with you, and do your best to reunite
your parents. You could not give yourself to a better task."

"She won't go without you."

"I think she will if you hold fast to your resolution. You won't
give that up, I hope?"

"No: I must go somewhere, for I can't stay here; and it may
as well be India, since that pleases father," answered Charlie,
doggedly.

"It will more than you can imagine. Tell him all the truth,
and see how glad he will be to help you, and how sincerely he
will respect you for what you've done."

"If you respect me, I don't care much about the opinion of anyone else," answered Charlie, clinging with a lover's pertinacity
to the hope that was dearest.

"I shall, if you go manfully away, and do the duty you owe
your father and yourself."

"And, when I've done it, may I come back to be rewarded,
Rose?" he asked, taking possession of the hand on his arm, as
if it was already his.

"I wish I could say what you want me to. But how can I promise when I am not sure of anything? I don't love you as I ought, and perhaps I never shall: so why persist in making me bind myself in this way? Be generous, Charlie, and don't ask it," implored Rose, much afflicted by his persistence.

"I thought you did love me: it looked very like it a month ago, unless you have turned coquette, and I can't quite believe that," he answered bitterly.

"I *was* beginning to love you, but you made me afraid to go on," murmured Rose, trying to tell the truth kindly.

"That cursed custom! What *can* a man do when his hostess asks him to drink wine with her?" And Charlie looked as if he could have cursed himself even more heartily.

"He can say 'No.' "

"I can't."

"Ah, that's the trouble! You never learned to say it even to yourself; and now it is so hard you want me to help you."

"And you won't."

"Yes, I will, by showing you that I *can* say it to myself, for your sake." And Rose looked up with a face so full of tender sorrow he could not doubt the words which both reproached and comforted him.

"My little saint! I don't deserve one half your goodness to me, but I will, and go away without one complaint to do my best, for your sake," he cried, touched by her grief, and stirred to emulation by the example of courage and integrity she tried to set him.

Here Steve and Kitty bore down upon them; and, obeying the impulse to put care behind them which makes it possible for young hearts to ache one minute and dance the next, Rose and Charlie banished their troubles, joined in the sport that soon turned the lonely little bay into a ballroom, and enjoyed the splendours of a winter sunset, forgetful of separation and Calcutta.

15
Alas For Charlie!

IN SPITE of much internal rebellion, Charlie held fast to his resolution; and Aunt Clara, finding all persuasions vain, gave in, and prepared to accompany him, in a state of chronic indignation against the world in general and Rose in particular. The poor girl had a hard time of it, and, but for her uncle, would have fared still worse. He was a sort of shield, upon which Mrs. Clara's lamentations, reproaches, and irate glances fell unavailingly, instead of wounding the heart against which they were aimed.

The days passed very quickly now; for everyone seemed anxious to have the parting over, and preparations went on rapidly. The big house was made ready to shut up for a year at least, comforts for the long voyage laid in, and farewell visits paid. The general activity and excitement rendered it impossible for Charlie to lead the life of an artistic hermit any longer: and he fell into a restless condition, which caused Rose to long for the departure of the "Rajah," when she felt that he would be safe; for these farewell festivities were dangerous to one who was just learning to say "No."

"Half the month safely gone. If we can only get well over these last weeks, a great weight will be off my mind," thought Rose, as she went down one wild, wet morning towards the end of February.

Opening the study door to greet her uncle, she exclaimed, "Why, Archie!" then paused upon the threshold, transfixed by fear; for in her cousin's white face she read the tidings of some great affliction.

180

"Hush! don't be frightened. Come in and I'll tell you," he whispered, putting down the bottle he had just taken from the doctor's medicine-closet.

Rose understood and obeyed; for Aunt Plenty was poorly with her rheumatism, and depended on her morning doze.

"What is it?" she said, looking about the room with a shiver, as if expecting to see again what she saw there New Year's night. Archie was alone, however, and, drawing her towards the closet, answered, with an evident effort to be quite calm and steady—

"Charlie is hurt! Uncle wants more ether, and the wide bandages in some drawer or other. He told me, but I forget. You keep this place in order: find them for me. Quick!"

Before he had done, Rose was at the drawer, turning over the bandages with hands that trembled as they searched.

"All narrow! I must make some. Can you wait?" And, catching up a piece of old linen, she tore it into wide strips, adding, in the same quick tone, as she began to roll them—

"Now tell me."

"I can wait: those are not needed just yet. I didn't mean anyone should know, you least of all," began Archie, smoothing out the strips as they lay across the table, and evidently surprised at the girl's nerve and skill.

"I can bear it: make haste! Is he much hurt?"

"I'm afraid he is. Uncle looks sober, and the poor boy suffers so I couldn't stay," answered Archie, turning still whiter about the lips that never had so hard a tale to tell before.

"You see, he went to town last evening to meet the man who is going to buy Brutus—"

"And Brutus did it? I knew he would!" cried Rose, dropping her work to wring her hands, as if she guessed the ending of the story now.

"Yes, and if he wasn't shot already I'd do it myself with pleasure; for he's done his best to kill Charlie," muttered Charlie's mate with a grim look; then gave a great sigh, and added with averted face—

"I shouldn't blame the brute; it wasn't his fault: he needed a firm hand, and—" he stopped there, but Rose said quickly—

"Go on. I *must* know."

"Charlie met some of his old cronies, quite by accident; there was a dinner-party, and they made him go, just for a good-bye they said. He couldn't refuse, and it was too much for him. He would come home alone in the storm, though they tried to keep him as he wasn't fit. Down by the new bridge—that high embankment you know—the wind had put the lantern out—he forgot— or something scared Brutus, and all went down together."

Archie had spoken fast and brokenly; but Rose understood, and at the last word hid her face with a little moan, as if she saw it all.

"Drink this and never mind the rest," he said, dashing into the next room and coming back with a glass of water, longing to be done and away; for this sort of pain seemed almost as bad as that he had left.

Rose drank, but held his arm tightly as he would have turned away, saying in a tone of command he could not disobey—

"Don't keep anything back: tell me the worst at once."

"We knew nothing of it," he went on obediently. "Aunt Clara thought he was with me, and no one found him till early this morning. A workman recognized him; and he was brought home, dead they thought. I came for uncle an hour ago. Charlie is conscious now, but awfully hurt; and I'm afraid from the way Mac and uncle look at one another that—Oh! think of it, Rose! crushed and helpless, alone in the rain all night, and I never knew, I never knew!"

With that poor Archie broke down entirely; and, flinging himself into a chair, laid his face on the table, sobbing like a girl. Rose had never seen a man cry before, and it was so unlike a woman's gentler grief that it moved her very much. Putting by her own anguish, she tried to comfort his, and going to him lifted up his head and made him lean on her; for in such hours as this women are the stronger. It was a very little to do, but it did comfort Archie; for the poor fellow felt as if fate was very hard upon him just then, and into this faithful bosom he could pour his brief but pathetic plaint.

"Phebe's gone, and now if Charlie's taken I don't see how I *can* bear it!"

"Phebe will come back, dear, and let us hope poor Charlie isn't going to be taken yet. Such things always seem worse at first, I've heard people say; so cheer up and hope for the best," answered Rose, seeking for some comfortable words to say, and finding very few.

They took effect, however; for Archie did cheer up like a man. Wiping away the tears which he so seldom shed that they did not know where to go, he got up, gave himself a little shake, and said with a long breath, as if he had been under water—

"Now I'm all right, thank you. I couldn't help it: the shock of being waked suddenly to find the dear old fellow in such a pitiful state upset me. I ought to go: are these ready?"

"In a minute. Tell uncle to send for me if I can be of any use. Oh, poor Aunt Clara! how does she bear it?"

"Almost distracted. I took mother to her, and she will do all that anybody can. Heaven only knows what aunt will do if—"

"And Heaven only can help her," added Rose, as Archie stopped at the words he could not utter. "Now take them, and let me know often."

"You brave little soul, I will," and Archie went away through the rain with his sad burden, wondering how Rose could be so calm, when the beloved Prince might be dying.

A long dark day followed, with nothing to break its melancholy monotony except the bulletins that came from hour to hour, reporting little change either for better or for worse. Rose broke the news gently to Aunt Plenty, and set herself to the task of keeping up the old lady's spirits; for, being helpless, the good soul felt as if everything would go wrong without her. At dusk she fell asleep, and Rose went down to order lights and fire in the parlour, with tea ready to serve at any moment; for she felt sure some of the men would come, and that a cheerful greeting and creature comforts would suit them better than tears, darkness, and desolation.

Presently Mac arrived, saying the instant he entered the room—

"More comfortable, cousin."

"Thank Heaven!" cried Rose, unclasping her hands. Then, seeing how worn out, wet, and weary Mac looked as he came into the light, she added in a tone that was a cordial in itself, "Poor boy, how tired you are! Come here, and let me make you comfortable."

"I was going home to freshen up a bit; for I must be back in an hour. Mother took my place so I could be spared, and came off, as uncle refused to stir."

"Don't go home; for if aunty isn't there it will be very dismal. Step into uncle's room and refresh, then come back and I'll give you your tea. Let me, let me! I can't help in any other way; and I *must* do something, this waiting is so dreadful."

Her last words betrayed how much suspense was trying her and Mac yielded at once, glad to comfort and be comforted. When he came back, looking much revived, a tempting little tea-table stood before the fire; and Rose went to meet him, saying with a faint smile, as she liberally bedewed him with the contents of a cologne flask—

"I can't bear the smell of ether: it suggests such dreadful things."

"What curious creatures women are! Archie told us you bore the news like a hero, and now you turn pale at a whiff of bad air. I can't explain it," mused Mac, as he meekly endured the fragrant shower-bath.

"Neither can I; but I've been imagining horrors all day, and made myself nervous. Don't let us talk about it; but come and have some tea."

"That's another queer thing. Tea is your panacea for all human ills; yet there isn't any nourishment in it. I'd rather have a glass of milk, thank you," said Mac, taking an easy-chair and stretching his feet to the fire.

She brought it to him and made him eat something; then, as he shut his eyes wearily, she went away to the piano, and having no heart to sing, played softly till he seemed asleep. But at the stroke of six, he was up and ready to be off again.

"He gave me that: take it with you and put some on his hair; he likes it, and I do so want to help a little," she said, slipping the pretty flagon into his pocket, with such a wistful look, Mac never thought of smiling at this very feminine request.

"I'll tell him. Is there anything else I can do for you, cousin?" he asked, holding the cold hand that had been serving him so helpfully.

"Only this: if there is any sudden change, promise to send for me, no matter at what hour it is: I *must* say 'Good-bye.' "

"I will come for you. But, Rose, I am sure you may sleep in peace to-night; and I hope to have good news for you in the morning."

"Bless you for that! Come early, and let me see him soon. I will be very good, and I know it will not do him any harm."

"No fear of that: the first thing he said when he could speak was, 'Tell Rose carefully;' and, as I came away, he guessed where I was going, and tried to kiss his hand in the old way, you know."

Mac thought it would cheer her to hear that Charlie remembered her; but the sudden thought that she might never see that familiar little gesture any more was the last drop that made her full heart overflow, and Mac saw the "hero" of the morning sink down at his feet in a passion of tears that frightened him. He took her to the sofa, and tried to comfort her; but, as soon as the bitter sobbing quieted, she looked up and said quite steadily, great drops rolling down her cheeks the while—

"Let me cry: it is what I need, and I shall be all the better for it by and by. Go to Charlie now, and tell him I said with all my heart, 'Good-night!' "

"I will!" and Mac trudged away, marvelling in his turn at the curiously blended strength and weakness of womankind.

That was the longest night Rose ever spent; but joy came in the morning with the early message, "He is better. You are to come by and by." Then Aunt Plenty forgot her lumbago and arose; Aunt Myra, who had come to have a social croak, took off her black bonnet as if it would not be needed at present, and the girl made ready to go and say "Welcome back," not the hard "Good-bye."

It seemed very long to wait; for no summons came till afternoon, then her uncle arrived, and at the first sight of his face Rose began to tremble.

"I came for my little girl myself, because we must go back at once," he said, as she hurried towards him hat in hand.

"I'm ready, sir;" but her hands shook as she tried to tie the ribbons, and her eyes never left the face that was so full of tender pity for her.

He took her quickly into the carriage, and, as they rolled away, said with the quiet directness which soothes such agitation better than any sympathetic demonstration—

"Charlie is worse. I feared it when the pain went so suddenly this morning; but the chief injuries are internal, and one can never tell what the chances are. He insists that he is better, but will soon begin to fail, I fear; become unconscious, and slip away without more suffering. This is the time for you to see him; for he has set his heart on it, and nothing can hurt him now. My child, it is very hard; but we must help each other bear it."

Rose tried to say, "Yes, uncle," bravely; but the words would not come; and she could only slip her hand into his with a look of mute submission. He laid her head on his shoulder, and went on talking so quietly that anyone who did not see how worn and haggard his face had grown with two days and a night of sharp anxiety might have thought him cold.

"Jessie has gone home to rest, and Jane is with poor Clara, who has dropped asleep at last. I've sent for Steve and the other boys. There will be time for them later; but he so begged to see you now, I thought it best to come while this temporary strength keeps him up. I have told him how it is, but he will not believe me. If he asks you, answer honestly; and try to fit him a little for this sudden ending of so many hopes."

"How soon, uncle?"

"A few hours, probably. This tranquil moment is yours: make the most of it; and, when we can do no more for him, we'll comfort one another."

Mac met them in the hall: but Rose hardly saw him; she was conscious only of the task before her; and, when her uncle led her to the door, she said quietly—

"Let me go in alone, please."

Archie, who had been hanging over the bed, slipped away into the inner room as she appeared; and Rose found Charlie waiting for her with such a happy face, she could not believe what she had heard, and found it easy to say almost cheerfully, as she took his eager hand in both of hers—

"Dear Charlie, I'm so glad you sent for me. I longed to come, but waited till you were better. You surely are?" she added, as a second glance showed her the indescribable change which had come upon the face which at first, seemed to have both light and colour in it.

"Uncle says not: but I think he is mistaken, because the agony is all gone; and, except for this odd sinking now and then, I don't feel so much amiss," he answered feebly, but with something of the old lightness in his voice.

"You will hardly be able to sail in the 'Rajah,' I fear; but you won't mind waiting a little, while we nurse you," said poor Rose, trying to talk on quietly, with her heart growing heavier every minute.

"I shall go if I'm carried! I'll keep that promise, though it costs me my life. O Rose! you know? they've told you?" and, with a sudden memory of what brought him there, he hid his face in the pillow.

"You broke no promise; for I would not let you make one,

you remember. Forget all that, and let us talk about the better
time that may be coming for you."

"Always so generous, so kind!" he murmured, with her hand
against his feverish cheek; then, looking up, he went on in a
tone so humbly contrite it made her eyes fill with slow, hot
tears.

"I tried to flee temptation: I tried to say 'No;' but I am so
pitiably weak, I couldn't. You must despise me. But don't give
me up entirely: for, if I live, I'll do better; I'll go away to
father and begin again."

Rose tried to keep back the bitter drops; but they would fall,
to hear him still speak hopefully when there was no hope.
Something in the mute anguish of her face seemed to tell him
what she could not speak; and a quick change came over him
as he grasped her hand tighter, saying in a sharp whisper—

"Have I really got to die, Rose?"

Her only answer was to kneel down and put her arms about
him, as if she tried to keep death away a little longer. He
believed it then, and lay so still, she looked up in a moment,
fearing she knew not what.

But Charlie bore it manfully; for he had the courage which
can face a great danger bravely, though not the strength to fight
a bosom-sin and conquer it. His eyes were fixed, as if trying to
look into the unseen world whither he was going, and his lips
firmly set that no word of complaint should spoil the proof he
meant to give that, though he had not known how to live, he
did know how to die. It seemed to Rose as if for one brief
instant she saw the man that might have been, if early training
had taught him how to rule himself; and the first words he
uttered with a long sigh, as his eye came back to her, showed
that he felt the failure and owned it with pathetic candour.

"Better so, perhaps; better go before I bring any more
sorrow to you, and shame to myself. I'd like to stay a little
longer, and try to redeem the past; it seems so wasted now:
but, if I can't, don't grieve, Rose; I'm no loss to anyone, and
perhaps it *is* too late to mend."

"Oh, don't say that! no one will fill your place among us: we
never can forget how much we loved you; and you must believe
how freely we forgive as we would be forgiven," cried Rose,
steadied by the pale despair that had fallen on Charlie's face with
those bitter words.

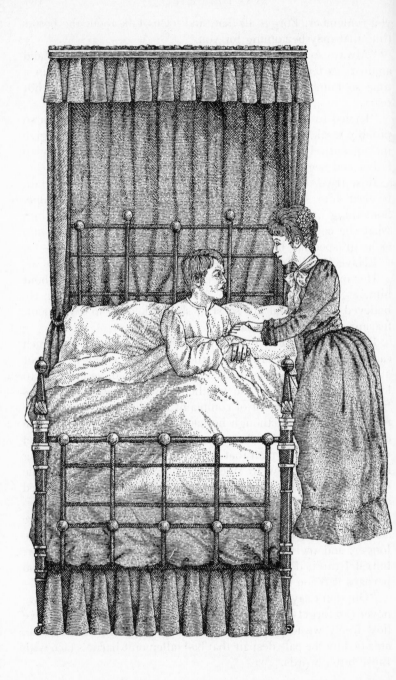

" 'Forgive us our trespasses!' Yes, I should say that. Rose, I'm not ready; it is so sudden: what can I do?" he whispered, clinging to her, as if he had no anchor except the creature whom he loved so much.

"Uncle will tell you: I am not good enough; I can only pray for you," and she moved as if to call in the help so sorely needed.

"No, no, not yet! stay by me, darling: read something; there, in grandfather's old book, some prayer for such as I. It will do me more good from you than any minister alive."

She got the venerable book—given to Charlie because he bore the good man's name—and, turning to the "Prayer for the Dying," read it brokenly; while the voice beside her echoed now and then some word that reproved or comforted.

"The testimony of a good conscience." "By the sadness of his countenance may his heart be made better." "Christian patience and fortitude." "Leave the world in peace." "Amen."

There was silence for a little; then Rose, seeing how wan he looked, said softly, "Shall I call uncle now?"

"If you will; but first—don't smile at my foolishness, dear— I want my little heart. They took it off: please give it back, and let me keep it always," he answered, with the old fondness strong as ever, even when he could only show it by holding fast the childish trinket which she found and gave him—the old agate heart with the faded ribbon. "Put it on, and never let them take it off," he said; and, when she asked if there was anything else she could do for him, he tried to stretch out his arms to her with a look which asked for more.

She kissed him very tenderly on lips and forehead, tried to say "Good-bye," but could not speak, and groped her way to the door. Turning for a last look, Charlie's hopeful spirit rose for a moment, as if anxious to send her away more cheerful, and he said with a shadow of the old blithe smile a feeble attempt at the familiar farewell gesture—

"Till tomorrow, Rose."

Alas, for Charlie! his tomorrow never came: and, when she saw him next, he lay there looking so serene and noble, it seemed as if it must be well with him; for all the pain was past; temptation ended; doubt and fear, hope and love, could no more stir his quiet heart, and in solemn truth he *had* gone to meet his Father, and begin again.

16
Good Works

THE "RAJAH" was delayed awhile, and when it sailed poor Mrs. Clara was on board; for everything was ready, all thought she had better go to comfort her husband, and since her boy died she seemed to care very little what became of her. So, with friends to cheer the long voyage, she sailed away, a heavy-hearted woman, yet not quite disconsolate; for she knew her mourning was excessively becoming, and felt sure that Stephen would not find her altered by her trials as much as might have been expected.

Then nothing was left of that gay household but the empty rooms, silence never broken by a blithe voice any more, and pictures full of promise, but all unfinished, like poor Charlie's life.

There was much mourning for the bonny Prince, but no need to tell of it except as it affected Rose; for it is with her we have most to do, the other characters being of secondary importance.

When time had soothed the first shock of sudden loss, she was surprised to find that the memory of his faults and failings, short life and piteous death, grew dim as if a kindly hand wiped out the record, and gave him back to her in the likeness of the brave, bright boy she had loved, not as the wayward, passionate young man who had loved her.

This comforted her very much; and, folding down the last blotted leaf where his name was written, she gladly turned back to reopen and reread the happier chapters which painted the youthful knight before he went out to fall in his first battle. None of the bitterness of love bereaved marred this memory for

Rose, because she found that the warmer sentiment, just budding in her heart, had died with Charlie, and lay cold and quiet in his grave. She wondered, yet was glad; though sometimes a remorseful pang smote her when she discovered how possible it was to go on without him, feeling almost as if a burden had been lifted off, since his happiness was taken out of her hands. The time had not yet come when the knowledge that a man's heart was in her keeping would make the pride and joy of her life; and while she waited for that moment she enjoyed the liberty she seemed to have recovered.

Such being her inward state, it much annoyed her to be regarded as a broken-hearted girl, and pitied for the loss of her young lover. She could not explain to all the world, so let it pass, and occupied her mind with the good works which always lie ready to be taken up and carried on. Having chosen philanthropy as her profession, she felt that it was high time to begin the task too long neglected.

Her projects were excellent, but did not prosper as rapidly as she hoped; for, having to deal with people, not things, unexpected obstacles were constantly arising. The "Home for Decayed Gentlewomen," as the boys insisted on calling her two newly repaired houses, started finely; and it was a pleasant sight to see the comfortable rooms filled with respectable women busy at their various tasks, surrounded by the decencies and many of the comforts which make life endurable. But, presently, Rose was disturbed to find that the good people expected her to take care of them in a way she had not bargained for. Buffum, her agent, was constantly reporting complaints, new wants, and general discontent if they were not attended to. Things were neglected, water-pipes froze and burst, drains got out of order, yards were in a mess, and rents behindhand. Worst of all, outsiders, instead of sympathizing, only laughed and said, "We told you so," which is a most discouraging remark to older and wiser workers than Rose.

Uncle Alec, however, stood by her staunchly, and helped her out of many of her woes by good advice, and an occasional visit of inspection, which did much to impress upon the dwellers there the fact that, if they did not do their part, their leases would be short ones.

"I didn't expect to make anything out of it, but I did think they would be grateful," said Rose, on one occasion when several complaints had come in at once, and Buffum had reported great difficulty in collecting the low rents.

"If you do this thing for the sake of the gratitude, then it *is* a failure: but if it is done for the love of helping those who need help it is a success; for in spite of their worry every one of those women feel what privileges they enjoy and value them highly," said Dr. Alec, as they went home after one of these unsatisfactory calls.

"Then the least they can do is to say 'Thank you.' I'm afraid I *have* thought more of the gratitude than the work; but if there isn't any I must make up my mind to go without," answered Rose, feeling defrauded of her due.

"Favours often separate instead of attracting people nearer to one another, and I've seen many a friendship spoilt by the obligation being all on one side. Can't explain it, but it is so; and I've come to the conclusion that it is as hard to give in the right spirit as it is to receive. Puzzle it out, my dear, while you are learning to do good for its own sake."

"I know one sort of people who *are* grateful, and I'm going to devote my mind to them. They thank me in many ways, and helping them is all pleasure and no worry. Come into the hospital and see the dear babies, or the Asylum and carry oranges to Phebe's orphans: *they* don't complain and fidget one's life out, bless their hearts!" cried Rose, clearing up suddenly.

After that she left Buffum to manage the "Retreat," and devoted her energies to the little folks, always so ready to receive the smallest gift, and repay the giver with their artless thanks. Here she found plenty to do, and did it with such sweet good-will that she won her way like sunshine, making many a little heart dance over splendid dolls, gay picture-books, and pots of flowers, as well as food, fire, and clothes for the small bodies pinched with want and pain.

As spring came, new plans sprung up as naturally as dandelions. The poor children longed for the country; and, as the green fields could not come to them, Rose carried them to the green fields. Down on the Point stood an old farmhouse, often used by the Campbell tribe for summer holidays. That spring it was set to rights unusually early, several women installed as housekeeper, cook, and nurses; and, when the May days grew bright and warm, squads of pale children came to toddle in the grass, run over the rocks, and play upon the smooth sands of the beach. A pretty sight, and one that well repaid those who brought it to pass.

Everyone took an interest in the "Rose Garden," as Mac named it; and the women-folk were continually driving over to the Point with something for the "poor dears." Aunt Plenty sowed gingerbread broadcast; Aunt Jessie made pinafores by the dozen; while Aunt Jane "kept her eye" on the nurses, and Aunt Myra supplied medicines so liberally that the mortality would have been awful, if Dr. Alec had not taken them in charge. To him this was the most delightful spot in the world: and well it might be; for he suggested the idea, and gave Rose all the credit of it. He was often there, and his appearance was always greeted with shrieks of rapture, as the children gathered from all quarters: creeping, running, hopping on crutches, or carried in arms which they gladly left to sit on "Uncle Doctor's" knee; for that was the title by which he went among them.

He seemed as young as any of his comrades, though the curly head was getting grey; and the frolics that went on when he arrived were better than any medicine to children who had never learned to play. It was a standing joke among the friends that the bachelor brother had the largest family, and was the most domestic man of the remaining four; though Uncle Mac did his part manfully, and kept Aunt Jane in a constant fidget, by his propositions to adopt the heartiest boys and prettiest girls to amuse him and employ her.

On one occasion she had a very narrow escape; and the culprit being her son, not her husband, she felt free to repay herself for many scares of this sort by a good scolding; which, unlike many, produced excellent results.

One bright June day, as Rose came cantering home from the Point on her pretty bay pony, she saw a man sitting on a fallen tree beside the road, and something in his despondent attitude arrested her attention. As she drew nearer, he turned his head, and she stopped short, exclaiming in great surprise—

"Why, Mac! what *are* you doing here?"

"Trying to solve a problem," he answered, looking up with a whimsical expression of perplexity and amusement in his face, which made Rose smile, till his next words turned her sober in a twinkling—

"I've eloped with a young lady, and don't know what to do

G

with her. I took her home, of course; but mother turned her out of the house, and I'm in a quandary."

"Is that her baggage?" asked Rose, pointing with her whip to the large bundle which he held; while the wild idea flashed through her head that perhaps he really *had* done some rash deed of this sort.

"No, this is the young lady herself;" and, opening a corner of the brown shawl, he displayed a child of three—so pale, so thin, and tiny, that she looked like a small scared bird just fallen from the nest, as she shrunk away from the light with great frightened eyes, and a hand like a little claw tightly clutching a button of Mac's coat.

"Poor baby! where did it come from?" cried Rose, leaning down to look.

"I'll tell you the story, and then you shall advise me what to do. At our hospital, we've had a poor woman who got hurt, and died two days ago. I had nothing to do with her, only took her a bit of fruit once or twice; for she had big, wistful sort of eyes that haunted me. The day she died I stopped a minute, and the nurse said she'd been wanting to speak to me, but didn't dare. So I asked if I could do anything for her; and, though she could hardly breathe for pain—being almost gone—she implored me to take care of baby. I found out where the child was, and promised I'd see after her; for the poor soul couldn't seem to die till I'd given her that comfort. I never can forget the look in her eyes, as I held her hand, and said, 'Baby shall be taken care of.' She tried to thank me, and died soon after quite peacefully. Well, I went today and hunted up the poor little wretch. Found her in a miserable place, left in the care of an old hag, who had shut her up alone to keep her out of the way, and there this mite was, huddled in a corner crying, 'Marmar, marmar!' fit to touch a heart of stone. I blew up the woman, and took baby straight away, for she had been abused; and it was high time. Look there, will you?"

Mac turned the little skinny arm, and showed a blue mark which made Rose drop her reins, and stretch out both hands, crying with a tender sort of indignation—

"How dared they do it? Give her to me; poor, little, motherless thing!"

Mac laid the bundle in her arms, and Rose began to cuddle it in the fond, foolish way women have—a most comfortable and

effective way, nevertheless; and baby evidently felt that things
were changing for the better, when warm lips touched her
cheeks, a soft hand smoothed her tumbled hair, and a womanly
face bent over her, with the inarticulate cooings and purrings
mothers make. The frightened eyes went up to this gentle
countenance, and rested there as if reassured; the little claw
crept to the girl's neck, and poor baby nestled to her with a long
sigh, and a plaintive murmur of "Marmar, marmar," that certainly would have touched a stony heart.

"Now, go on. No, Rosa, not you," said the new nurse, as the
intelligent animal looked round to see if things were all right
before she proceeded.

"I took the child home to mother, not knowing what else to
do; but she she wouldn't have it at any price, even for a night.
She doesn't like children, you know, and father has joked so
much about the Pointers that she is quite rampant at the mere
idea of a child in the house. She told me to take it to the Rose
Garden. I said it was running over now, and no room even for a
mite like this. 'Go to the Hospital,' says she. 'Baby isn't ill,
ma'am,' says I. 'Orphan Asylum,' says she. 'Not an orphan:
got a father who can't take care of her,' says I. 'Take her to the
Foundling place, or Mrs. Gardener, or someone whose business
it is. I will *not* have the creature here, sick and dirty and noisy.
Carry it back, and ask Rose to tell you what to do with it.' So
my cruel parent cast me forth; but relented as I shouldered baby,
gave me a shawl to put her in, a jumble to feed her with, and
money to pay her board in some good place. Mother's bark is
always worse than her bite, you know."

"And you were trying to think of the 'good place' as you sat
here?" asked Rose, looking down at him with great approval,
as he stood patting Rosa's glossy neck.

"Exactly. I didn't want to trouble you, for you have your
house full already; and I really couldn't lay my hands on any
good soul who would be bothered with this little forlornity.
She has nothing to recommend her, you see—not pretty, feeble,
and shy as a mouse; no end of care, I dare say: yet she needs
every bit she can get to keep soul and body together, if I'm
any judge."

Rose opened her lips impulsively, but closed them without
speaking, and sat a minute looking straight between Rosa's
ears, as if forcing herself to think twice before she spoke. Mac

watched her out of the corner of his eye, as he said, in a musing tone, tucking the shawl round a pair of shabby little feet the while—

"This seems to be one of the charities that no one wants to undertake; yet I can't help feeling that my promise to the mother binds me to something more than merely handing baby over to some busy matron or careless nurse in any of our over-crowded institutions. She is such a frail creature she won't trouble any one long, perhaps; and I *should* like to give her just a taste of comfort, if not love before she finds her 'Marmar' again."

"Lead Rosa: I'm going to take this child home; and, if uncle is willing, I'll adopt her, and she *shall* be happy!" cried Rose, with the sudden glow of feeling that always made her lovely. And, gathering poor baby close, she went on her way like a modern Britomart, ready to redress the wrongs of any who had need of her.

As he led the slowly stepping horse along the quiet road, Mac could not help thinking that they looked a little like the Flight into Egypt: but he did not say so, being a reverent youth—only glanced back now and then at the figure above him; for Rose had taken off her hat to keep the light from baby's eyes, and sat with the sunshine turning her uncovered hair to gold, as she looked down at the little creature resting on the saddle before her, with the sweet thoughtfulness one sees in some of Cor-regio's young Madonnas.

No one else saw the picture, but Mac long remembered it; and ever after there was a touch of reverence added to the warm affection he had always borne his cousin Rose.

"What is the child's name?" was the sudden question which disturbed a brief silence, broken only by the sound of pacing hoofs, the rustle of green boughs overhead, and the blithe carolling of birds.

"I'm sure I don't know," answered Mac, suddenly aware that he had fallen out of one quandary into another.

"Didn't you ask?"

"No: the mother called her 'Baby;' the old woman, 'Brat.' And that is all I know of the first name: the last is Kennedy. You can Christen her what you like."

"Then I shall name her Dulcinea, as you are her knight, and call her Dulce for short. That is a sweet diminutive, I'm sure," laughed Rose, much amused at the idea.

Don Quixote looked pleased, and vowed to defend his little lady stoutly, beginning his services on the spot by filling the small hands with buttercups, thereby winning for himself the first smile baby's face had known for weeks.

When they got home, Aunt Plenty received her new guest with her accustomed hospitality, and, on learning the story, was as warmly interested as even enthusiastic Rose could desire, bustling about to make the child comfortable with an energy pleasant to see; for the grandmotherly instincts were strong in the old lady, and of late had been beautifully developed.

In less than half an hour from the time baby went upstairs, she came down again on Rose's arm, freshly washed and brushed in a pink gown much too large, and a white apron decidedly too small; an immaculate pair of socks but no shoes; a neat bandage on the bruised arm, and a string of spools for a plaything hanging on the other. A resigned expression sat upon her little face; but the frightened eyes were only shy now, and the forlorn heart evidently much comforted.

"There! how do you like your Dulce now?" said Rose, proudly displaying the work of her hands, as she came in with her habit pinned up, and carrying a silver porringer of bread and milk.

Mac knelt down, took the small, reluctant hand, and kissed it as devoutly as ever good Alonzo Quixada did that of the Duchess; while he said, merrily quoting from the immortal story—

" 'High and Sovereign Lady, thine till death, the Knight of the Rueful Countenance.' "

But baby had no heart for play, and, withdrawing her hand, pointed to the porringer, with the suggestive remark—

"Din-din, *now.*"

So Rose sat down and fed the Duchess, while the Don stood by and watched the feast with much satisfaction.

"How nice she looks! Do you consider shoes unhealthy?" he asked, surveying the socks with respectful interest.

"No: her shoes are drying. You must have let her go in the mud."

"I only put her down for a minute when she howled; and she made for a puddle, like a duck. I'll buy her some new ones— clothes too. Where do I go, what do I ask for, and how much do I get?" he said, diving for his pocket-book, amiably anxious, but pitiably ignorant.

"I'll see to that. We always have things on hand for the Pointers as they come along, and can soon fit Dulce out. You may make some inquiries about the father if you will; for I don't want to have her taken away just as I get fond of her. Do you know anything about him?"

"Only that he is in State Prison for twenty-one years and not likely to trouble you."

"How dreadful! I really think Phebe was better off to have none at all. I'll go to work at once, then, and try to bring up the convict's little daughter to be a good woman; so that she will have an honest name of her own, since he has nothing but disgrace to give her."

"Uncle can show you how to do that, if you need any help. He has been so successful in his first attempt I fancy you won't require much," said Mac, picking up the spools for the sixth time.

"Yes, I shall; for it is a great responsibility, and I do not undertake it lightly," answered Rose, soberly; though the double-barrelled compliment pleased her very much.

"I'm sure Phebe has turned out splendidly, and you began very early with her."

"So I did! that's encouraging. Dear thing, how bewildered she looked when I proposed adopting her. I remember all about it; for uncle had just come, and I was quite crazy over a box of presents, and rushed at Phebe as she was cleaning brasses. How little I thought my childish offer would end so well!" and Rose fell a musing with a happy smile on her face, while baby picked the last morsels out of the porringer with her own busy fingers.

It certainly had ended well; for Phebe at the end of six months not only had a good place as choir singer, but several young pupils, and excellent prospects for the next winter.

> " 'Accept the blessing of a poor young man,
>   Whose lucky steps have led him to your door,'

and let me help as much as I can. Good-bye, my Dulcinea," and, with a farewell stroke of the smooth head, Mac went away to report his success to his mother, who, in spite of her seeming harshness, was already planning how she could best befriend this inconvenient baby.

17

Among the Haycocks

UNCLE ALEC did not object; and, finding that no one had any claim upon the child, permitted Rose to keep it for a time at least. So little Dulce, newly equipped even to a name, took her place among them and slowly began to thrive. But she did not grow pretty, and never was a gay, attractive child; for she seemed to have been born in sorrow and brought up in misery. A pale, pensive little creature, always creeping into corners and looking timidly out, as if asking leave to live, and, when offered playthings, taking them with a meek surprise that was very touching.

Rose soon won her heart, and then almost wished she had not; for baby clung to her with inconvenient fondness, changing her former wail of "Marmar" into a lament for "Aunty Wose" if separated long. Nevertheless, there was great satisfaction in cherishing the little waif; for she learned more than she could teach, and felt a sense of responsibility which was excellent ballast for her enthusiastic nature.

Kitty Van, who made Rose her model in all things, was immediately inspired to go and do likewise, to the great amusemend as well as annoyance of her family. Selecting the prettiest, liveliest child in the Asylum, she took it home on trial for a week. "A perfect cherub" she pronounced it the first day, but an *"enfant terrible"* before the week was over; for the young hero rioted by day, howled by night, ravaged the house from top to bottom, and kept his guardians in a series of panics by his hairbreadth escapes. So early on Saturday, poor, exhausted Kitty restored the "cherub" with many thanks, and decided to wait till her views of education were rather more advanced.

199

As the warm weather came on, Rose announced that Dulce needed mountain air; for she dutifully repeated as many of Dr. Alec's prescriptions as possible, and, remembering how much good Cosy Corner did her long ago, resolved to try it on her baby. Aunt Jessie and Jamie went with her, and Mother Atkinson received them as cordially as ever. The pretty daughters were all married and gone, but a stout damsel took their place; and nothing seemed changed except that the old heads were greyer and the young ones a good deal taller than six years ago.

Jamie immediately fraternized with neighbouring boys, and devoted himself to fishing with an ardour which deserved greater success. Aunt Jessie revelled in the reading, for which she had no time at home; and lay in her hammock a happy woman, with no socks to darn, buttons to sew, or housekeeping cares to vex her soul.

Rose went about with Dulce like a very devoted hen with one rather feeble chicken; for she was anxious to have this treatment work well, and tended her little patient with daily increasing satisfaction. Dr. Alec came up to pass a few days, and pronounced the child in a most promising condition. But the grand event of the season was the unexpected arrival of Phebe.

Two of her pupils had invited her to join them in a trip to the mountains, and she ran away from the great hotel to surprise her little mistress with a sight of her, so well and happy that Rose had no anxiety left on her account.

Three delightful days they spent, roaming about together, talking as only girls can talk after a long separation, and enjoying one another like a pair of lovers. As if to make it quite perfect, by one of those remarkable coincidences which sometimes occur, Archie happened to run up for the Sunday; so Phebe had *her* surprise, and Aunt Jessie and the telegraph kept their secret so well, no one ever knew what maternal machinations brought the happy accident to pass.

Then Rose saw a very pretty, pastoral bit of love-making, and long after it was over, and Phebe gone one way, Archie another, the echo of sweet words seemed to linger in the air, tender ghosts to haunt the pine-grove, and even the big coffee-pot had a halo of romance about it; for its burnished sides reflected the soft glances the lovers interchanged, as one filled the other's cup at that last breakfast.

Rose found these reminiscences more interesting than any

novel she had read, and often beguiled her long leisure by planning a splendid future for her Phebe, as she trotted about after
her baby in the lovely July weather.

On one of the most perfect days, she sat under an old apple-
tree on the slope behind the house where they used to play.
Before her opened the wide inter-vale, dotted with hay-makers
at their picturesque work. On the left, flowed the swift river
fringed with graceful elms in their bravest greenery; on the
right, rose the purple hills serene and grand; and overhead
glowed the midsummer sky which glorified it all.

Little Dulce tired of play, lay fast asleep in the nest she had
made in one of the haycocks close by; and Rose leaned against
the gnarled old tree, dreaming day-dreams with her work at her
feet. Happy and absorbing fancies they seemed to be; for her
face was beautifully tranquil, and she took no heed of the train
which suddenly went speeding down the valley, leaving a white
cloud behind. Its rumble concealed the sound of approaching
steps, and her eyes never turned from the distant hills, till the
abrupt appearance of a very sunburnt but smiling young man
made her jump up, exclaiming joyfully—

"Why Mac! where did you drop from?"

"The top of Mount Washington. How do you do?"

"Never better. Won't you go in? You must be tired after
such a fall."

"No, thank you; I've seen the old lady. She told me Aunt
Jessie and the boy had gone to town, and that you were 'settin'
round' in the old place; so I came on at once, and will take a
lounge here, if you don't mind," answered Mac, unstrapping his
knapsack, and taking a haycock as if it were a chair.

Rose subsided into her former seat, surveying her cousin with
much satisfaction, as she said—

"This is the third surprise I've had since I came. Uncle
popped in upon us first, then Phebe, and now you. Have you had
a pleasant tramp? Uncle said you were off."

"Delightful! I feel as if I'd been in heaven, or near it, for
about three weeks; and thought I'd break the shock of coming
down to the earth by calling here on my way home."

"You look as if heaven suited you. Brown as a berry; but so
fresh and happy, I should never guess you had been scrambling
down a mountain," said Rose, trying to discover why he looked
so well in spite of the blue-flannel suit and dusty shoes; for there

G*

was a certain sylvan freshness about him, as he sat there full of
the reposeful strength the hills seemed to have given, the wholesome cheerfulness days of air and sunshine put into a man, and
the clear, bright look of one who had caught glimpses of a new
world from the mountain-top.

"Tramping agrees with me. I took a dip in the river as I came
along, and made my toilet in a place where Milton's Sabrina
might have lived," he said, shaking back his damp hair, and
settling the knot of scarlet bunch-berries stuck in his button-
hole.

"You look as if you found the nymph at home," said Rose,
knowing how much he liked the Comus.

"I found her *here*," and he made a little bow.

"That's very pretty; and I'll give you one in return. You
grow more like Uncle Alec every day, and I think I'll call you
Alec, Jr."

"Alexander the Great wouldn't thank you for that," said
Mac and did not look as grateful as she had expected.

"Very like, indeed, except the forehead. His is broad and
benevolent; yours high and arched. Do you know if you had no
beard, and wore your hair long, I really think you'd look like
Milton," added Rose, sure that would please him.

It certainly did amuse him; for he lay back on the hay and
laughed so heartily that his merriment scared the squirrel on
the wall and woke Dulce.

"You ungrateful boy! will nothing suit you? When I say you
look like the best man I know, you give a shrug; and, when I
liken you to a great poet, you shout: I'm afraid you are very
conceited, Mac;" and Rose laughed too, glad to see him so gay.

"If I am, it is your fault. Nothing I can do will ever make a
Milton of me, unless I go blind some day," he said, sobering at
the thought.

"You once said a man could be what he liked if he tried hard
enough; so why shouldn't you be a poet?" asked Rose, liking to
trip him up with his own words, as he often did her.

"I thought I was to be an M.D."

"You might be both. There have been poetical doctors, you
know."

"Would you like me to be such an one?" asked Mac, looking
at her as seriously as if he really thought of trying it.

"No: I'd rather have you one or the other. I don't care which,

only you must be famous in either you choose. I'm very ambitious for you; because, I insist upon it, you are a genius of some
sort. I think it is beginning to simmer already, and I've a great
curiosity to know what it will turn out to be."

Mac's eyes shone as she said that, but before he could speak
a little voice said, "Aunty Wose!" and he turned to find Dulce
sitting up in her nest, staring at the broad blue back before her
with round eyes.

"Do you know your Don?" he asked, offering his hand with
respectful gentleness; for she seemed a little doubtful whether
he was friend or stranger.

"It is 'Mat,'" said Rose, and that familiar word seemed to
reassure the child at once; for, leaning forward, she kissed him
as if quite used to doing it.

"I picked up some toys for her by the way, and she shall have
them at once to pay for that. I didn't expect to be so graciously
received by this shy mouse," said Mac, much gratified; for
Dulce was very chary of her favours.

"She knew you; for I always carry my home-album with me,
and when she comes to your picture she always kisses it, because
I never want her to forget her first friend," explained Rose,
pleased with her pupil.

"First, but not best," answered Mac, rummaging in his
knapsack for the promised toys, which he set forth upon the hay
before delighted Dulce.

Neither picture-books nor sweeties; but berries strung on
long stems of grass, acorns and pretty cones, bits of rock shining
with mica, several bluebirds' feathers, and a nest of moss with
white pebbles for eggs.

"Dearest Nature, strong and kind," knows what children love,
and has plenty of such playthings ready for them all, if one only
knows how to find them. These were received with rapture; and,
leaving the little creature to enjoy them in her own quiet way,
Mac began to tumble the things back into his knapsack again.
Two or three books lay near Rose, and she took up one which
opened at a place marked by a scribbled paper.

"Keats? I didn't know you condescended to read anything so
modern," she said, moving the paper to see the page
beneath.

Mac looked up, snatched the book out of her hand, and shook
down several more scraps; then returned it with a curiously

shame-faced expression, saying, as he crammed the papers into his pocket—

"I beg pardon, but it was full of rubbish. Oh, yes! I'm fond of Keats; don't you know him?"

"I used to read him a good deal; but uncle found me crying over the 'Pot of Basil,' and advised me to read less poetry for a while or I should get too sentimental," answered Rose, turning the pages without seeing them; for a new idea had just popped into her head.

" 'The Eve of St. Agnes' is the most perfect love-story in the world, I think," said Mac, enthusiastically.

"Read it to me. I feel just like hearing poetry, and you will do it justice if you are fond of it," said Rose, handing him the book with an innocent air.

"Nothing I'd like better; but it is rather long."

"I'll tell you to stop if I get tired. Baby won't interrupt; she will be contented for an hour with those pretty things."

As if well pleased with his task, Mac laid himself comfortably on the grass, and leaning his head on his hand read the lovely story as only one could who entered fully into the spirit of it. Rose watched him closely, and saw how his face brightened over some quaint fancy, delicate description, or delicious word; heard how smoothly the melodious measures fell from his lips, and read something more than admiration in his eyes, as he looked up now and then to mark if she enjoyed it as much as he.

She could not help enjoying it; for the poet's pen painted as well as wrote, and the little romance lived before her: but she was not thinking of John Keats as she listened; she was wondering if this cousin was a kindred spirit, born to make such music and leave as sweet an echo behind him. It seemed as if it might be; and, after going through the rough caterpillar and the pent-up chrysalis changes, the beautiful butterfly would appear to astonish and delight them all. So full of this fancy was she that she never thanked him when the story ended; but, leaning forward, asked in a tone that made him start and look as if he had fallen from the clouds—

"Mac, do you ever write poetry?"

"Never."

"What do you call the song Phebe sang with her bird chorus?"

"That was nothing till she put the music to it. But she promised not to tell."

"She didn't; I suspected, and now I know," laughed Rose, delighted to have caught him.

Much discomfited, Mac gave poor Keats a fling, and leaning on both elbows tried to hide his face; for it had reddened like that of a modest girl when teased about her lover.

"You needn't look so guilty; it is no sin to write poetry," said Rose, amused at his confusion.

"It's a sin to call that rubbish poetry," muttered Mac, with great scorn.

"It is a greater sin to tell a fib, and say you never write it."

"Reading so much sets one thinking about such things, and every fellow scribbles a little jingle when he is lazy or in love, you know," explained Mac, looking very guilty.

Rose could not quite understand the change she saw in him, till his last words suggested a cause which she knew by experience was apt to inspire young men. Leaning forward again, she asked solemnly, though her eyes danced with fun—

"Mac, are you in love?"

"Do I look like it?" and he sat up with such an injured and indignant face, that she apologized at once; for he certainly did not look lover-like with hay-seed in his hair, several lively crickets playing leap-frog over his back, and a pair of long legs stretching from tree to haycock.

"No, you don't; and I humbly beg your pardon for making such an unwarrantable insinuation. It merely occurred to me that the general upliftedness I observe in you might be owing to that since it wasn't poetry."

"It is the good company I've been keeping, if anything. A fellow can't spend 'A Week' with Thoreau and not be the better for it. I'm glad I show it; because in the scramble life is to most of us, even an hour with such a sane, simple, and sagacious soul as his must help one," said Mac, taking a much worn book out of his pocket with the air of introducing a dear and honoured friend.

"I've read bits, and liked them: they are so original and fresh and sometimes droll," said Rose, smiling to see what natural and appropriate marks of approbation the elements seemed to set upon the pages Mac was turning eagerly; for one had evidently been rained on, a crushed berry stained another, some appreciative field-mouse or squirrel had nibbled one corner, and the cover was faded with the sunshine, which seemed to have filtered through to the thoughts within.

"Here's a characteristic bit for you:—

" 'I would rather sit on a pumpkin, and have it all to myself, than be crowded on a velvet cushion. I would rather ride on earth in an ox-cart, with free circulation, than go to heaven in the fancy car of an excursion train, and breathe malaria all the way.'

"I've tried both and quite agree with him," laughed Mac; and, skimming down another page, gave her a paragraph here and there.

" 'Read the best books first, or you may not have a chance to read them at all.'

" 'We do not learn much from learned books, but from sincere human books: frank, honest biographies.'

" 'At least let us have healthy books. Let the poet be as vigorous as sugar-maple, with sap enough to maintain his own verdure, besides what runs into the trough; and not like a vine which, being cut in the spring, bears no fruit, but bleeds to death in the endeavour to heal its wounds.' "

"That will do for you," said Rose, still thinking of the new suspicion which pleased her by its very improbability.

Mac flashed a quick look at her and shut the book, saying quietly, though his eyes shone, and a conscious smile lurked about his mouth—

"We shall see, and no one need meddle; for, as my Thoreau says—

" 'Whate'er we leave to God, God does
And blesses us:
The work we choose should be our own
God lets alone.' "

Rose sat silent, as if conscious that she deserved his poetical reproof.

"Come, you have catechised me pretty well; now I'll take my turn and ask why *you* look 'uplifted,' as you call it. What have you been doing to make yourself more like your namesake than ever?" asked Mac, carrying war into the enemy's camp with the sudden question.

"Nothing but live, and enjoy doing it. I actually sit here, day after day, as happy and contented with little things as Dulce is, and feel as if I wasn't much older than she," answered the girl, feeling as if some change was going on in that pleasant sort of pause, but unable to describe it.

" 'As if a rose should shut and be a bud again,' "

murmured Mac, borrowing from his beloved Keats.

"Ah, but I can't do that! I must go on blooming whether I like it or not, and the only trouble I have is to know what leaf I ought to unfold next," said Rose, playfully smoothing out the white gown, in which she looked very like a daisy among the green.

"How far have you got?" asked Mac, continuing his catechism as if the fancy suited him.

"Let me see. Since I came home last year, I've been gay, then sad, then busy, and now I am simply happy. I don't know why; but seem to be waiting for what is to come next, and getting ready for it, perhaps unconsciously," she said, looking dreamily away to the hills again, as if the new experience was coming to her from afar.

Mac watched her thoughtfully for a minute, wondering how many more leaves must unfold, before the golden heart of this human flower would lie open to the sun. He felt a curious desire to help in some way, and could think of none better than to offer her what he had found most helpful to himself. Picking up another book, he opened it at a place where an oak leaf lay, and, handing it to her, said, as if presenting something very excellent and precious—

"If you want to be ready to take whatever comes in a brave and noble way, read that, and the one where the page is turned down."

Rose took it, saw the words "Self-Reliance," and, turning the leaves, read here and there a passage which was marked:—

" 'My life is for itself, and not for a spectacle.'

" 'Insist on yourself: never imitate. That which each can do best, none but his Maker can teach him.'

" 'Do that which is assigned to you, and you cannot hope or dare too much.'

Then coming to the folded leaf, whose title was "Heroism," she read, and brightened as she read—

" 'Let the maiden, with erect soul, walk serenely on her way; accept the hint of each new experience; search in turn all the objects that solicit her eye, that she may learn the power and the charm of her new-born being.'

" 'The fair girl who repels interference by a decided and proud choice of influences inspires every beholder with something of her own nobleness; and the silent heart encourages her. O friend, never strike sail to a fear! Come into port greatly, or sail with God the seas.'

"You understand that, don't you?" asked Mac, as she glanced up with the look of one who had found something suited to her taste and need.

"Yes, but I never dared to read these Essays, because I thought they were too wise for me."

"The wisest things are sometimes the simplest, I think. Everyone welcomes light and air, and cannot do without them; yet very few could explain them truly. I don't ask you to read or understand all of that—don't myself—but I do recommend the two essays I've marked, as well as 'Love and Friendship.' Try them, and let me know how they suit. I'll leave you the book."

"Thanks. I wanted something fine to read up here; and, judging by what I see, I fancy this *will* suit. Only Aunt Jessie may think I'm putting on airs, if I try Emerson."

"Why should she? He has done more to set young men and women thinking than any man in this century at least. Don't you be afraid: if it is what you want, take it, and go ahead as he tells you—

" 'Without halting, without rest,
Lifting Better up to Best.' "

"I'll try," said Rose, meekly; feeling that Mac had been going ahead himself much faster than she had any suspicion.

Here a voice exclaimed "Hallo!" and, looking round, Jamie was discovered surveying them critically, as he stood in an independent attitude, like a small Colossus of Rhodes in brown linen, with a bundle of molasses-candy in one hand, several new fish-hooks cherished carefully in the other, and his hat well on the back of his head, displaying as many freckles as one somewhat limited nose could reasonably accommodate.

"How are you, young one?" said Mac, nodding.

"Tip-top. Glad it's you: thought Archie might have turned up again, and he's no fun. Where did you come from? What did you come for? How long are you going to stay? Want a bit? It's jolly good."

With which varied remarks Jamie approached, shook hands

in a manly way, and, sitting down beside his long cousin, hospitably offered sticks of candy all round.

"Did you get any letters?" asked Rose, declining the sticky treat.

"Lots: but mamma forgot to give 'em to me, and I was rather in a hurry; for Mrs. Atkinson said somebody had come, and I couldn't wait," explained Jamie, reposing luxuriously with his head on Mac's legs, and his mouth full.

"I'll step and get them. Aunty must be tired, and we should enjoy reading the news together."

"She is the most convenient girl that ever was," observed Jamie, as Rose departed, thinking Mac might like some more substantial refreshment than sweetmeats.

"I should think so, if you let her run your errands, you lazy little scamp," answered Mac, looking after her as she went up the green slope; for there was something very attractive to him about the slender figure in a plain white gown, with a black sash about the waist, and all the wavy hair gathered to the top of the head with a little black bow.

"Sort of pre-Raphaelite, and quite refreshing after the fur-belowed creatures at the hotels," he said to himself, as she vanished under the arch of scarlet-runners over the garden-gate.

"Oh, well! she likes it. Rose is fond of me, and I'm very good to her when I have time," continued Jamie, calmly explaining. "I let her cut out a fish-hook, when it caught in my leg, with a sharp pen-knife; and you'd better believe it hurt: but I never squirmed a bit, and she said I was a brave boy. And then, one day I got left on my desert island—out in the pond, you know— the boat floated off, and there I was for as much as an hour before I could make anyone hear. But Rose thought I might be there; and down she came, and told me to swim ashore. It wasn't far; but the water was horrid cold, and I didn't like it. I started though, just as she said, and got on all right, till about half way, then cramp or something made me shut up and howl, and she came after me slapdash and pulled me ashore. Yes, sir, as wet as a turtle, and looked so funny I laughed; and that cured the cramp. Wasn't I good to mind when she said, 'Come on?' "

"She was, to dive after such a scapegrace. I guess you lead her a life of it, and I'd better take you home with me in the morning," suggested Mac, rolling the boy over, and giving him a good-natured pummelling on the haycock, while Dulce applauded from her nest.

When Rose returned with ice-cold milk, ginger-bread, and letters, she found the reader of Emerson up in the tree, pelting and being pelted with green apples, as Jamie vainly endeavoured to get at him. The siege ended when Aunt Jessie appeared; and the rest of the afternoon was spent in chat about home affairs.

Early the next morning Mac was off, and Rose went as far as the old church with him.

"Shall you walk all the way?" she asked, as he strode along beside her, in the dewy freshness of the young day.

"Only about twenty miles, then take the car and whisk back to my work," he answered, breaking a delicate fern for her.

"Are you never lonely?"

"Never: I take my best friends along, you know," and he gave a slap to the pocket from which peeped the volume of Thoreau.

"I'm afraid you leave your very best behind you," said Rose, alluding to the book he had lent her yesterday.

"I'm glad to share it with you. I have much of it here; and a little goes a great way, as you will soon discover," he answered, tapping his head.

"I hope the reading will do as much for me as it seems to have done for you. I'm happy; but you are wise and good: I want to be, also."

"Read away, and digest it well; then write, and tell me what you think of it. Will you?" he asked, as they paused where the four roads met.

"If you will answer. Shall you have time with all your other work? Poetry—I beg pardon—medicine is very absorbing, you know," answered Rose, mischievously; for just then, as he stood bareheaded with the shadows of the leaves playing over his fine forehead, she remembered the chat among the haycocks, and he did not look at all like an M.D.

"I'll make time."

"Good-bye, Milton."

"Good-bye, Sabrina."

18

Which Was It?

Rose did read and digest, and found her days much richer for the good company she kept; for an introduction to so much that was wise, beautiful, and true, could not but make that month a memorable one. It is not strange that while the young man most admired "Heroism" and "Self-Reliance," the girl preferred "Love" and "Friendship," reading them over and over like prose poems, as they are, to the fitting accompaniment of sunshine, solitude, and sympathy; for letters went to and fro, with praiseworthy regularity.

Rose much enjoyed this correspondence, and found herself regretting that it was at an end when she went home in September; for Mac wrote better than he talked, though he could do that remarkably well when he chose. But she had no chance to express either pleasure or regret; for, the first time she saw him after her return, the great change in his appearance made her forget everything else. Some whim had seized him to be shaven and shorn, and when he presented himself to welcome Rose she hardly knew him; for the shaggy hair was nicely trimmed and brushed, the cherished brown beard entirely gone, showing a well cut mouth and handsome chin, and giving a new expression to the whole face.

"Are you trying to look like Keats?" she asked after a critical glance, which left her undecided whether the change was an improvement or not.

"I am trying not to look like uncle," answered Mac, coolly.

"And why, if you please?" demanded Rose, in great surprise.

212

"Because I prefer to look like myself, and not resemble any other man, no matter how good or great he may be."

"You haven't succeeded then; for you look now very much like the Young Augustus," returned Rose, rather pleased, on the whole, to see what a finely shaped head appeared after the rough thatch was off.

"Trust a woman to find a comparison for everything under the sun!" laughed Mac, not at all flattered by the one just made. "What do you think of me, on the whole?" he asked a minute later, as he found Rose still scrutinizing him with a meditative air.

"Haven't made up my mind. It is such an entire change I don't know you, and feel as if I ought to be introduced. You certainly look much more tidy; and I fancy I *shall* like it, when I'm used to seeing a somewhat distinguished-looking man about the house instead of my old friend Orson," answered Rose, with her head on one side to get a profile view.

"Don't tell uncle why I did it, please: he thinks it was for the sake of coolness, and likes it, so take no notice; they are all used to me now, and don't mind," said Mac, roving about the room as if rather ashamed of his whim after all.

"No, I won't; but you mustn't mind if I'm not as sociable as usual for a while. I never can be with strangers, and you really do seem like one. That will be a punishment for your want of taste and love of originality," returned Rose, resolved to punish him for the slight put upon her beloved uncle.

"As you like. I won't trouble you much anyway; for I'm going to be very busy. May go to L. this winter, if uncle thinks best; and then my 'originality' can't annoy you."

"I hope you won't go. Why, Mac, I'm just getting to know and enjoy you, and thought we'd have a nice time this winter reading something together. Must you go?" and Rose seemed to forget his strangeness, as she held him still by one button while she talked.

"That *would* be nice. But I feel as if I must go: my plans are all made, and I've set my heart on it," answered Mac, looking so eager that Rose released him, saying sadly—

"I suppose it is natural for you all to get restless, and push off; but it is hard for me to let you go one after the other, and stay here alone. Charlie is gone, Archie and Steve are wrapt up in their sweethearts, the boys away, and only Jamie left to 'play with Rose.' "

"But I'll come back, and you'll be glad I went if I bring you my—" began Mac, with sudden animation; then stopped abruptly to bite his lips, as if he had nearly said too much.

"Your what?" asked Rose, curiously; for he neither looked nor acted like himself.

"I forgot how long it takes to get a diploma," he said, walking away again.

"There will be one comfort if you go: you'll see Phebe, and can tell me all about her; for she is so modest she doesn't half do it. I shall want to know how she gets on, if she is engaged to sing ballads in the concerts they talk of for next winter. You will write, won't you?"

"Oh, yes! no doubt of that," and Mac laughed low to himself, as he stooped to look at the little Psyche on the mantel-piece. "What a pretty thing it is!" he added soberly, as he took it up.

"Be careful. Uncle gave it to me last New Year, and I'm very fond of it. She is just lifting her lamp to see what Cupid is like; for she hasn't seen him yet," said Rose, busy putting her work-table in order.

"You ought to have a Cupid for her to look at. She has been waiting patiently a whole year, with nothing but a bronze lizard in sight," said Mac, with the half-shy, half-daring look which was so new and puzzling.

"Cupid flew away as soon as she woke him, you know, and she had a bad time of it. She must wait longer till she can find and keep him."

"Do you know she looks like you? Hair tied up in a knot, and a spiritual sort of face. Don't you see it?" asked Mac, turning the graceful little figure towards her.

"Not a bit of it. I wonder whom I shall resemble next! I've been compared to a Fra Angelico angel, Saint Agnes, and now 'Syke,' as Annabel once called her."

"You'd see what I mean, if you'd ever watched your own face when you were listening to music, talking earnestly, or much moved; then your soul gets into your eyes and you are—like Psyche."

"Tell me the next time you see me in a 'soulful' state, and I'll look in the glass; for I'd like to see if it is becoming," said Rose, merrily, as she sorted her gay worsteds.

" 'Your feet in the full-grown grasses
    Moved soft as a soft wind blows;
You passed me as April passes,
    With a face made out of a rose,' "

murmured Mac, under his breath, thinking of the white figure going up a green slope one summer day; then, as if chiding himself for sentimentality, he set Psyche down with great care, and began to talk about a course of solid reading for the winter.

After that, Rose saw very little of him for several weeks, as he seemed to be making up for lost time, and was more odd and absent than ever when he did appear. As she became accustomed to the change in his external appearance, she discovered that he was altering fast in other ways and watched the "distinguished-looking gentleman" with much interest; saying to herself, when she saw a new sort of dignity about him alternating with an unusual restlessness of manner, and now and then a touch of sentiment, "Genius is simmering, just as I predicted."

As the family were in mourning, there were no festivities on Rose's twenty-first birthday, though the boys had planned all sorts of rejoicings. Everyone felt particuarly tender towards their girl on that day, remembering how "poor Charlie" had loved her; and they tried to show it in the gifts and good wishes they sent her. She found her sanctum all aglow with autumn leaves, and on her table so many rare and pretty things she quite forgot she was an heiress, and only felt how rich she was in loving friends.

One gift greatly pleased her, though she could not help smiling at the source from whence it came; for Mac sent her a Cupid—not the chubby child with a face of naughty merriment, but a slender, winged youth, leaning on his unstrung bow, with a broken arrow at his feet. A poem, "To Psyche," came with it: and Rose was much surprised at the beauty of the lines; for, instead of being witty, complimentary, or gay, there was something nobler than mere sentiment in them, and the sweet old fable lived again in language which fitly painted the maiden Soul looking for a Love worthy to possess it.

Rose read them over and over, as she sat among the gold and scarlet leaves which glorified her little room, and each time found new depth and beauty in them; looking from the words that made music in her ear to the lovely shapes that spoke with their mute grace to her eye. The whole thing suited her exactly, it was so delicate and perfect in its way; for she was tired of costly gifts, and valued very much this proof of her cousin's taste and talent, seeing nothing in it but an affectionate desire to please her.

All the rest dropped in at intervals through the day to say a loving word, and last of all came Mac. Rose happened to be alone with Dulce, enjoying a splendid sunset from her western window; for October gave her child a beautiful good-night.

Rose turned round as he entered, and, putting down the little girl, went to him with the evening red shining on her happy face, as she said gratefully—

"Dear Mac, it was *so* lovely! I don't know how to thank you for it in any way but this." And, drawing down his tall head, she gave him the birthday kiss she had given all the others.

But this time it produced a singular effect: for Mac turned scarlet, then grew pale; and when Rose added playfully, thinking to relieve the shyness of so young a poet, "Never say again you don't write poetry, or call your verses rubbish: I *knew* you were a genius, and now I'm sure of it," he broke out, as if against his will—

"No. It isn't genius: it is—love!" Then, as she shrunk a little, startled at his energy, he added, with an effort at self-control which made his voice sound strange—

"I didn't mean to speak, but I can't suffer you to deceive yourself so. I *must* tell the truth, and not let you kiss me like a cousin when I love you with all my heart and soul!"

"O Mac, don't joke!" cried Rose, bewildered by this sudden glimpse into a heart she thought she knew so well.

"I'm in solemn earnest," he answered, steadily, in such a quiet tone that, but for the pale excitement of his face, she might have doubted his words. "Be angry, if you will. I expect it, for I know it is too soon to speak. I ought to wait for years, perhaps; but you seemed so happy I dared to hope you had forgotten."

"Forgotten what?" asked Rose, sharply.

"Charlie."

"Ah! you all will insist on believing that I loved him better than I did!" she cried, with both pain and impatience in her voice; for the family delusion tried her very much at times.

"How could we help it, when he was everything women most admire?" said Mac, not bitterly, but as if he sometimes wondered at their want of insight.

"*I* do not admire weakness of any sort: I could never love

without either confidence or respect. Do me the justice to believe that, for I'm tired of being pitied."

She spoke almost passionately, being more excited by Mac's repressed emotion than she had ever been by Charlie's most touching demonstration, though she did not know why.

"But he loved you so!" began Mac; feeling as if a barrier had suddenly gone down, but not daring to venture in as yet.

"That was the hard part of it! That was why I tried to love him—why I hoped he would stand fast for my sake, if not for his own; and why I found it so sad sometimes not to be able to help despising him for his want of courage. I don't know how others feel, but, to me, love isn't all. I must look up, not down, trust and honour with my whole heart, and find strength and integrity to lean on. I have had it so far, and I know I could not live without it."

"Your ideal is a high one. Do you hope to find it, Rose?" Mac asked, feeling, with the humility of a genuine love, that *he* could not give her all she desired.

"Yes," she answered, with a face full of the beautiful confidence in virtue, the instinctive desire for the best which so many of us lose too soon, to find again after life's great lessons are well learned. "I do hope to find it, because I try not to be unreasonable and expect perfection. Smile if you will, but I won't give up my hero yet," and she tried to speak lightly, hoping to lead him away from a more dangerous topic.

"You'll have to look a long while, I'm afraid," and all the glow was gone out of Mac's face; for he understood her wish, and knew his answer had been given.

"I have uncle to help me; and I think my ideal grew out of my knowledge of him. How can I fail to believe in goodness, when he shows me what it can be and do?"

"It is no use for me to say any more; for I have very little to offer. I did not mean to say a word, till I'd earned a right to hope for something in return. I cannot take it back; but I can wish you success, and I do, because you deserve the very best," and Mac moved, as if he was going away without more words, accepting the inevitable as manfully as he could.

"Thank you: that makes me feel very ungrateful and unkind. I wish I could answer as you want me to; for, indeed, dear Mac, I'm very fond of you in my own way," and Rose looked up with such tender pity and frank affection in her face, it was no wonder the poor fellow caught at a ray of hope, and, brightening suddenly, said in his own odd way—

"Couldn't you take me on trial, while you are waiting for the true hero? It may be years before you find him; meantime, you could be practising on me in ways that would be useful when you get him."

"O Mac! what *shall* I do with you?" exclaimed Rose, so curiously affected by this very characteristic wooing, that she did not know whether to laugh or cry; for he was looking at her with his heart in his eyes, though his proposition was the queerest ever made at such a time.

"Just go on being fond of me in your own way, and let me love you as much as I like in mine. I'll try to be satisfied with that," and he took both her hands so beseechingly that she felt more ungrateful than ever.

"No, it would not be fair: for you would love the most; and, if the hero did appear, what would become of you?"

"I should resemble Uncle Alec in one thing at least—fidelity; for my first love would be my last."

That went straight to Rose's heart; and for a minute she stood silent, looking down at the two strong hands that held hers so firmly, yet so gently; and the thought went through her mind, "Must he too be solitary all his life? I have no dear lover as my mother had, why cannot I make him happy and forget myself?"

It did not seem very hard; and she owned that, even while she told herself to remember that compassion was no equivalent for love. She wanted to give all she could, and keep as much of Mac's affection as she honestly might; because it seemed to grow more sweet and precious when she thought of putting it away.

"You will be like uncle in happier ways than that, I hope; for you, too, must have a high ideal, and find her and be happy," she said, resolving to be true to the voice of conscience, not be swayed by the impulse of the moment.

"I *have* found her, but I don't see any prospect of happiness, do you?" he asked, wistfully.

"Dear Mac, I cannot give you the love you want, but I do trust and respect you from the bottom of my heart, if that is any comfort," began Rose, looking up with eyes full of contrition, for the pain her reply must give.

She got no further, however; for those last words wrought a

marvellous change in Mac. Dropping her hands, he stood erect, as if inspired with sudden energy and hope, while over his face there came a brave, bright look, which for the moment made him a nobler and a comelier man than ever handsome Prince had been.

"It *is* a comfort!" he said in a tone of gratitude, that touched her very much. "You said your love must be founded on respect, and that you have given me: why can I not earn the rest? I'm nothing now; but everything is possible when one loves with all his heart and soul and strength. Rose, *I* will be your hero if a mortal man can, even though I have to work and wait for years. I'll *make* you love me, and be glad to do it. Don't be frightened. I've not lost my wits: I've just found them. I don't ask anything: I'll never speak of my hope, but it is no use to stop me; I *must* try it, and I *will* succeed!"

With the last words, uttered in a ringing voice, while his face glowed, his eyes shone, and he looked as if carried out of himself by the passion that possessed him, Mac abruptly left the room, like one eager to change words to deeds and begin his task at once.

Rose was so amazed by all this, that she sat down trembling a little, not with fear or anger, but a feeling half pleasure, half pain; and a sense of some new power—subtle, strong, and sweet —that had come into her life. It seemed as if another Mac had taken the place of the one she had known so long—an ardent, ambitious man, ready for any work, now that the magical moment had come, when everything seems possible to love. If hope could work such a marvellous change for a moment, could not happiness do it for a lifetime? It would be an exciting experiment to try, she thought, remembering the sudden illumination which made that familiar face both beautiful and strange.

She could not help wondering how long this unsuspected sentiment had been growing in his heart, and felt perplexed by its peculiar demonstration; for she had never had a lover like this before. It touched and flattered her nevertheless: and she could not but feel honoured by a love so genuine and generous; for it seemed to make a man of Mac all at once, and a manly man too, who was not daunted by disappointment, but could "hope against hope," and resolve to *make* her love him if it took years to do it.

There was the charm of novelty about this sort of wooing,

and she tried to guess how he would set about it, felt curious to see how he would behave when next they met, and was half angry with herself for not being able to decide how she ought to act. The more she thought the more bewildered she grew; for, having made up her mind that Mac was a genius, it disturbed all her plans to find him a lover, and such an ardent one. As it was impossible to predict what would come next, she gave up trying to prepare for it; and, tired with vain speculations, carried Dulce off to bed, wishing she could tuck away her love-troubles as quietly and comfortably as she did her sleepy little charge.

Simple and sincere in all things, Mac gave Rose a new surprise by keeping his promise to the letter—asked nothing of her, said nothing of his hope, and went on as if nothing had happened, quite in the old friendly way. No, not quite; for now and then, when she least expected it, she saw again that indescribable expression in his face, a look that seemed to shed a sudden sunshine over her, making her eyes fall involuntarily, her colour rise, and her heart beat quicker for a moment. Not a word did he say, but she felt that a new atmosphere surrounded her when he was by; and, although he used none of the little devices most lovers employ to keep the flame alight, it was impossible to forget that underneath his quietude there was a hidden world of fire and force, ready to appear at a touch, a word from her.

This was rather dangerous knowledge for Rose, and she soon began to feel that there were more subtle temptations than she had suspected; for it was impossible to be unconscious of her power, or always to resist the trials of it which daily came unsought. She had never felt this desire before: for Charlie was the only one who had touched her heart; and he was constantly asking as well as giving, and wearied her by demanding too much, or oppressed by offering more than she could accept.

Mac did neither: he only loved her, silently, patiently, hopefully; and this generous sort of fidelity was very eloquent to a nature like hers. She could not refuse or chide, since nothing was asked or urged; there was no need of coldness, for he never presumed; no call for pity, since he never complained. All that could be done was to try and be as just and true as he was, and to wait as trustfully for the end, whatever it was to be.

For a time she liked the new interest it put into her life, yet did nothing to encourage it; and thought that if she gave this love no food it would soon starve to death. But it seemed to thrive on air; and presently she began to feel as if a very strong will was slowly but steadily influencing her in many ways. If Mac had never told her that he meant to "*make* her love him," she might have yielded unconsciously; but now she mistook the impulse to obey this undercurrent for compassion, and resisted stoutly, not comprehending yet the reason of the unrest which took possession of her about this time.

She had as many moods as an April day; and would have much surprised Dr. Alec by her vagaries, had he known them all. He saw enough, however, to guess what was the matter, but took no notice; for he knew this fever must run its course, and much medicine only does harm. The others were busy about their own affairs, and Aunt Plenty was too much absorbed in her rheumatism to think of love; for the cold weather set in early, and the poor lady kept her room for days at a time, with Rose as nurse.

Mac had spoken of going away in November, and Rose began to hope he would; for she decided that this silent sort of adoration was bad for her, as it prevented her from steadily pursuing the employments she had marked out for that year. What was the use of trying to read useful books, when her thoughts continually wandered to those charming essays on "Love and Friendship"? to copy antique casts, when all the masculine heads looked like Cupid, and the feminine ones like the Psyche on her mantel-piece? to practise the best music, if it ended in singing over and over the pretty spring-song without Phebe's bird-chorus? Dulce's company was pleasantest now; for Dulce seldom talked, so much meditation was possible. Even Aunt Plenty's red flannel, camphor, and Pond's Extract were preferable to general society; and long solitary rides on Rosa seemed the only thing to put her in tune after one of her attempts to find out what she ought to do or leave undone.

She made up her mind at last; and arming herself with an unmade pen, like Fanny Squeers, she boldly went into the study to confer with Dr. Alec, at an hour when Mac was usually absent.

"I want a pen for marking: can you make me one, uncle?" she asked, popping in her head to be sure he was alone.

"Yes, my dear," answered a voice so like the doctor's that she entered without delay.

But before she had taken three steps she stopped, looking

rather annoyed; for the head that rose from behind the tall desk
was not rough and grey, but brown and smooth, and Mac, not
Uncle Alec, sat there writing. Late experience had taught her
that she had nothing to fear from a *tête-à-tête*; and, having with
difficulty taken a resolution, she did not like to fail of carrying
it out.

"Don't get up: I won't trouble you if you are busy; there is
no hurry," she said, not quite sure whether it were wiser to
stay or run away.

Mac settled the point, by taking the pen out of her hand and
beginning to cut it, as quietly as Nicholas did on that "thrilling"
occasion. Perhaps he was thinking of that; for he smiled as he
asked—

"Hard or soft?"

Rose had forgotten that the family of Squeers ever existed,
for she answered—

"Hard, please," in a voice to match. "I'm glad to see you
doing that," she added, taking courage from his composure,
and going as straight to her point as could be expected of a
woman.

"And I am very glad to do it."

"I don't mean making pens, but the romance I advised," and
she touched the closely written page before him, looking as if
she would like to read it.

"That is my abstract of a lecture on the circulation of the
blood," he answered, kindly turning it so that she could see.
"I don't write romances: I'm living one," and he glanced up
with the happy hopeful expression which always made her feel
as if he was heaping coals of fire on her head.

"I wish you wouldn't look at me in that way: it fidgets me,"
she said a little petulantly; for she had been out riding, and knew
that she did not present a "spiritual" appearance, after the frosty
air had reddened nose as well as cheeks.

"I'll try to remember. It does itself before I know it. Perhaps
this may mend matters," and, taking out the blue glasses he
sometimes wore in the wind, he gravely put them on.

Rose could not help laughing: but his obedience only aggra-
vated her for she knew he could observe her all the better
behind his ugly screen.

"No, it won't: they are not becoming; and I don't want to
look blue when I do not feel so," she said, finding it impossible

to guess what he would do next, or to help enjoying his peculiarities.

"But you don't to me; for in spite of the goggles everything is rose-coloured now," and he pocketed the glasses, without a murmur at the charming inconsistency of his idol.

"Really, Mac, I'm tired of this nonsense; it worries me and wastes your time."

"Never worked harder. But does it *really* trouble you to know I love you?" he asked anxiously.

"Don't you see how cross it makes me?" and she walked away, feeling that things were not going as she intended to have them at all.

"I don't mind the thorns if I get the rose at last; and I still hope I may, some ten years hence," said this persistent suitor, quite undaunted by the prospect of a "long wait."

"I think it is rather hard to be loved whether I like it or not," objected Rose, at a loss how to make any headway against such indomitable hopefulness.

"But you can't help it, nor can I: so I must go on doing it with all my heart till you marry; and then—well, then I'm afraid I may hate somebody instead," and Mac spoilt the pen by an involuntary slash of his knife.

"Please don't, Mac!"

"Don't which, love or hate?"

"Don't do either: go and care for someone else; there are plenty of nice girls who will be glad to make you happy," said Rose, intent upon ending her disquiet in some way.

"That is too easy. I enjoy working for my blessings; and the harder I have to work the more I value them when they come."

"Then if I suddenly grew very kind would you stop caring about me?" asked Rose, wondering if that treatment would free her from a passion which both touched and tormented her.

"Try and see;" but there was a traitorous glimmer in Mac's eyes which plainly showed what a failure it would be.

"No, I'll get something to do, so absorbing I shall forget all about you."

"Don't think about me if it troubles you," he said tenderly.

"I can't help it." Rose tried to catch back the words: but it was too late; and she added hastily, "That is, I cannot help wishing you would forget *me*. It is a great disappointment to find I was mistaken when I hoped such fine things of you."

"Yes, you were very sure that it was love when it was poetry; and now you want poetry when I've nothing on hand but love. Will both together please you?"

"Try and see."

"I'll do my best. Anything else?" he asked, forgetting the small task she had given him, in his eagerness to attempt the greater.

"Tell me one thing. I've often wanted to know; and now you speak of it I'll venture to ask. Did you care about me when you read Keats to me last summer?"

"No."

"When *did* you begin?" asked Rose, smiling in spite of herself at his unflattering honesty.

"How can I tell? Perhaps it did begin up there, though; for that talk set us writing, and the letters showed me what a beautiful soul you had. I loved that first: it was so quick to recognize good things, to use them when they came, and give them out again as unconsciously as a flower does its breath. I longed for you to come home, and wanted you to find me altered for the better in some way as I had found you. And when you came it was very easy to see why I needed you—to love you entirely, and to tell you so. That's all, Rose."

A short story, but it was enough: the voice that told it with such simple truth made the few words so eloquent Rose felt strongly tempted to add the sequel Mac desired. But her eyes had fallen as he spoke; for she knew his were fixed upon her, dark and dilated with the same repressed emotion that put such fervour into his quiet tones, and, just as she was about to look up, they fell on a shabby little footstool. Trifles affect women curiously, and often most irresistibly when some agitation sways them: the sight of the old hassock vividly recalled Charlie; for he had kicked it on the night she never liked to remember; like a spark it fired a long train of recollections, and the thought went through her mind—

"I fancied I loved him, and let him see it; but I deceived myself, and he reproached me for a single look that said too much. This feeling is very different, but too new and sudden to be trusted. I'll neither look nor speak till I am quite sure; for Mac's love is far deeper than poor Charlie's, and I must be very true."

Not in words did the resolve shape itself, but in a quick

impulse, which she obeyed—certain that it was right, since it was hard to yield to it. Only an instant's silence followed Mac's answer, as she stood looking down with fingers intertwined, and colour varying in her cheeks. A foolish attitude; but Mac thought it a sweet picture of maiden hesitation, and began to hope that a month's wooing was about to end in winning for a lifetime. He deceived himself, however; and cold water fell upon his flame, subduing but by no means quenching it, when Rose looked up with an air of determination, which could not escape eyes that were growing wonderfully far-sighted lately.

"I came in here to beg uncle to advise you to go away soon. You are very patient and forbearing, and I feel it more than I can tell. But it is not good for you to depend on anyone so much for your happiness, I think; and I know it is bad for me to feel that I have so much power over a fellow-creature. Go away, Mac, and see if this isn't all a mistake. Don't let a fancy for me change or delay your work, because it may end as suddenly as it began, and then we should both reproach ourselves and each other. Please do! I respect and care for you so much, I can't be happy to take all and give nothing. I try to, but I'm not sure— I want to think—it is too soon to know yet—"

Rose began bravely, but ended in a fluttered sort of way, as she moved towards the door; for Mac's face, though it fell at first, brightened as she went on, and at the last word, uttered almost involuntarily, he actually laughed low to himself, as if this order into exile pleased him much.

"Don't say that you give nothing, when you've just shown me that I'm getting on. I'll go; I'll go at once; and see if absence won't help you 'to think, to know, and to be sure,' as it did me. I wish I could do something more for you; as I can't, good-bye."

"Are you going *now?*" and Rose paused in her retreat, to look back with a startled face, as he offered her a badly made pen, and opened the door for her just as Dr. Alec always did; for, in spite of himself, Mac did resemble the best of uncles.

"Not yet; but you seem to be."

Rose turned as red as a poppy, snatched the pen, and flew upstairs, to call herself hard names, as she industriously spoiled all Aunt Plenty's new pocket-handkerchiefs by marking them "A.M.C."

Three days later Mac said "Good-bye" in earnest; and no

H

one was surprised that he left somewhat abruptly, such being his way, and a course of lectures by a famous physician the ostensible reason for a trip to L. Uncle Alec deserted most shamefully at the last moment by sending word that he would be at the station to see the traveller off: Aunt Plenty was still in her room; so, when Mac came down from his farewell to her, Rose met him in the hall, as if anxious not to delay him. She was a little afraid of another *tête-à-tête*, as she fared so badly at the last, and had assumed a calm and cousinly air, which she flattered herself would plainly show on what terms she wished to part.

Mac apparently understood, and not only took the hint, but surpassed her in cheerful composure; for, merely saying, "Good-bye, cousin; write when you feel like it," he shook hands, and walked out of the house as tranquilly as if only a day instead of three months were to pass before they met again. Rose felt as if a sudden shower-bath had chilled her, and was about to retire, saying to herself with disdainful decision—

"There's no love about it after all; only one of the eccentricities of genius," when a rush of cold air made her turn, to find herself in what appeared to be the embrace of an impetuous overcoat, which wrapt her close for an instant, then vanished as suddenly as it came, leaving her to hide in the sanctum, and confide to Psyche with a tender sort of triumph in her breathless voice—

"No, no, it isn't genius: *that* must be love!"

19

Behind the Fountain

TWO DAYS after Christmas, a young man of a serious aspect might have been seen entering one of the large churches at L——. Being shown to a seat, he joined in the services with praiseworthy devotion, especially the music, to which he listened with such evident pleasure that a gentleman who sat near by felt moved to address this appreciative stranger after church.

"Fine sermon today. Ever heard our minister before, sir?" he began, as they went down the aisle together among the last; for the young man had lingered as if admiring the ancient building.

"Very fine. No, sir, I have never had that pleasure. I've often wished to see this old place, and am not at all disappointed. Your choir, too, is unusually good," answered the stranger, glancing up at several bonnets bobbing about behind the half-drawn curtains above.

"Finest in the city, sir. We pride ourselves on our music, and always have the best. People often come for that alone," and the old gentleman looked as satisfied as if a choir of cherubim and seraphim "continually did cry" in his organ-loft.

"Who is the contralto? That solo was beautifully sung," observed the younger man, pausing to read a tablet in the wall.

"That is Miss Moore. Been here about a year, and is universally admired. Excellent young lady: couldn't do without her. Sings superbly in oratorios. Ever heard her?"

"Never. She came from X——, I believe?"

"Yes; highly recommended. She was brought up by one of

the first families there. Campbell is the name. If you come
from X——, you doubtless know them."

"I have met them. Good morning." And with bows the
gentlemen parted; for at that instant the young man caught
sight of a tall lady going down the church-steps, with a devout
expression in her fine eyes, and a prayer-book in her hand.

Hastening after her, the serious-minded young man accosted
her just as she turned into a quiet street.

"Phebe!"

Only a word, but it wrought a marvellous change, for the
devout expression vanished in the drawing of a breath, and the
quiet face blossomed suddenly with colour, warmth, and "the
light that never was on sea or land," as she turned to meet her
lover, with an answering word as eloquent as his—

"Archie!"

"The year is out today. I told you I should come. Have you
forgotten?"

"No; I knew you'd come."

"And you are glad?"

"How can I help it?"

"You can't: don't try. Come into this little park, and let us
talk." And, drawing her hand through his arm, Archie led her
into what to other eyes was a very dismal square, with a
boarded-up fountain in the middle, sodden grass-plots, and dead
leaves dancing in the wintry wind.

But to them it was a summery Paradise; and they walked to
and fro in the pale sunshine, quite unconscious that they were
objects of interest to several ladies and gentlemen waiting
anxiously for their dinner, or yawning over the dull books kept
for Sunday reading.

"Are you ready to come home now, Phebe?" asked Archie,
tenderly, as he looked at the downcast face beside him, and
wondered why all women did not wear delightful little black
velvet bonnets, with one deep-red flower against their hair.

"Not yet. I haven't done enough," began Phebe, finding it
very hard to keep the resolution made a year ago.

"You have proved that you can support yourself; make
friends, and earn a name, if you choose. No one can deny that;
and we are all getting proud of you. What more can you ask,
my dearest?"

"I don't quite know, but I am very ambitious. I want to be

amous, to do something for you all, to make some sacrifice for
Rose, and, if I can, to have something to give up for your sake.
Let me wait and work longer: I know I haven't earned my
welcome yet," pleaded Phebe, so earnestly that her lover knew
it would be vain to try and turn her; so wisely contented himself
with half, since he could not have the whole.

"Such a proud woman! Yet I love you all the better for it,
and understand your feeling. Rose made me see how it seems to
you; and I don't wonder that you cannot forget the unkind
things that were looked, if not said, by some of my amiable
aunts. I'll try to be patient on one condition, Phebe."

"And what is that?"

"You are to let me come sometimes while I wait, and wear
this lest you should forget me," he said, pulling a ring from his
pocket, and gently drawing a warm, bare hand out of the muff
where it lay hidden.

"Yes, Archie, but not here—not now!" cried Phebe, glancing
about her, as if suddenly aware that they were not alone.

"No one can see us here: I thought of that. Give me one
happy minute, after this long, long year of waiting," answered
Archie, pausing just where the fountain hid them from all eyes,
for there were houses only on one side.

Phebe submitted; and never did a plain gold ring slip more
easily to its place than the one he put on in such a hurry that
cold December day. Then one hand went back into the muff red
with the grasp he gave it, and the other to its old place on his
arm, with a confiding gesture, as if it had a right there.

"Now I feel sure of you," said Archie, as they went on again,
and no one the wiser for that tender transaction behind the ugly
pyramid of boards. "Mac wrote me that you were much admired
by your church people, and that certain wealthy bachelors
evidently had designs on the retiring Miss Moore. I was horribly
jealous, but now I defy every man of them."

Phebe smiled with the air of proud humility that was so
becoming, and answered briefly—

"There was no danger: kings could not change me, whether
you ever came or not. But Mac should not have told you."

"You shall be revenged on him, then; for as he told secrets
about you, I'll tell you one about him. Phebe, he loves Rose!"
And Archie looked as if he expected to make a great sensation
with his news.

"I know it." And Phebe laughed at his sudden change of countenance, as he added inquiringly—

"She told you, then?"

"Not a word. I guessed it from her letters: for lately she says nothing about Mac, and before there was a good deal; so I suspected what the silence meant, and asked no questions."

"Wise girl! then you think she does care for the dear old fellow?"

"Of course she does. Didn't he tell you so?"

"No, he only said when he went away, 'Take care of my Rose, and I'll take care of your Phebe,' and not another thing could I get out of him; for I did ask questions. He stood by me like a hero, and kept Aunt Jane from driving me stark mad with her 'advice.' I don't forget that, and burned to lend him a hand somewhere; but he begged me to let him manage his wooing in his own way. And from what I see I should say he knew how to do it," added Archie, finding it very delightful to gossip about love affairs with his sweetheart.

"Dear little mistress! how does she behave?" asked Phebe, longing for news, but too grateful to ask at headquarters; remembering how generously Rose had tried to help her, even by silence, the greatest sacrifice a woman can make at such interesting periods.

"Very sweet and shy and charming. I try not to watch: but upon my word I cannot help it sometimes; she is so 'cunning,' as you girls say. When I carry her a letter from Mac she tries so hard not to show how glad she is, that I want to laugh, and tell her I know all about it. But I look as sober as a judge, and as stupid as an owl by daylight; and she enjoys her letter in peace, and thinks I'm so absorbed by my own passion that I'm blind to hers."

"But why did Mac come away? He says lectures brought him, and he goes; but I am sure something else is in his mind, he looks so happy at times. I don't see him very often, but when I do I'm conscious that he isn't the Mac I left a year ago," said Phebe, leading Archie away: for inexorable propriety forbade a longer stay, even if prudence and duty had not given her a reminding nudge; as it was very cold, and afternoon church came in an hour.

"Well, you see Mac was always peculiar, and he cannot even grow up like other fellows. I don't understand him yet, and am sure he's got some plan in his head that no one suspects, unless it is Uncle Alec. Love makes us all cut queer capers; and I've an idea that the Don will distinguish himself in some uncommon way. So be prepared to applaud whatever it is. We owe him that, you know."

"Indeed we do! If Rose ever speaks of him to you, tell her I shall see that he comes to no harm, and she must do the same for my Archie."

That unusual demonstration of tenderness from reserved Phebe very naturally turned the conversation into a more personal channel; and Archie devoted himself to building castles in the air so successfully that they passed the material mansion without either being aware of it.

"Will you come in?" asked Phebe, when the mistake was rectified, and she stood on her own steps looking down at her escort, who had discreetly released her before a pull at the bell caused five heads to pop up at five different windows.

"No, thanks. I shall be at church this afternoon, and the Oratorio this evening. I must be off early in the morning, so let me make the most of precious time, and come home with you tonight as I did before," answered Archie, making his best bow, and quite sure of consent.

"You may," and Phebe vanished, closing the door softly, as if she found it hard to shut out so much love and happiness as that in the heart of the sedate young gentleman, who went briskly down the street, humming a verse of old "Clyde" like a tuneful bass viol.

> " 'Oh, let our mingling voices rise
> In grateful rapture to the skies,
> Where love has had its birth.
>
> Let songs of joy this day declare
> That spirits come their bliss to share
> With all the sons of earth.' "

That afternoon Miss Moore sang remarkably well, and that evening quite electrified even her best friends by the skill and power with which she rendered "Inflammatus" in the oratorio.

"If that is not genius, I should like to know what it is?" said one young man to another, as they went out just before the general crush at the end.

"Some genius and a great deal of love. They are a grand

team, and, when well driven, astonish the world by the time they make in the great race," answered the second young man, with the look of one inclined to try his hand at driving that immortal span.

"Dare say you are right. Can't stop now: she's waiting for me. Don't sit up, Mac."

"The gods go with you, Archie."

And the cousins separated: one to write till midnight, the other to bid his Phebe good-bye, little dreaming how unexpectedly and successfully she was to earn her welcome home.

20

What Mac Did

Rose, meantime, was trying to find out what the sentiment was with which she regarded her cousin Mac. She could not seem to reconcile the character she had known so long with the new one lately shown her; and the idea of loving the droll, bookish, absent-minded Mac of former times appeared quite impossible and absurd: but the new Mac, wide awake, full of talent, ardent and high-minded, was such a surprise to her she felt as if her heart was being won by a stranger, and it became her to study him well before yielding to a charm which she could not deny.

Affection came naturally, and had always been strong for the boy; regard for the studious youth easily deepened to respect for the integrity of the young man: and now something warmer was growing up within her; but at first she could not decide whether it was admiration for the rapid unfolding of talent of some sort, or love answering to love.

As if to settle that point, Mac sent her on New Year's day a little book plainly bound and modestly entitled "Songs and Sonnets." After reading this with ever-growing surprise and delight, Rose never had another doubt about the writer's being a poet; for, though she was no critic, she had read the best authors and knew what was good. Unpretending as it was, this had the true ring, and its very simplicity showed conscious power; for, unlike so many first attempts, the book was not full of "My Lady," neither did it indulge in Swinburnian convulsions about

"The lilies and languors of peace,
The roses and raptures of love;"

or contain any of the highly coloured mediæval word pictures
so much in vogue. "My book should smell of pines, and resound
with the hum of insects," might have been its motto: so sweet
and wholesome was it with a spring-like sort of freshness, which
plainly betrayed that the author had learned some of Nature's
deepest secrets, and possessed the skill to tell them in tuneful
words. The songs went ringing through one's memory long
after they were read; and the sonnets were full of the subtle
beauty, insight, and half-unconscious wisdom, which seem to
prove that "genius is divine when young."

Many faults it had, but was so full of promise that it was
evident Mac had not "kept good company, read good books,
loved good things, and cultivated soul and body as faithfully as
he could," in vain. It all told now; for truth and virtue had
blossomed into character, and had a language of their own more
eloquent than the poetry to which they were what the fragrance
is to the flower. Wiser critics than Rose felt and admired this;
less partial ones could not deny their praise to a first effort,
which seemed as spontaneous and aspiring as a lark's song; and,
when one or two of these Jupiters had given a nod of approval,
Mac found himself, not exactly famous, but much talked about.
One set abused, the other set praised, and the little book was
sadly mauled among them: for it was too original to be ignored,
and too robust to be killed by hard usage; so it came out of the
fray none the worse, but rather brighter, if anything, for the
friction which proved the gold genuine.

This took time, however, and Rose could only sit at home
reading all the notices she could get, as well as the literary
gossip Phebe sent her: for Mac seldom wrote, and never a word
about himself; so Phebe skilfully extracted from him in their
occasional meetings all the personal news her feminine wit could
collect, and faithfully reported it.

It was a little singular that without a word of inquiry on either
side, the letters of the girls were principally filled with tidings
of their respective lovers. Phebe wrote about Mac; Rose
answered with minute particulars about Archie; and both added
hasty items concerning their own affairs, as if these were of
little consequence.

Phebe got the most satisfaction out of the correspondence; for, soon after the book appeared, Rose began to want Mac home again, and to be rather jealous of the new duties and delights that kept him. She was immensely proud of her poet, and had little jubilees over the beautiful fulfilment of her prophecies; for even Aunt Plenty owned now with contrition that "the boy was not a fool." Every word of praise was read aloud on the house-tops, so to speak, by happy Rose; every adverse criticism was hotly disputed; and the whole family were in a great state of pleasant excitement over this unexpectedly successful first flight of the Ugly Duckling, now generally considered by his relatives as the most promising young swan of the flock.

Aunt Jane was particularly funny in her new position of mother to a callow poet, and conducted herself like a proud but bewildered hen when one of her brood takes to the water. She pored over the poems trying to appreciate them, but quite failing to do so; for life was all prose to her, and she vainly tried to discover where Mac got his talent from. It was pretty to see the new respect with which she treated his possessions now; the old books were dusted with a sort of reverence; scraps of paper laid carefully by lest some immortal verse be lost; and a certain shabby velvet jacket fondly smoothed, when no one was by to smile at the maternal pride which filled her heart, and caused her once severe countenance to shine with unwonted benignity.

Uncle Mac talked about "my son" with ill-concealed satisfaction, and evidently began to feel as if his boy was going to confer distinction upon the whole race of Campbell, which had already possessed one poet. Steve exulted with irrepressible delight, and went about quoting "Songs and Sonnets," till he bored his friends dreadfully by his fraternal raptures.

Archie took it more quietly, and even suggested that it was too soon to crow yet; for the dear old fellow's first burst might be his last, since it was impossible to predict what he would do next. Having proved that he *could* write poetry, he might drop it for some new world to conquer, quoting his favourite Thoreau, who, having made a perfect pencil, gave up the business, and took to writing books with the sort of indelible ink which grows clearer with time.

The aunts of course had their "views," and enjoyed much prophetic gossip, as they wagged their caps over many social cups of tea. The younger boys thought it "very jolly, and hoped the Don would go ahead and come to glory as soon as possible," which was all that could be expected of "Young America," with whom poetry is not usually a passion.

But Dr. Alec was a sight for "sair een:" so full of concentrated contentment was he. No one but Rose, perhaps, knew how proud and pleased the good man felt at this first small success of his godson; for he had always had high hopes of the boy, because in spite of his oddities he had such an upright nature, and promising little did much, with the quiet persistence which foretells a manly character. All the romance of the doctor's heart was stirred by this poetic bud of promise, and the love that made it bloom so early: for Mac had confided his hopes to uncle, finding great consolation and support in his sympathy and advice. Like a wise man, Dr. Alec left the young people to learn the great lesson in their own way, counselling Mac to work, and Rose to wait, till both were quite certain that their love was built on a surer foundation than admiration or youthful romance.

Meantime he went about with a well-worn little book in his pocket, humming bits from a new set of songs, and repeating with great fervour certain sonnets which seemed to him quite equal, if not superior, to any that Shakespeare ever wrote. As Rose was doing the same thing, they often met for a private "read and warble," as they called it; and, while discussing the safe subject of Mac's poetry, both arrived at a pretty clear idea of what Mac's reward was to be when he came home.

He seemed in no hurry to do this, however, and continued to astonish his family by going into society, and coming out brilliantly in that line. It takes very little to make a lion, as everyone knows who has seen what poor specimens are patted and petted every year, in spite of their bad manners, foolish vagaries, and very feeble roaring. Mac did not want to be lionized and took it rather scornfully, which only added to the charm that people suddenly discovered about the nineteenth cousin of Thomas Campbell, the poet. He desired to be distinguished in the best sense of the word, as well as to look so, and thought a little of the polish society gives would not be amiss, remembering Rose's efforts in that line. For her sake he came out of his shell, and went about seeing and testing all sorts of people with those observing eyes of his, which saw so much in spite of their nearsightedness. What use he meant to make of these new experiences no one knew; for he wrote short letters, and, when questioned, answered with imperturbable patience—

"Wait till I get through; then I'll come home and talk about it."

So everyone waited for the poet, till something happened which produced a greater sensation in the family than if all the boys had simultaneously taken to rhyming.

Dr. Alec got very impatient, and suddenly announced that he was going to L. to see after those young people; for Phebe was rapidly singing herself into public favour, with the sweet old ballads which she rendered so beautifully that hearts were touched as well as ears delighted, and her prospects brightening every month.

"Will you come with me, Rose, and surprise this ambitious pair, who are getting famous so fast they'll forget their home-keeping friends if we don't remind them of us now and then?" he said, when he proposed the trip one wild March morning.

"No, thank you, sir; I'll stay with auntie: that is all I'm fit for; and I should only be in the way among those fine people," answered Rose, snipping away at the plants blooming in the study window.

There was a slight bitterness in her voice and a cloud on her face, which her uncle heard and saw at once, half-guessed the meaning of, and could not rest till he had found out.

"Do you think Phebe and Mac would not care to see you?" he asked, putting down a letter in which Mac gave a glowing account of a concert at which Phebe surpassed herself.

"No, but they must be very busy," began Rose, wishing she had held her tongue.

"Then what is the matter?" persisted Dr. Alec.

Rose did not speak for a moment, and decapitated two fine geraniums with a reckless slash of her scissors, as if pent-up vexation of some kind must find a vent. It did in words also; for, as if quite against her will, she exclaimed impetuously—

"The truth is, I'm jealous of them both!"

"Bless my soul! what now?" ejaculated the doctor, in great surprise.

Rose put down her watering-pot and shears, came and stood before him with her hands nervously twisted together, and said, just as she used to do when she was a little girl confessing some misdeed—

"Uncle, I must tell you; for I've been getting very envious, discontented, and bad lately. No, don't be good to me yet; for you don't know how little I deserve it. Scold me well, and make me see how wicked I am."

"I will as soon as I know what I am to scold about. Unburden yourself, child, and let me see all your iniquity; for, if you begin by being jealous of Mac and Phebe, I'm prepared for anything," said Dr. Alec, leaning back as if nothing could surprise him now.

"But I am not jealous in that way, sir. I mean I want to be or do something splendid as well as they. I can't write poetry or sing like a bird; but I *should* think I might have my share of glory in some way. I thought perhaps I could paint, and I've tried, but I can only copy: I've no power to invent lovely things and I'm so discouraged; for that is my one accomplishment. Do you think I have *any* gift that could be cultivated, and do me credit like theirs?" she asked so wistfully that her uncle felt for a moment as if he never could forgive the fairies, who endow babies in their cradles, for being so niggardly to his girl. But one look into the sweet, open face before him, reminded him that the good elves *had* been very generous, and he answered cheerfully—

"Yes, I do; for you have one of the best and noblest gifts a woman can possess. Music and poetry are fine things; and I don't wonder you want them, or that you envy the pleasant fame they bring. I've felt just so, and been ready to ask why it didn't please heaven to be more generous to some people; so you needn't be ashamed to tell me all about it."

"I know I ought to be contented, but I'm not. My life is very comfortable, but so quiet and uneventful I get tired of it, and want to launch out as the others have, and do something, or at least try. I'm glad you think it isn't very bad of me, and I'd like to know what my gift is," said Rose, looking less despondent already.

"The art of living for others so patiently and sweetly that we enjoy it as we do the sunshine, and are not half grateful enough for the great blessing."

"It is very kind of you to say so, but I think I'd like a little fun and fame, nevertheless," and Rose did not look as thankful as she ought.

"Very natural, dear; but the fun and the fame do not last; while the memory of a real helper is kept green long after poetry is forgotten and music silent. Can't you believe that, and be happy?"

"But I do so little, nobody sees or cares, and I don't feel as if I was really of any use," sighed Rose, thinking of the long, dull winter, full of efforts that seemed fruitless.

"Sit here, and let us see if you really do very little, and if no one cares," and, drawing her to his knee, Dr. Alec went on, telling off each item on one of the fingers of the soft hand he held.

"First, an infirm old aunt is kept very happy by the patient, cheerful care of this good-for-nothing niece. Secondly, a crotchety uncle, for whom she reads, runs, writes, and sews so willingly that he cannot get on without her. Thirdly, various relations who are helped in various ways. Fourthly, one dear friend never forgotten, and a certain cousin cheered by the praise which is more to him than the loudest blast Fame could blow. Fifthly, several young girls find her an example of many good works and ways. Sixthly, a motherless baby is cared for as tenderly as if she was a little sister. Seventhly, half a dozen poor ladies made comfortable; and, lastly, some struggling boys and girls with artistic longings are put into a pleasant room furnished with casts, studies, easels, and all manner of helpful things, not to mention free lessons given by this same idle girl, who now sits upon my knee owning to herself that her gift *is* worth having after all."

"Indeed, I am! Uncle, I'd no idea I had done so many things to please you, or that anyone guessed how hard I try to fill my place usefully. I've learned to do without gratitude: now I'll learn not to care for praise, but to be contented to do my best, and have only God know."

"He knows, and He rewards in His own good time. I think a quiet life like this often makes itself felt in better ways than one that the world sees and applauds; and some of the noblest are never known till they end, leaving a void in many hearts. Yours may be one of these if you choose to make it so, and no one will be prouder of this success than I, unless it be—Mac."

The clouds were quite gone now, and Rose was looking straight into her uncle's face with a much happier expression, when that last word made it colour brightly, and the eyes glance away for a second. Then they came back full of a tender sort of resolution, as she said—

"That will be the reward I work for," and rose, as if ready to be up and doing with renewed courage.

But her uncle held her long enough to ask quite soberly, though his eyes laughed—

"Shall I tell him that?"

"No, sir, please don't! When he is tired of other people's praise, he will come home, and then—I'll see what I can do for him," answered Rose, slipping away to her work with the shy, happy look that sometimes came to give her face the charm it needed.

"He is such a thorough fellow he never is in a hurry to go from one thing to another. An excellent habit, but a trifle trying to impatient people like me," said the doctor, and picking up Dulce, who sat upon the rug with her dolly, he composed his feelings by tossing her till she crowed with delight.

Rose heartily echoed that last remark, but said nothing aloud, only helped her uncle off with dutiful alacrity, and, when he was gone, began to count the days till his return, wishing she had decided to go too.

He wrote often, giving excellent accounts of the "great creatures," as Steve called Phebe and Mac, and seemed to find so much to do in various ways that the second week of absence was nearly over before he set a day for his return, promising to astonish them with the account of his adventures.

Rose felt as if something splendid was going to happen, and set her affairs in order, so that the approaching crisis might find her fully prepared. She had "found out" now, was quite sure, and put away all doubts and fears to be ready to welcome home the cousin whom she was sure uncle would bring as her reward. She was thinking of this one day, as she got out her paper to write a long letter to poor Aunt Clara, who pined for news far away there in Calcutta.

Something in the task reminded her of that other lover whose wooing ended so tragically, and opening the little drawer of keepsakes, she took out the blue bracelet, feeling that she owed Charlie a tender thought in the midst of her new happiness; for of late she *had* forgotten him.

She had worn the trinket hidden under her black sleeve for a long time after his death, with the regretful constancy one sometimes shows in doing some little kindness all too late. But her arm had grown too round to hide the ornament, the forget-me-nots had fallen one by one, the clasp had broken; and that autumn she laid the bracelet away, acknowledging that she had outgrown the souvenir as well as the sentiment that gave it.

She looked at it in silence for a moment, then put it softly back, and, shutting the drawer, took up the little grey book which was her pride, thinking as she contrasted the two men and their influence on her life—the one sad and disturbing, the other sweet and inspiring—"Charlie's was passion: Mac's is love."

"Rose! Rose!" called a shrill voice, rudely breaking the pensive reverie, and with a start she shut the desk exclaiming as she ran to the door—

"They have come! They have come!"

21

How Phebe Earned her Welcome

DR. ALEC had not arrived, but bad tidings had, as Rose
guessed the instant her eye fell upon Aunt Plenty, hobbling
downstairs with her cap awry, her face pale, and a letter flap-
ping wildly in her hand, as she cried distractedly—

"Oh, my boy! my boy! sick, and I not there to nurse him!
Malignant fever, so far away. What can those children do?
why did I let Alec go?"

Rose got her into the parlour; and, while the poor old lady
lamented, she read the letter which Phebe had sent to her that
she might "break the news carefully to Rose."

"DEAR MISS PLENTY,—Please read this to yourself first, and
tell my little mistress as you think best. The dear doctor is very
ill; but I am with him, and shall not leave him day or night till he
is safe. So trust me, and do not be anxious; for everything shall
be done that care and skill and entire devotion can do. He would
not let us tell you before, fearing you would try to come at the
risk of your health. Indeed it would be useless; for only one nurse
is needed, and I came first, so do not let Rose or anybody else rob
me of my right to the danger and the duty. Mac has written to
his father; for Dr. Alec is now too ill to know what we do, and we
both felt that you ought to be told without further delay. He has
a bad malignant fever, caught no one can tell how, unless among
some poor emigrants whom he met wandering about quite forlorn
in a strange city. He understood Portuguese, and sent them to a
proper place when they had told their story. But I fear he has
suffered for his kindness; for this fever came on rapidly, and before
he knew what it was I was there, and it was too late to send me
away.

"*Now* I can show you how grateful I am, and if need be give my life so gladly for this friend who has been a father to me. Tell Rose his last conscious word and thought were for her. 'Don't let her come; keep my darling safe.' Oh, do obey him! Stay safely at home; and, God helping me, I'll bring Uncle Alec back in time. Mac does all I will let him. We have the best physicians, and everything is going as well as can be hoped till the fever turns.

"Dear Miss Plenty, pray for him and for me, that I may do this one happy thing for those who have done so much for

Your ever dutiful and loving

PHEBE."

As Rose looked up from the letter, half stunned by the sudden news and the great danger, she found that the old lady had already stopped useless bewailing, and was praying heartily, like one who knew well where help was to be found. Rose went and knelt down at her knee, laying her face on the clasped hands in her lap, and for a few minutes neither wept nor spoke. Then a stifled sob broke from the girl, and Aunt Plenty gathered the young head in her arms, saying, with the slow tears of age trickling down her own withered cheeks—

"Bear up, my lamb, bear up. The good Lord won't take him from us I am sure: and that brave child *will* be allowed to pay her debt to him; I feel she will."

"But I want to help. I *must* go, aunty, I must: no matter what the danger is," cried Rose, full of a tender jealousy of Phebe for being first to brave peril for the sake of him who had been a father to them both.

"You can't go, dear, it's no use now; and she is right to say 'Keep away.' I know those fevers, and the ones who nurse often take it, and fare worse for the strain they've been through. Good girl to stand by so bravely, to be so sensible, and not let Mac go too near! She's a grand nurse: Alec couldn't have a better, and she'll never leave him till he's safe," said Miss Plenty, excitedly.

"Ah, you begin to know her now, and value her as you ought. I think few would have done as she has; and if she does get ill and die it will be our fault partly; because she'd go through fire and water to make us do her justice, and receive her as we ought," cried Rose, proud of an example which she longed to follow.

"If she brings my boy home, I'll never say another word.

She may marry every nephew I've got, if she likes, and I'll give her my blessing," exclaimed Aunt Plenty, feeling that no price would be too much to pay for such a deed.

Rose was going to clap her hands, but wrung them instead; remembering with a sudden pang that the battle was not over yet, and it was much too soon to award the honours.

Before she could speak Uncle Mac and Aunt Jane hurried in; for Mac's letter had come with the other, and dismay fell upon the family at the thought of danger to the well-beloved Uncle Alec. His brother decided to go at once, and Aunt Jane insisted on accompanying him: though all agreed that nothing could be done but wait, and leave Phebe at her post as long as she held out; since it was too late to save her from danger now, and Mac reported her quite equal to the task.

Great was the hurry and confusion till the relief party was off. Aunt Plenty was heart-broken that she could not go with them, but felt that she was too infirm to be useful; and, like a sensible old soul, tried to content herself with preparing all sorts of comforts for the invalid. Rose was less patient, and at first had wild ideas of setting off alone, and forcing her way to the spot where all her thoughts now centred. But before she could carry out any rash project, Aunt Myra's palpitations set in so alarmingly that they did good service for once, and kept Rose busy taking her last directions, and trying to soothe her dying-bed; for each attack was declared fatal, till the patient demanded toast and tea when hope was again allowable and the rally began.

The news flew fast, as such tidings always do: and Aunt Plenty was constantly employed in answering inquiries; for her knocker kept up a steady tattoo for several days. All sorts of people came; gentle-folk and paupers, children with anxious little faces, old people full of sympathy, pretty girls sobbing as they went away, and young men who relieved their feelings by swearing at all emigrants in general and Portuguese in particular. It was touching and comforting to see how many loved the good man who was known only by his benefactions, and now lay suffering far away, quite unconscious how many unsuspected charities were brought to light by this grateful solicitude, as hidden flowers spring up when warm rains fall.

If Rose had ever felt that the gift of living for others was a poor one, she saw now how beautiful and blest it was—how rich the returns, how wide the influence, how much more precious the tender tie which knit so many hearts together, than any breath of fame, or brilliant talent, that dazzled, but did not win and warm. In after years she found how true her uncle's words had been; and, listening to eulogies of great men, felt less moved and inspired by praises of their splendid gifts than by the sight of some good man's patient labour for the poorest of his kind. Her heroes ceased to be the world's favourites; and became such as Garrison fighting for his chosen people; Howe restoring lost senses to the deaf, the dumb, and blind; Sumner unbribable, when other men were bought and sold: and many a large-hearted woman working as quietly as Abby Gibbons, who for thirty years has made Christmas merry for two hundred little paupers in a city almshouse, beside saving Magdalens and teaching convicts.

The lesson came to Rose when she was ready for it, and showed her what a noble profession philanthropy is, made her glad of her choice, and helped fit her for a long life full of the loving labour, and sweet satisfaction unostentatious charity brings to those who ask no reward, and are content if "only God knows."

Several anxious weeks went by with wearing fluctuations of hope and fear; for Life and Death fought over the prize each wanted, and more than once Death seemed to have won. But Phebe stood at her post, defying both danger and death with the courage and devotion women often show. All her soul and strength were in her work; and, when it seemed most hopeless, she cried out with the passionate energy which seems to send such appeals straight up to Heaven—

"Grant me this one boon, dear Lord, and I will never ask another for myself!"

Such prayers avail much, and such entire devotion often seems to work miracles when other aids are vain. Phebe's cry was answered; her self-forgetful task accomplished, and her long vigil rewarded with a happy dawn. Dr. Alec always said that she kept him alive by the force of her will; and that, during the hours when he seemed to lie unconscious, he felt a strong, warm hand holding his, as if keeping him from the swift current trying to sweep him away. The happiest hour of all her life was that in which he knew her, looked up with the shadow of a smile in his hollow eyes, and tried to say in his old cheery way—

"Tell Rose I've turned the corner, thanks to you, my child."

She answered very quietly, smoothed the pillow, and saw him drop asleep again, before she stole away into the other room, meaning to write the good news; but could only throw herself down, and find relief for a full heart in the first tears she had shed for weeks. Mac found her there, and took such care of her that she was ready to go back to her place—now indeed a post of honour—while he ran off to send home a telegram which made many hearts sing for joy, and caused Jamie, in his first burst of delight, to propose to ring all the city bells and order out the cannon.

"Saved: thanks to God and Phebe."

That was all; but everyone was satisfied, and everyone fell a-crying, as if hope needed much salt water to strengthen it. That was soon over, however, and then people went about smiling and saying to one another, with hand-shakes or embraces, "He is better: no doubt of it now!" A general desire to rush away and assure themselves of the truth pervaded the family for some days; and nothing but awful threats from Mac, mandates from the doctor, and entreaties from Phebe not to undo her work, kept Miss Plenty, Rose, and Aunt Jessie at home.

As the only way in which they could ease their minds and bear the delay, they set about spring cleaning, with an energy which scared the spiders, and drove char-women distracted. If the old house had been infected with small-pox, it could not have been more vigorously scrubbed, aired, and refreshed. Early as it was, every carpet was routed up, curtains pulled down, cushions banged, and glory-holes turned out, till not a speck of dust, a last year's fly, or stray straw could be found. Then they all sat down and rested in such an immaculate mansion that one hardly dared to move for fear of destroying the shining order everywhere visible.

It was late in April before this was accomplished, and the necessary quarantine of the absentees well over. The first mild days seemed to come early, so that Dr. Alec might return with safety from the journey which had so nearly been his last. It was perfectly impossible to keep any member of the family away on that great occasion. They came from all quarters in spite of express directions to the contrary; for the invalid was still very feeble, and no excitement must be allowed. As if the wind had carried the glad news, Uncle Jem came into port the night before; Will and Geordie got a leave on their own responsibility; Steve would have defied the entire Faculty, had it been necessary; and Uncle Mac and Archie said simultaneously, "Business be hanged today."

Of course, the aunts arrived all in their best; all cautioning everybody else to keep quiet, and all gabbling excitedly at the least provocation. Jamie suffered most during that day, so divided was he between the desire to behave well and the frantic impulse to shout at the top of his voice, turn somersaults, and race all over the house. Occasional bolts into the barn, where he let off steam by roaring and dancing jigs, to the great dismay of the fat old horses and two sedate cows, helped him to get through that trying period.

But the heart that was fullest beat and fluttered in Rose's bosom, as she went about putting spring flowers everywhere; very silent, but so radiant with happiness that the aunts watched her, saying softly to one another, "Could an angel look sweeter?"

If angels ever wore pale-green gowns and snowdrops in their hair, had countenances full of serenest joy, and large eyes shining with an inward light that made them very lovely, then Rose did look like one. But she felt a like a woman: and well she might; for was not life very rich that day, when uncle, friend, and lover were coming back to her together? Could she ask anything more, except the power to be to all of them the creature they believed her, and to return the love they gave her with one as faithful, pure, and deep?

Among the portraits in the hall hung one of Dr. Alec, taken soon after his return by Charlie, in one of his brief fits of inspiration. Only a crayon, but wonderfully life-like and carefully finished, as few of the others were. This had been handsomely framed, and now held the place of honour, garlanded with green wreaths, while the great Indian jar below blazed with a pyramid of hot-house flowers sent by Kitty. Rose was giving these a last touch, with Dulce close by, cooing over a handful of sweet "daffydowndillies," when the sound of wheels sent her flying to the door. She meant to have spoken the first welcome and had the first embrace; but when she saw the altered face in the carriage, the feeble figure being borne up the steps by all the boys, she stood motionless till Phebe caught her in her arms, whispering with a laugh and a cry struggling in her voice—

"I did it for you, my darling, all for you!"

"Oh Phebe, never say again you owe me anything! I never can repay you for this," was all Rose had time to answer, as they stood one instant cheek to cheek, heart to heart, both too full of happiness for many words.

Aunt Plenty had heard the wheels also, and, as everybody rose *en masse*, had said as impressively as extreme agitation would allow, while she put her glasses on upside-down, and seized a lace tidy instead of her handkerchief—

"Stop! all stay here, and let *me* receive Alec. Remember his weak state, and be calm, quite calm, as I am."

"Yes, aunt, certainly," was the general murmur of assent: but it was as impossible to obey as it would have been to keep feathers still in a gale; and one irresistible impulse carried the whole roomful into the hall, to behold Aunt Plenty beautifully illustrate her own theory of composure by waving the tidy wildly, rushing into Dr. Alec's arms, and laughing and crying with an hysterical abandonment which even Aunt Myra could not have surpassed.

The tearful jubilee was soon over, however, and no one seemed the worse for it: for the instant his arms were at liberty Uncle Alec forgot himself, and began to make other people happy, by saying seriously, though his thin face beamed paternally, as he drew Phebe forward—

"Aunt Plenty, but for this good daughter I never should have come back to be so welcomed. Love her for my sake."

Then the old lady came out splendidly, and showed her mettle; for, turning to Phebe, she bowed her grey head as if saluting an equal; and, offering her hand, answered with repentance, admiration, and tenderness trembling in her voice—

"I'm proud to do it for her own sake. I ask pardon for my silly prejudices, and I'll prove that I'm sincere by—where's that boy?"

There were six boys present: but the right one was in exactly the right place at the right moment; and, seizing Archie's hand, Aunt Plenty put Phebe's into it, trying to say something appropriately solemn, but could not; so hugged them both, and sobbed out—

"If I had a dozen nephews, I'd give them *all* to you, my dear, and dance at the wedding, though I had rheumatism in every limb."

That was better than any oration; for it set them all to laughing, and Dr. Alec was floated to the sofa on a gentle wave of merriment. Once there, everyone but Rose and Aunt Plenty was ordered off by Mac, who was in command now, and seemed to have sunk the poet in the physician.

"The house must be perfectly quiet, and he must go to sleep as soon as possible after the journey; so all say 'Good-bye' now, and call again tomorrow," he said, watching his uncle anxiously, as he leaned in the sofa corner, with four women taking off his wraps, three boys contending for his overshoes, two brothers shaking hands at short intervals, and Aunt Myra holding a bottle of strong salts under his devoted nose every time there was an opening anywhere.

With difficulty the house was partially cleared: and then while Aunt Plenty mounted guard over her boy, Rose stole away to see if Mac had gone with the rest; for as yet they had hardly spoken in the joyful flurry, though eyes and hands had met.

22

Short and Sweet

IN THE HALL she found Steve and Kitty; for he had hidden his little sweetheart behind the big couch, feeling that she had a right there, having supported his spirits during the late anxiety with great constancy and courage. They seemed so cosy, billing and cooing in the shadow of the gay vase, that Rose would have slipped silently away if they had not seen and called to her.

"He's not gone: I guess you'll find him in the parlour," said Steve, divining with a lover's instinct the meaning of the quick look she had cast at the hat-rack, as she shut the study-door behind her.

"Mercy, no! Archie and Phebe are there, so he'd have the sense to pop into the sanctum and wait; unless you'd like me to go and bring him out?" added Kitty, smoothing Rose's ruffled hair, and settling the flowers on the bosom where Uncle Alec's head had laid until he fell asleep.

"No, thank you, I'll go to him when I've seen my Phebe. She won't mind me," answered Rose, moving on to the parlour.

"Look here," called Steve, "do advise them to hurry up and all be married at once. We were just ready when uncle fell ill, and now we can *not* wait a day later than the first of May."

"Rather short notice," laughed Rose, looking back with the door-knob in her hand.

"We'll give up all our splendour, and do it as simply as you like, if *you* will only come too. Think how lovely! three weddings at once! Do fly round and settle things: there's a dear," implored Kitty, whose imagination was fired with this romantic idea.

"How can I, when I have no bridegroom yet?" began Rose, with conscious colour in her tell-tale face.

"Sly creature! you know you've only got to say a word and have a famous one. Una and her lion will be nothing to it," cried Steve, bent on hastening his brother's affair, which was much too dilatory and peculiar for his taste.

"He has been in no haste to come home, and I am in no haste to leave it. Don't wait for me, 'Mr. and Mrs. Harry Walmers, Jr.;' I shall be a year at least making up my mind: so you may lead off as splendidly as you like, and I'll profit by your experience;" and Rose vanished into the parlour, leaving Steve to groan over the perversity of superior women, and Kitty to comfort him by promising to marry him on May-day "all alone."

A very different couple occupied the drawing-room, but a happier one; for they had known the pain of separation, and were now enjoying the bliss of a reunion which was to last unbroken for their lives. Phebe sat in an easy-chair, resting from her labours, pale and thin and worn, but lovelier in Archie's eyes than ever before. It was very evident that he was adoring his divinity; for, after placing a footstool at her feet, he had forgotten to get up, and knelt there, with his elbow on the arm of her chair, looking like a thirsty man drinking long draughts of the purest water.

"Shall I disturb you if I pass through?" asked Rose, loth to spoil the pretty tableau.

"Not if you stop a minute on the way and congratulate me, cousin; for she says 'Yes' at last!" cried Archie, springing up to go and bring her to the arms Phebe opened as she appeared.

"I knew she would reward your patience, and put away her pride when both had been duly tried," said Rose, laying the tired head on her bosom, with such tender admiration in her eyes that Phebe had to shake some bright drops from her own before she could reply in a tone of grateful humility, that showed how much her heart was touched—

"How can I help it, when they all are so kind to me? Any pride would melt away under such praise and thanks and loving wishes as I've had today; for every member of the family has taken pains to welcome me, to express far too much gratitude, and to beg me to be one of you. I needed very little urging; but, when Archie's father and mother came and called me 'daughter,' I would have promised anything to show my love for them."

"And him," added Rose; but Archie seemed quite satisfied, and kissed the hand he held as if it had been that of a beloved princess, while he said with all the pride Phebe seemed to have lost—

"Think what she gives up for me: fame and fortune and the admiration of many a better man. You don't know what a splendid prospect she has of becoming one of the sweet singers who are loved and honoured everywhere; and all this she puts away for my sake, content to sing for me alone, with no reward but love."

"I am so glad to make a little sacrifice for a great happiness: I never shall regret it or think my music lost, if it makes home cheerful for my mate. Birds sing sweetest in their own nests, you know," and Phebe bent towards him with a look and gesture which plainly showed how willingly she offered up all ambitious hopes upon the altar of a woman's happy love.

Both seemed to forget that they were not alone, and in a moment they were; for a sudden impulse carried Rose to the door of her sanctum, as if the south wind which seemed to have set in was wafting this little ship also towards the Islands of the Blest, where the others were safely anchored now.

The room was a blaze of sunshine and a bower of spring freshness and fragrance: for here Rose had let her fancy have free play; and each garland, fern, and flower had its meaning. Mac seemed to have been reading this sweet language of symbols, to have guessed why Charlie's little picture was framed in white roses, why pansies hung about his own, why Psyche was half hidden among feathery sprays of maiden's-hair, and a purple passion-flower lay at Cupid's feet. The last fancy evidently pleased him; for he was smiling over it, and humming to himself, as if to beguile his patient waiting, the burden of the air Rose so often sung to him—

"Bonny lassie, will ye gang, will ye gang
To the birks of Aberfeldie?"

"Yes, Mac, anywhere!"

He had not heard her enter, and wheeling round looked at her with a radiant face, as he said, drawing a long breath—

"At last! you were so busy over the dear man, I got no word. But I can wait: I'm used to it."

Rose stood quite still, surveying him with a new sort of reverence in her eyes, as she answered with a sweet solemnity, that made him laugh and redden with the sensitive joy of one to whom praise from her lips was very precious.

"You forget that you are not the Mac who went away. I should have run to meet my cousin, but I did not dare to be familiar with the poet whom all begin to honour."

"You like the mixture then? You know I said I'd try to give you love and poetry together."

"Like it! I'm so glad, so proud, I haven't any words strong and beautiful enough to half express my wonder and my admiration. How *could* you do it, Mac?" and a whole face full of smiles broke loose, as Rose clapped her hands, looking as if she could dance with sheer delight at his success.

"It did itself, up there among the hills, and here with you, or out alone upon the sea. I could write a heavenly poem this very minute, and put you in as Spring; you look like her in that green gown with snowdrops in your bonny hair! Rose, am I getting on a little? Does a hint of fame help me nearer to the prize I'm working for? Is your heart more willing to be won?"

He did not stir a step, but looked at her with such intense longing that his glance seemed to draw her nearer like an irresistible appeal; for she went and stood before him, holding out both hands, as if she offered all her little store, as she said with simplest sincerity—

"It is not worth so much beautiful endeavour; but, if you still want so poor a thing, it is yours."

He caught the hands in his, and seemed about to take the rest of her, but hesitated for an instant, unable to believe that so much happiness was true.

"Are you sure, Rose—very sure? Don't let a momentary admiration blind you: I'm not a poet yet; and the best are but mortal men, you know."

"It is not admiration, Mac."

"Nor gratitude for the small share I've taken in saving uncle? I had my debt to pay, as well as Phebe, and was as glad to risk my life."

"No: it is not gratitude."

"Nor pity for my patience? I've only done a little yet, and am as far as ever from being like your hero. I can work and wait still longer, if you are not sure; for I must have all or nothing."

"O Mac! why will you be so doubtful? You said you'd make me love you, and you've done it. Will you believe me now?" And, with a sort of desperation, she threw herself into his arms, clinging there in eloquent silence, while he held her close; feeling, with a thrill of tender triumph, that this was no longer little Rose, but a loving woman ready to live and die for him.

"Now I'm satisfied!" he said presently, when she lifted up her face, full of maidenly shame at the sudden passion which had carried her out of herself for a moment. "No: don't slip away so soon; let me keep you for one blessed minute, and feel that I have really found my Psyche."

"And I my Cupid," answered Rose, laughing, in spite of her emotion, at the idea of Mac in that sentimental character.

He laughed too, as only a happy lover could; then said, with sudden seriousness—

"Sweet Soul! lift up your lamp, and look well before it is too late; for I'm no god, only a very faulty man."

"Dear Love! I will. But I have no fear, except that you will fly too high for me to follow, because I have no wings."

"You shall live the poetry, and I will write it; so my little gift will celebrate your greater one."

"No: you shall have all the fame, and I'll be content to be known only as the poet's wife."

"And I'll be proud to own that my best inspiration comes from the beneficent life of a sweet and noble woman."

"O Mac! we'll work together, and try to make the world better by the music and the love we leave behind us when we go."

"Please God, we will!" he answered fervently; and, looking at her as she stood there in the spring sunshine, glowing with the tender happiness, high hopes, and earnest purposes that make life beautiful and sacred, he felt that now the last leaf had folded back, the golden heart lay open to the light, and his Rose had bloomed.

Plato and Milton

BY IRENE SAMUEL

Plato's thought is built into the ethics of Milton's poems as substantially as some parts of the Bible are built into their plots.

MERRITT Y. HUGHES, *John Milton,*
'Paradise Regained,' the Minor Poems,
and 'Samson Agonistes,' p. 411.

How little the commentators of Milton have availed themselves of the writings of Plato, Milton's darling! SAMUEL TAYLOR COLERIDGE, Letter to W. Sotheby, September 10, 1802.

Next to Homer and the inspired Hebrew poets, no author exercised a more powerful influence on the congenial sublimity of Milton's genius than Plato.

BENJAMIN JOWETT, 'The Genius of Plato,'
Edinburgh Review 87 (1848). 335.

PLATO *and* MILLTON

IRENE SAMUEL

Associate Professor of English at Hunter College

Cornell Paperbacks

CORNELL UNIVERSITY PRESS

ITHACA, NEW YORK

ox 4/25

CORNELL UNIVERSITY PRESS

First published 1947 as Volume XXXV of Cornell Studies in English
First printing for Cornell Paperbacks 1965

Contents

	Preface	vii
I	Milton as a Student of Plato	3
II	'Academics Old and New'	27
III	'Himself a True Poem'	45
IV	The Good Life: Pleasure, Wealth, Fame	69
V	The Good Life: Knowledge	101
VI	The Theory of Ideas	131
VII	The Doctrine of Love	149
	A List of References to Publications	173
	Index of Names and Titles	177

TO LANE COOPER
Late Professor of the English Language
and Literature in Cornell University

Preface

No ONE, to my knowledge, has ever doubted that Milton knew the Dialogues and Epistles of Plato—along with very nearly everything else a man of his time might read. Indeed, a list of those who have written, cursorily or at length, of the relation between the two men might be extended far beyond the one appended to this volume. But in spite of the liberal use of Plato in annotated texts of Milton, and even after the work of Dr. Herbert Agar on *Milton and Plato*, the extent to which Milton accepted Platonic teaching has still to be appraised.

My own work began with the study of Plato. Coming to Milton with the Dialogues and Epistles fresh in mind, I could not read *Paradise Lost* and *Paradise Regained* as Puritan poems, nor see Milton as a mere Satanic rebel. Everywhere in his work there were echoes of Plato, many that might have come from intermediate sources, some of them Christian, but many, too, that only a close reading of Plato by Milton himself could produce. Whoever wishes may cull three shoe-boxes of such parallels; I wished to, and did, in my graduate study at Cornell University. For my doctoral dissertation, written under the direction of Professor Lane Cooper, I used only the passages from Milton's poems—one boxful. My notes on the Platonic origins of those passages are available on pages 258-386 of a typewritten dissertation entitled *Platonism in the Poetry of John Milton*.

In the present study, the reader has been spared the notes. Early in the collection of them it became clear that the works of Plato had been not merely a source, but a stimulant, to Milton, and had acted as a catalytic agent on the heterogeneous materials of pagan, Biblical, and Christian learning in his mind. Moreover, the Platonic pattern into which these materials were fused seemed to explain some troublesome questions about the poems of Milton. The apparently inconsistent treatment of knowledge in *Areopagitica* and *Paradise Lost,* the paradox of Adam's fall, the discrepant rejection and use of the pagan classics in *Paradise Regained;* these and the like questions resolved themselves when held to the light of Plato's thought.

Lest the pattern here traced seem strained to my reader, I have devoted the first two chapters to a factual account of Milton as a student of Plato and Platonists. Of his unconscious or 'native' Platonism I can pretend to no knowledge. Certainly much of his Platonizing, especially in early works, was derivative, and certainly he did not check every thought that entered his head against the canon of Plato. But his assimilation of Platonic teaching was reasonably conscious.

In the light, then, of Milton's avowed study of Plato I have sought to explain the poetic and ethical theories that underlie *Paradise Lost, Paradise Regained,* and, less ostensibly since it is a less discursive poem, *Samson Agonistes.* I have followed the argument where it led, and, I trust, duly acknowledged the fact when it led beyond Plato. Although no appraisal of Milton's Christian doctrine is attempted, the reader will see that Milton takes his place, along with Augustine and Dean Inge, among Christian Platonists. He is also, like Spenser and Shelley, a Platonic poet; and it is thus that he here concerns us. Plato did not affect Milton precisely as he affected Shelley or Spenser; for the effect of any writer varies with the reader. But the use Milton made of Plato can tell us much about the relation between a philosopher and a poet, and perhaps even about that between a poet's philosophy and his poetry.

It is, at any rate, in that hope that I offer the following pages. For the sake of readability I have reduced the footnotes to a minimum; used translations for most passages in Greek, Latin, and Italian; in the main normalized the spelling and punctuation of Milton's prose; and in general tried to give the results and conceal the process of research. The editions and translations employed in the text are given in the List of References to Publications on pp. 173-175. I wish here to acknowledge my indebtedness to the following publishers and persons for permission to quote from works in their copyright: the Macmillan Company for Milton's *Private Correspondence and Academic Exercises* translated by Phyllis B. Tillyard, Augustine's *De Civitate Dei* edited by J. E. C. Welldon, *The English Grammar Schools to 1660* by Foster Watson; the Oxford University Press and the Clarendon Press for the edition and translation of the *Hermetica* by Walter Scott, the translations by Lane Cooper of Plato's dialogues on art, by Benjamin Jowett of *The Dialogues of Plato,* and by W. W. Jackson of Dante's *Convivio;* E. P. Dutton and Company for *The Republic of Plato* translated by A. D. Lindsay; Jackson, Son and Company for *The Sonnets of Milton* edited and translated by John S. Smart; the Odyssey Press for the Preface to an edition of Milton's poems by Merritt Y. Hughes; the Princeton University Press for *Milton and Plato* by Herbert Agar; the University of Michigan Press and Professor James Holly Hanford for his essay on 'The Youth of Milton' in *Studies in Shakespeare, Milton, and Donne;* and the Columbia University Press for *The Works of John Milton,* from which most of my quotations from Milton's prose works are taken. I have also to thank the editors of *Studies in Philology* for permission to use in modified form as the first chapter of this book my article on 'Milton's References to Plato and Socrates,' which appeared in that periodical. Mr. Herbert Agar gave me permission in 1939 to use his *Milton and Plato* as the starting point of my work.

Most of this study had been written before I read C. S. Lewis's *Preface to Paradise Lost*, and all of it before the work of Douglas Bush, *'Paradise Lost' in Our Time*, appeared. But I am indebted to both volumes for confirming me in views independently arrived at. My work owes much to the encouragement and advice of my teachers, Professor Lane Cooper and Professor Charles W. Jones of Cornell University, and of Professor John S. Diekhoff, formerly my colleague at Queens College. Among other friends who have helped me in ways too numerous to list, I wish especially to thank Dr. Mary Campbell Brill for her careful and generous assistance in proof-reading and compiling the Index.

IRENE SAMUEL

Hunter College
1946

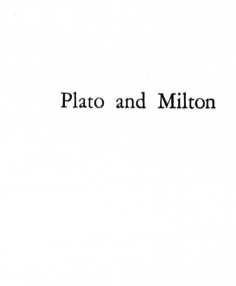

Plato and Milton

CHAPTER I

Milton as a Student of Plato

THE DOCTRINE which we find in the writings of John
Milton shows an unusual degree of consistency; and
while in a mind as complex as his, consistency is not same-
ness, we may draw from his work the principles that generally guided his thought. They do not belong to any one
philosophical system. Indeed, a man of his endowment and
learning necessarily agrees with some part of most systems;
the better part, we may suppose. But the correspondence
between his doctrine and that of Plato is remarkably close;
moreover, as we shall see, we have Milton's own warrant
for thinking the correspondence important.

In order to appraise the influence of one writer on another, we must start, of course, from explicit references.
But we need not take a narrow view of the transmission
of thought from mind to mind. Only a pedant would lift
word after word from another's page, or retain in separate
compartments of his mind what he has learned from this
source and what from that. A thought once assimilated will
readily flow into channels far from its original source. Thus,
if Milton truly accepts some definite view from Plato, he
is not likely to tag it at every use, much less to name the
dialogue or epistle in which he found it. In large part the
effect of a writer upon any reader cannot be traced back
to isolated passages; the spirit of the whole is more likely
to remain with him than a series of excerpts.

Both sympathy and caution must, therefore, guide the interpreter. To the commentators who name the Cabala as a primary source of Milton's thought, we may fairly object that they show little caution, since his one reference to this 'source' is a disparaging use of the term 'Cabalists' in *Eikonoclastes* (5. 252). Conversely, Dr. Herbert Agar shows too much caution, and too little sympathy, when, after finding the Platonic origin of many passages in the works of Milton, he hesitates to assert that 'Plato's effect upon Milton's thought, or upon his spiritual development, was of major importance.' Milton did assert it.

In the year 1642, looking back over his past in order to answer a libelous attack on his conduct, he reviewed the course of his reading. He said in effect: This is what my mind fed on, and feeding on this, it reached these decisions; how could I then have acted as my accuser says? Apparently he believed that knowledge determines choice, and therefore offered his doctrine as a proof of his character, and his literary preferences as a proof of his doctrine. Whether or not the argument was of a kind to convince opponents, it provides a key to the mind of the man who used it. And Plato is a part of that key; here Milton spoke unmistakably:

Thus, from the laureate fraternity of poets, riper years and the ceaseless round of study and reading led me to the shady spaces of philosophy, but chiefly to the divine volumes of Plato and his equal Xenophon: where, if I should tell ye what I learned of chastity and love, I mean that which is truly so, whose charming cup is only virtue, which she bears in her hand to those who are worthy (the rest are cheated with a thick intoxicating potion, which a certain sorceress, the abuser of love's name, carries about), and how the first and chiefest office of love begins and ends in the soul, producing those happy twins of her divine generation, knowledge and virtue, with such abstracted sublimities as these, it might be worth your listening, readers,

4

as I may one day hope to have ye in a still time, when there
shall be no chiding. (3. 305.)[1]

To be sure, this passage in the *Apology for Smectymnuus*
looks backward, and is concerned with a doctrine of love.
How much more of its author does it reveal, and for how
long a period? How much of the thought of Plato, moreover, do the words allude to? The references Milton made
to Plato and Socrates answer these questions.

Now such references are, of course, hardly a matter for
surprise. An Englishman of the seventeenth century, trained
at St. Paul's and Cambridge, at home in the academies of
Italy, and in correspondence with the learned men of his
time, who had *not* found occasion to mention Plato and
Socrates would astonish us. And Milton, before he entered
school at the age of twelve, had already studied languages
with Thomas Young. The curriculum at St. Paul's, from
what we know of its founders and its headmaster in Milton's time, Alexander Gill, doubtless included selections
from Plato.[2] We may surmise from the popular handbook
of Erasmus, *De Duplici Copia rerum ac verborum Commentarii duo,* that schoolboys of the Renaissance knew
parts, at least, of Plato's *Symposium, Apology, Crito,
Phaedo,* and *Republic,* as well as the Socratic writings of
Xenophon, Cebes' *Picture of Human Life,* and the fragment of Aeschines—all perhaps in translation. Milton,
we know, thought reading like this suited to young students; he must have had in mind when he wrote *Of Education* his own happy years at St. Paul's. He may even
have read in the headmaster's *Logonomia Anglica* (p. 83)
this English and Latin illustration of the superlative de-

---

[1] The numbers in parenthesis, when no other source is indicated,
refer to the Columbia edition of *The Works of John Milton.*

[2] See J. H. Lupton, *Life of Dean Colet,* pp. 168-9, 171; Foster Watson, *The English Grammar Schools to 1660;* and Arthur Barker, 'Milton's Schoolmasters,' *MLR.* 32 (1937). 517-36.

gree: 'Among ðe Filosoferz, Plato was ðe most lerned; *inter Philosophos Plato doctissimus fuit.*' And he may have had to debate a question like that which John Clarke recorded among *Quaestiones aliquot declamatoriae* at the Lincoln Grammar-School: *'Utrum utilius sit Socratem de moribus quam Hippocratem de humoribus disputantem audire.'*[3]

In any case, Milton had learned something of Plato and his master at St. Paul's, had heard them praised, and probably used only a commonplace of the schools when he addressed Thomas Young in his Fourth *Elegy:*

> Carior ille mihi quam tu, doctissime Graium,
> Cliniadi, pronepos qui Telamonis erat;
> Quamque Stagirites generoso magnus alumno,
> Quem peperit Libyco Chaonis alma Iovi.

Clearly, he had not yet studied Plato intensively.

Did he reach 'the shady spaces of philosophy' at Christ's College? His undergraduate writings contain several allusions to Socrates and Plato. In his Second *Prolusion* (12. 150), Plato is *'ille Naturae Matris optimus interpres'* for describing the Sirens on the edge of each sphere, and Aristotle is *'Pythagorae et Platonis aemulus et perpetuus Calumniator.'* We read in the Sixth *Prolusion:*

Moreover Socrates, according to the Pythian Apollo the wisest of men, is said often to have bridled his wife's shrewish tongue with a jesting word. Besides, we read that the conversation of the ancient philosophers was always sprinkled with witty sayings and enlivened by a pleasant sparkle. (Tillyard, pp. 90-1.)[4]

And again:

We too keep the custom of amusing ourselves as Socrates advised. (*Ibid.,* p. 98.)

---

[3] See Watson, *op. cit.,* pp. 454, 466.

[4] The translations of Milton's letters and prolusions are taken from Phyllis B. Tillyard, *Milton, Private Correspondence and Academic Exercises.*

In the Seventh *Proclusion,* Milton derides *'illud nescire Socraticum,'* but speaks with delight of conferences

such as those which the divine Plato is said often to have held in the shade of that famous plane-tree, conversations which all mankind might well have flocked to hear in spell-bound silence. (*Ibid.,* p. 111.)

But these remarks may all be as conventional as that in the Fourth *Elegy.* In Milton's age, as in ours, a good many persons doubtless referred to Plato and Socrates even among those who knew little more of the one than that he might be called divine and of the other that he was called the wisest of men. The references to Plato and Socrates in Milton's Academic Exercises and Elegies might have come from any one of similar training. They are vague, reveal no special insight into the teaching of Plato, and have no close tie to their writer's own belief. The like may be said of the verses *De Idea Platonica,* whenever they were composed. The lines show some knowledge and some affection, but even their 'sportive' tone and the precedent of Renaissance Platonism hardly excuse Milton for accepting Hermes Trismegistus as a valid interpreter of Platonic thought.[5] So too with *Il Penseroso,* where Plato is to be unsphered for such work as had better been left to 'thrice-great Hermes':

> Or let my Lamp at midnight hour,
> Be seen in some high lonely Tow'r,
> Where I may oft out-watch the Bear,
> With thrice-great Hermes, or unsphere
> The spirit of Plato to unfold
> What Worlds, or what vast Regions hold
> The immortal mind that hath forsook
> Her mansion in this fleshly nook:

[5] Cf. W. Skeat and E. H. Visiak, *Milton's Lament for Damon and His Other Latin Poems,* p. 66; and Walter Mac Kellar, *The Latin Poems of John Milton,* pp. 17, 51-3.

> And of those Daemons that are found
> In fire, air, flood, or under ground,
> Whose power hath a true consent
> With Planet, or with Element. (85-96.)[6]

Such words reflect a contemporary enthusiasm, but reveal little independent study. Evidently the name of Plato had long been impressed upon Milton as that of an eminent, perhaps the most eminent, philosopher; and though Milton was seldom content to take impressions at second hand, Plato had not yet begun to exercise a determinant influence upon him.

The verses added by Milton to the Seventh *Elegy* when he published his Latin poems in 1645 confirm the conventionality of his earlier Platonism:

> These vain trophies of my idleness I once set up in foolish mood and with supine endeavor. Injurious error, forsooth, led me astray, and untutored youth was a bad teacher; until the shady Academy offered its Socratic streams, and freed me from the yoke to which I had submitted. At once these flames were extinguished, and thenceforth my breast has been stiff with encircling ice, whence Cupid has feared a frost for his arrows, and Venus fears my Diomedean strength! (Mac Kellar, p. 107.)[7]

This recantation has an evident purpose. At a definite time in Milton's life, we are to understand, Plato with his Socratic teaching profoundly altered the poet's habit of thought. And this difference in emphasis is what chiefly distinguishes the Platonizing of the early works from that zest for Plato which began at some definite period in Milton's 'riper years'; the account of his education in the

---

[6] Cf. E. C. Baldwin, 'A Note on *Il Penseroso*,' *MLN*. 33 (1918). 184-5. Quotations from Milton's English poems are taken from the text of H. J. C. Grierson, *The Poems of John Milton*, except where another source is indicated.

[7] The translations of Milton's Latin poems are taken from Walter Mac Kellar, *The Latin Poems of John Milton*.

Apology, and the late postscript to the Seventh *Elegy,* assert the influence of Plato on Milton's *ethical* theory, and particularly on his theory of love. The Platonic citations and allusions in the Academic Exercises, the Latin poems, and *Il Penseroso,* while in all probability drawn from the Dialogues, nowhere indicate that those Dialogues have a central and unifying doctrine. The music of the spheres, the conference under the plane-tree, the Socratic sportiveness and pretended ignorance, the idea distinct from phenomena, the immortal mind freed of its 'fleshly nook,' all these are related to a view of human life with which Milton's early writings were scarcely concerned.

No such doubt can touch his letter to Charles Diodati, dated from London, September 23, 1637:

Though I know not God's intent toward me in other respects, yet of this I am sure, that he has imbued me especially with a mighty passion for Beauty. Ceres never sought her daughter Proserpine (as the legend tells) with greater ardor than I do this Idea of Beauty, like some image of loveliness; ever pursuing it, by day and by night, in every shape and form ('for many forms there are of things divine') and following close in its footprints as it leads. And so, whensover I find one who spurns the base opinions of common men, and dares to be, in thought and word and deed, that which the wisest minds throughout the ages have approved; whensoever, I say, I find such a man, to him I find myself impelled forthwith to cleave. And if I am fated, either by nature or destiny, never to attain this high honor and glory in my own proper person, for all my toil and striving, yet sure I am that neither god nor man shall forbid me to honor and revere all my days those who have won such glory as this, or are happily striving toward it.

To change the subject, I know it is time to satisfy your curiosity. You make many eager enquiries, even asking about my thoughts. I will tell you, Diodati, but let me whisper it in your ear, to spare my blushes, and allow me for a moment to speak to you in a boastful strain. What am I thinking about? you ask. So help me God, of immortality. What am I doing? Growing wings and learning to fly; but my Pegasus can only rise on tender pinions as yet, so let my new wisdom be humble. (Tillyard, p. 14.)

This is Milton's first intimate use of Plato. Though *Phaedrus* is not named, Diodati is expected to place the allusion and understand the Platonic language. Evidently Milton had known an Italian Platonist before ever he entered an *accademia*. And the whole passage differs from the commonplaces of school and society on the Idea of the Beautiful. Here is no mistress praised as the very incarnation of that glorious idea, but a friend is told that he, but not he alone, is loved because this Idea of Beauty leaves its print on many shapes and forms, and especially on the spirit of an uncommonly good man. The friend is even told his use; by his aid the soul grows its wings to its own end, immortality, that it may have vision of the very 'image of loveliness,' and fly its Pegasus, if it be the soul of a poet, to the rim of heaven itself. Here is that love 'which is truly so,' the doctrine that Milton thought among the most important sources of his essential education. Here is the authentic note of ardent Platonism.

But was it the first time Milton sounded that note? *Comus*, written three years earlier, contains a similar paraphrase, from *Phaedo* 81. And surely much in *Comus* comes from the Dialogues, and much is ardent. Still, is its Platonizing exactly Platonic? Coleridge thought so, and most commentators since have found the Mask the most Platonic of Milton's works. Hanford suggests a more likely explanation: 'That a poet should be a poet's guide to emotional Platonism is very natural. That Spenser should have been the guide of Milton is particularly so.'[8] Put the question thus: Is the conversation of the Mask such a dialogue as Plato might have written on the subject, or

[8] James Holly Hanford, 'The Youth of Milton,' in *Studies in Shakespeare, Milton, and Donne*, p. 139.

the saintly Lady a second Diotima versed in the deep mysteries of Love? Surely no more than Comus with his bestiality resembles the Aristophanes created by Plato. The theories of the Mask, like its men and women, are such as the Platonic Spenser loved to present, but not Plato. The 'divine Philosophy' had begun to 'charm' Milton long before; it had not yet pervaded his thought.

Doubtless the writer of *Comus* did not set himself to expound the doctrines of Plato, but, like poets from Homer to Yeats, simply used what in doctrine, as in image, legend, and myth, he found to his purpose. A great deal of what he found useful came originally from Plato, some of it directly; but genuine Platonism like the words to Diodati we can scarcely call it. The Platonism of *Comus* is still largely conventional because the author, though familiar with the Dialogues, and even partly under their sway, was not immediately concerned with them. What the letter to Diodati reveals was, then, not a new acquaintance with the Dialogues, but a new grasp of their bearing on Milton's own life.

Look again at the passage from the *Apology for Smectymnuus* quoted a few pages back. If Milton wrote thus, many years after *Comus* had been performed, clearly he did not feel that his Mask told what he had learned about chastity and love from the Dialogues. Far from it. Those 'divine volumes' have supplied him with matter for work yet unborn. And now, be it noted, the epithet 'divine' is no longer merely conventional, but granted by a disciple to the 'abstracted sublimities' into which he has himself been initiated. This is the language of an initiate, of one for whom the heart of an ethical doctrine has come alive. Knowing that Milton since his student days had been acquainted with Platonism, we recognize this experience of his 'riper years' as the winning of a new insight. The letter to Diodati, the postscript to the Elegies, the words in the *Apology,* all bear the mark of emotion, the two passages in prose, of strong emotion as well as clear understanding; they suggest, as it were, a philosophical conversion.

But we need not dwell on the emotional phase of Milton's Platonism. The bare references of his middle years alone warrant our finding in the Dialogues a major source of his theories on all the many problems of human life with which he then was dealing.

Thenceforth, at any rate, the authority of Plato assumed an ever-increasing importance. In the letter to Diodati, Milton had quoted from *Phaedrus* without giving his source; a year later he was more explicit. He wrote to Buommattei:

> It is Plato's opinion that an alteration in the style and fashion of dress portends grave disorders and changes in the State. (Tillyard, p. 16.)

That is Plato's opinion in the *Laws* (7. 797-8); the illustration of clothes is given only once, but in connection with a doctrine basic to the *Laws* as a whole, that unnecessary and careless change, like all instability, is at once a cause and sign of decay. Though it may seem strange for an advocate of divorce and regicide, Milton accepted the principle, applying it here to language as earnestly as Plato had applied it to dress. Indeed it became for Milton a constant guide, too little observed by readers of his prose, who naturally are more struck by its more striking corollary, that needed and deliberate corrections of evil signify and produce vitality.

And now, with Milton's entrance into the struggles of politics, his citations from Plato become more frequent. Their manner, too, changes; for controversial writing is of another sort than academic orations and verses, or even friendly letters, and demands from a writer a much clearer statement of the ground of his assertions. Schoolmasters and friends presumably know what we have read, and will accept allusive references; but opponents need to be convinced. The reader of poetry does not wish to have footnotes thrust into the text; the reader of polemic writing insists upon them. Whether or not this difference in the type of Milton's writing was responsible, he seemingly became a careful student of the Dialogues during the years of England's civil war. In his various treatises, the allusions and citations are specific and detailed, so much so that a scholar must still read the words of Plato as carefully as Milton did in order to find the exact source. But even more striking than this exactness is the manifest wish to grasp Plato's thought and hold it steadily in view. The reference, while imbedded in argument, often has a bit of commentary attached; that is, Milton comments not merely on its relevance to the argument, but on the reasonableness of the position taken by Plato. Most important of all, these citations of Plato as an authority show not understanding alone, but an incorporation of the thought into Milton's own doctrine; they do not simply add the prop of a great name to the argument, they guide it.

In his first political writing, *Of Reformation* (3.39), Milton cites for the organic conception of the State the authority of Plato, Aristotle, and the Bible. The following year, in the *Reason of Church-Government,* he gives Plato more prominence, opening his treatise with these words:

> In the publishing of human laws, which for the most part aim not beyond the good of civil society, to set them barely forth to the people without reason or preface like a physical prescript, or only with threatenings as it were a lordly command, in the judgment of Plato was thought to be done neither generously nor wisely. (3.181.)[9]

The advice of Plato is then given in detail, and confirmed by the example of Moses. A little further in the Preface (3.182), Plato is called 'the wisest of the heathen.' Naturally Milton's interest in political theory led him to a care-

---

[9] Cf. Plato, *Laws* 4.718 and elsewhere, and the Third *Epistle.*

ful study of the two great political theorists of antiquity; but since Plato, unlike Aristotle, presented his politics as an integrated part of his ethics, and indeed of his entire body of thought, Milton would consider works other than the *Republic* and *Laws* in order to grasp the meaning of Plato's doctrines on the State. It is, therefore, not strange to find in the *Reason of Church-Government* allusions to *Protagoras* and the *Sophist*. 'I read,' says Milton,

of no Sophister among the Greeks that was so dear, neither Hippias nor Protagoras, nor any whom the Socratic school famously refuted without hire. (3. 202.)

And later:

And he that will not let these [admonition and reproof] pass into him, though he be the greatest king, as Plato affirms, must be thought to remain impure within, and unknowing of those things wherein his pureness and his knowledge should most appear. (3. 264.)

Milton's very use of the term 'Sophist'—and he uses it with growing frequency and scorn in his controversial writings—apparently comes from his reading in the Dialogues, though the word was common in his time as now. At any rate, in his *Apology for Smectymnuus,* he again associates refutation of sophistry with the Socratic method, and elsewhere repeats the argument of Plato that those who deal in truth for hire cannot be true teachers.[10]

From the *Apology* we may cull further passages bearing on his Platonic studies:

This we know in Laertius, that the mimes of Sophron were of such reckoning with Plato as to take them nightly to read on and after make them his pillow. (3. 293.)[11]

---

[10] See *Apology for Smectymnuus* (3. 293-4), and cf. *Pro Se Defensio* (9. 284) and *The Means to Remove Hirelings* (6. 46).

[11] See Diogenes Laertius, *Life of Plato* 18; and cf. Olympiodorus, *Life of Plato,* and Athenaeus, *Deipnosophists* 11. 504 b.

If every book which may by chance excite to laugh here and there must be termed thus, then may the Dialogues of Plato, who for those his writings hath obtained the surname of Divine, be esteemed, as they are by that detractor in Athenaeus, no better than mimes. Because there is scarce one of them, especially wherein some notable Sophister lies sweating and turmoiling under the inevitable and merciless dilemmas of Socrates, but that he who reads, were it Saturn himself, would be often robbed of more than a smile. (3. 293-4.)[12]

That grave and noble invention which the greatest and sublimest wits in sundry ages, Plato in *Critias,* and our own two famous countrymen, the one in his *Utopia,* the other in his *New Atlantis,* chose, I may not say as a field, but as a mighty continent wherein to display the largeness of their spirits by teaching this our world better and exacter things than were yet known or used. (3. 294.)

[I have] read of heathen philosophers some to have taught that whosoever would but use his ear to listen might hear the voice of his guiding Genius ever before him, calling and as it were pointing to that way which is his part to follow. (3. 318.)[13]

Milton has read Diogenes Laertius' *Life of Plato* and the discussions of Plato in Athenaeus' *Deipnosophists.* He is, then, familiar not only with the works of Plato, but with some writings about them. He has analyzed the method of Socratic refutation. He recognizes in *Critias* the pattern of More's *Utopia* and Bacon's *New Atlantis,* and here praises the Utopian fiction as a means of teaching—a point to remember when we come upon his criticism in *Areopagitica* of 'Atlantic and Utopian polities.'

Thus from the year 1637, at latest, until 1642, the Socratic doctrine given in 'the divine volumes of Plato,' and

[12] See Athenaeus, *Deipnosophists* 11. 504 b-509 e, where Pontianus speaks scornfully of Plato's Dialogues, and 10. 440 b, where Plato is called ὁ Θειότατος.

[13] See Plato's *Apology* 27 and 31, *Symposium* 175 and 220, and especially *Phaedo* 107-8, 113. And cf. Xenophon, *Apology* 3-9, and *Memorabilia* 1.4.15-16; 4.3.12; and 4.8.1.

reinforced by the writings of Xenophon, represents an important element in Milton's thought; and not only the Socratic doctrine of love, though that itself is the whole ethical doctrine, as Milton explains:

> The first and chiefest office of love begins and ends in the soul, producing those happy twins of her divine generation, knowledge and virtue.

Moreover, he not only recognizes, but insists upon, the Platonic view that ethics is the inclusive study of moral theory for the individual, and political theory for the State. It is, indeed, because this is his own belief that Milton as poet and Milton as political writer are one, with the one consistent purpose of leading men through knowledge and virtue to happiness individual and communal.

Accordingly, if we ask to which realm of Milton's thought Platonic doctrine is the key, the answer must be to all of it, since for Milton as for Plato, the parts of life are not separate, but in organic unity; and what is now treated as the law of ecclesiastical organization is again the principle of writing poetry. We can distinguish only phases, not disjunct components, of his philosophy. But if Platonism helps to explain the entire range of Milton's views, it explains them only in part, or only as fused with other doctrines and modified by them. Of these, the most important is, of course, Christianity; the rest, with a man of such varied reading and high power of assimilation as Milton, can scarcely be analyzed here. Perhaps we must even hesitate to assign to Platonism the second highest power in forming Milton's mature thought. But the emphasis on Plato in the *Apology for Smectymnuus* confirms our view: Milton himself did not hesitate to assert a momentous debt to Plato, and besides the Bible, he pays to no other writings an equally high compliment.

The question to which part of Plato's writing he gave this praise must be answered as generally. In the Tractate

Of Education, he prescribes the 'moral works of Plato,' perhaps meaning the dialogues which Diogenes Laertius classified as 'ethical': the *Apology, Crito, Phaedo, Phaedrus,* the *Symposium, Menexenus, Clitophon,* the Epistles, *Philebus, Hipparchus,* and the *Rivals.* Perhaps he knew some of these to be spurious. But since he also wished to have the principles of rhetoric 'taught out of the rule of Plato,' he would add at least *Gorgias* to the list. His own references to Plato up through the publication of the *Apology for Smectymnuus* include specific citations of *Phaedrus,* the *Laws,* the *Sophist,* and *Critias,* with probable allusions to *Protagoras* and the *Symposium,* and general remarks on Plato that suggest a familiarity with all his writings. In later works,[14] he specifically mentions the *Symposium, Protagoras, Gorgias,* the *Republic,* and the Eighth *Epistle;* and he often alludes to the dialogues listed above. If we are to include the examples in his *Logic* among his own citations of Plato, other dialogues must be added: *Cratylus* and the *First Alcibiades, Philebus, Crito, Phaedo, Meno,* and the *Statesman.* There are, in addition, numerous places where he cites an opinion of Plato's without naming the dialogue or epistle in which it appears. We have every reason to think him familiar with all the writings commonly ascribed to Plato.

One further question remains: granted that Milton was deeply impressed by Platonic doctrine some time before 1642, how permanent was the impression? We may continue through his writings, no longer quoting every reference, but only those which suggest either continuity or a break in the Platonic influence. In the *Doctrine and Discipline of Divorce,* Diotima's myth of the birth of love is compared with the Mosaic account of the Garden of Eden (3. 398). Later in that treatise, Milton asks 'what would Plato have deemed' of England's inconsistent laws on marriage (3. 458-9), and associates with his own belief

---

[14] See the appended table, p. 22.

in the identity of good laws and the law of nature the 'high principles' of Socrates in *Gorgias* (3. 500-1).

Areopagitica is the one work in which Milton ever disparaged any writing of Plato; and even there Plato remains 'a man of high authority indeed,' though 'least of all for his Commonwealth, in the book of his *Laws*' (4. 316). Since Milton elsewhere often uses the authority of that very work to support his own arguments, we may suppose that not the *Laws* in its entirety, but only its advocacy of censorship roused his dissent; and many another Platonist has found it as hard to reconcile himself to some of the legal constraints Plato seemingly urged. But Milton, be it noted, ends his discussion of the censorship in the *Laws* by commending in its place another principle from the same work:

> Nor is it Plato's licensing of books will do this [that is, mend our condition], which necessarily pulls along with it so many other kinds of licensing; . . . but those unwritten or at least unconstraining laws of virtuous education, religious and civil nurture, which Plato there mentions as the bonds and ligaments of the Commonwealth, the pillars and the sustainers of every written statute, these they be which will bear chief sway in such matters as these. (4. 318.)

Plato naturally has a large part in the Tractate *Of Education*, not only among the books to be given to students, but in the theory and plan of instruction there set forth. And later works show how large a part the Dialogues had in Milton's self-education. In *Tetrachordon* he cites Plato three times; in the first *Defensio*, repeatedly turns to the *Laws* and Eighth *Epistle* to confirm his political theory; and in the *Defensio*, nine years after the *Apology for Smectymnuus*, reasserts his old judgment by naming Plato among the 'best and wisest men of old,' and once more calling him 'divine' (7. 349-51).

The Dialogues kept their hold upon Milton. Although the *Defensio Secunda, Pro Se Defensio,* and *Accidence*

Commenced Grammar have fewer references, the choice of Ramus' *Dialectica* as the basis for his *Logic* still shows a decided Platonic bent.[15] And finally the controversy between Satan and Jesus in *Paradise Regained* illuminates Milton's latest views on Plato. The first part of Athens to which Satan points in his last desperate attempt to win Jesus is

> the Olive Grove of Academe,
> Plato's retirement, where the Attic Bird
> Trills her thick-warbl'd notes the summer long. (4. 244-6.)

The first of the philosophers whose knowledge is offered are Socrates and his most illustrious pupil:

> To sage Philosophy next lend thine ear,
> From Heaven descended to the low-rooft house
> Of Socrates, see there his Tenement,
> Whom well inspir'd the Oracle pronounc'd
> Wisest of men; from whose mouth issu'd forth
> Mellifluous streams that water'd all the schools
> Of Academics old and new. (4. 272-8.)

Jesus had previously said:

> Poor Socrates (who next more memorable?)
> By what he taught and suffer'd for so doing,
> For truth's sake suffering death unjust, lives now
> Equal in fame to proudest Conquerours. (3. 96-9.)

But now he modifies Satan's compliment to Socrates:

> The first and wisest of them all profess'd
> To know this only, that he nothing knew. (4. 293-4.)[16]

Of Plato, all that Jesus says is

> The next to fabling fell and smooth conceits. (4. 295.)

---

[15] See Frank Pierrepont Graves, *Peter Ramus and the Educational Reformation of the Sixteenth Century*.

[16] Note that while Satan calls Socrates 'wisest of men,' Jesus calls him wisest only of the pagan philosophers.

Now since the other pagan philosophers are criticized in terms of their doctrine, Plato appears to come off easily in this stern rejection of all pagan learning. At any rate, next to Socrates, he is the Greek thinker least denounced. And Milton's words are not a very serious charge for a poet to bring against a philosopher; for if Plato 'fell' to 'fabling and smooth conceits,' his fall was from philosophy to poetry.

Milton did indeed think Plato poetical, recognizing in him the 'grave and noble' faculty of invention. He thought Plato a master of comic invention too (*Ap. Smect.* 3. 293-4; *Tetrach.* 4. 76), an authority on educational theory (*Of Ed.* 4. 287), a model of literary decorum (*Pro Se Def.* 9. 176), and an expert in law (*D.D.D.* 3. 458-9). In short he gave to Plato a position far above any other author, pagan or Christian, save the authors of the Bible. Never to Augustine, his favorite among Church-Fathers, to Spenser, his favorite among English poets, to Cicero, Erasmus, or Bacon, did he apply the epithet he granted to Plato. And far from merely adopting a conventional term of praise, he showed that he independently approved the common judgment, explaining that Plato 'for those his writings hath obtained the surname of Divine' (3. 293).

We can see that Milton was well-equipped by study to confirm and explain the ancient judgment. Note in the table of references how often he alludes to a specific passage in Plato, from how wide a range in the Dialogues and Epistles his allusions are drawn, and with what precision he refers to the *Laws* and Epistles, which are among the least generally read of Plato's works. If the references he took from Downham's commentary on Ramus should not be counted as his own, the choice at least is his, since he omitted innumerable others in condensing the commentary. And two changes he made suggest that what he took unchanged, he took with full knowledge of the works alluded to. Once, where Downham had omitted the specific source, Milton supplied *Phaedrus;*[17] and again, to Downham's illustrative phrase, *'philosophus pro Aristotele,'* Milton significantly added *'aut Platone.'*[18]

The two amendments confirm Milton's thorough knowledge of and enthusiastic admiration for Plato. What that knowledge and enthusiasm meant in his own thought and writing as yet has hardly been probed. For put *Paradise Lost* and *Paradise Regained* to the same test as we earlier put *Comus,* and we get a different result. Suppose Plato were dealing with the loss of human happiness, would he give the same explanation as Milton in the tale of man's fall? On the whole, we may say yes. True, he would conceive of no such perfect Providence watching—and waiting to relieve—mankind's errors. And Plato, to be sure, never plumbed so deep in Hell as Milton. Doubtless the Hebraic view of life brings to its disciples greater struggles as well as greater aspirations than Hellenism at its best. But if we look aside from Hell and Heaven to Earth, where Milton after all wished us most steadily to fix our gaze, and discern in the struggle there the meaning it had for Milton, we see that, however little the words and acts resemble those of a Platonic dialogue, the underlying argument is largely that of Plato. And when we turn to *Paradise Regained,* where a bolder Sophist than any opponent of Socrates defies a more glorious seeker after truth, even if the very dialectical method by which Jesus wins his victory did not point to the Dialogues as a model, the themes and arguments show how much Milton had assimilated from Plato.

---

[17] See in the appended table the note to the reference *Logic,* C. E. II. * 22.

[18] See the note to *Logic,* C. E. II. ** 334.

A TABLE OF MILTON'S REFERENCES TO SOCRATES AND PLATO[1]

	Passage	Date	Source	Quoted
S	*Eleg.* 4. 23-4	1627	? I *Alcib.*, 103 ff., 135	Agar 15
P	*Idea Plat.*	1628 or later	*passim;* esp. ?*Phaedo*, ?*Phaedr.*, ?*Sym.*, ?*Rep.*	Agar 16
P	*Prolus.* 2, C. E. 12. 150	1625-9	?*Rep.* 10. 616-7	Agar 76
	Prolus. 6, C. E. 12	1625-9		
S	*218		?*Apol.* 20-3[2]	
S	*238		*passim*	
	Prolus. 7, C. E. 12	1625-9		
P	262-4			Agar 77
S	*280		*passim*	
P	*Il Pen.* 87-96	1631-4	?*Tim.* 41-2	Agar 5
[P]	To Dio., C. E. 12. 26	1637	*Phaedr.*	Agar 72
P	To Buom., C. E. 12. 32	1638	*Laws* 7. 797-8	Agar 73
P	*Of Ref.*, C. E. 3. 39	1641	?*Rep.*, esp. 4. 420; ?*Laws*, esp. 5. 739	Agar 53
S	*Animad.*, C. E. 3. 161	1641	(Xenophon)[3]	

[1] The symbols used in the table are as follows:

S and *P* indicate references to Socrates and Plato. Parentheses are used to distinguish implicit references, as in the letter to Diodati, where Milton quotes *Phaedrus*, but does not name his source.

The single asterisk marks a reference not given in Agar's *Milton and Plato*. The double asterisk marks a reference given neither in the Columbia Index nor by Agar.

C.E. with Arabic numbers following refers to the Columbia edition of *The Works of John Milton*, volume and page. The numbers in parentheses correspond to Milton's own divisions.

A question mark before a title indicates uncertainty in assigning the allusion to any specific work of Plato.

The number after *Agar* refers to the passage in the Appendix of Agar's volume where the selection is quoted.

The page-number under *Downham* marks the place in the work of George Downham, *Rami Dialecticae Libri Duo cum Commentariis* (London, 1669), which is the source of Milton's reference. Milton, of course, used an earlier edition of Downham's commentary.

The list does not include those passages in the *Logic* where Socrates is named merely as a convenient Everyman of argument.

[2] The most likely source is Diogenes Laertius, *Life of Socrates*, 36-8. See also Xenophon's *Banquet* 2. 10. Diogenes Laertius seems to take the statement of the oracle from Plato's *Apology* and the character of Xanthippe from Xenophon.

[3] This is the sole reference to Socrates in which Milton uses Xenophon alone as the authority. See Xenophon, *Apology* 26; *Memorabilia* 1. 2. 1-8; 1. 6. 11-3.

	Passage	Date	Source	Quoted
	Church-Gov., C. E. 3	1642		
P	*181-2 (Preface)		*Laws* 4. 718 ff.	
S	*202 (1. 5)		*passim;* esp. *Protag.,* ?*Hipp. Min.*	
P	264 (2. 3)		*Soph.* 230; ?*Gorg.* 476 ff.	Agar 54
	Ap. Smect., C. E. 3	1642		
PS	293-4		*passim*[4]	Agar 55
P	*294		*Critias*	
P	305		*passim;* esp. *Phaedr., Sym.*	Agar 57
	D.D.D., C. E. 3	1643		
PS	398 (1. 4)		*Sym.* 203	Agar 58
P	441 (2. 3)		*passim;* esp. ?*Laws* 1. 644-5; ?*Meno 99-100*	Agar 60
P	*458-9 (2. 9)		*Laws* 4. 719	
P	464 (2. 11)		*Protag.* 354 e, 355-8; *et al.* Cf. *Meno* 77-8, *Tim.* 86	Agar 61
SP	500-1 (2. 21)		*Gorg.* 482-4, 488-510	Agar 62
	Judg. Bucer, C. E. 4	1644		
P	*24 (17 on Matth. v. 19)		(Bucer)[5] ?*Rep.,* ?*Laws*	
	Areop., C. E. 4	1644		
P	299			Agar 44
P	316		*Rep., Laws*	Agar 46
P	317		*Rep.* 3; *Laws* 2, 7	Agar 47
P	318		*Rep.* 4; *Laws* 1, 7	Agar 48
	Of Ed., C. E. 4	1644		
S	281			Agar 66
P	284		*passim*	Agar 67
P	286		*passim;* esp. *Phaedr., Gorg.*	Agar 68
P	287		*passim* and *Laws* 1. 634-5	Agar 69
[P]S	*Eleg.* 7, Postscript	before 1645	*passim;* esp. *Phaedr., Sym.*	Agar 14
	Tetrach., C. E. 4	1645		
S	*70 (To Parl.)		?*Apol.* 19	
P	*76 (on Gen. i. 27)		*Sym.* 189-93	
P	81 (on Gen. i. 28)		*Laws* 6. 773-6, 783-5	Agar 63

[4] The first part of the reference comes from Diogenes Laertius, *Life of Plato* 18; the second from Milton's own reading of the Dialogues. 'That detractor in Athenaeus' is probably Pontianus in *Deipnosophists* 2. 504 b-509 e.

[5] Apparently taken from Martin Bucer, *Of the Kingdom of Christ*, Chap. 17.

Passage	Date	Source	Quoted
P *157-8 (on Matth. xix. 7-8)		*Rep.*	
Def., C. E. 7	1651		
P *158 (3)		*Rep.* 5. 463. Cf. *Laws* 4. 715	
P 166-8 (3)		*Laws* 4. 715; VIII *Epist.* 354	Agar 40
P 304 (5)		VIII *Epist.* 355	Agar 41
P *348-50 (6)		VIII *Epist.* 354-5	
S *Def. Sec.*, C. E. 8 192	1654	?*Apol.* 20-3	
Pro Se Def., C. E. 9	1655		
S *52		?*Apol.*	
S[P] *112		*passim*	
PS *176		*passim*	
P *180-2			
P *P. L.* 3. 471-3	before 1667		Agar 18
Grammar, C. E. 6	1669		
P **329 (2. Of the Concords)			
SP **349 (2. Of the Conjunctions)			
Logic, C. E. 11	1670		Downham
P *10 (Preface)		*Theaet.* 202 e	Proleg., p. 19
P **12 (Preface)		*Gorg.* 448	Proleg., p. 22
P *18-20 (1.1)		*Crat.*, I *Alcib.* 129 c	pp. 3-4
P *22 (1.2)		*Phaedr.* 235-6, 264	p. 15[6]
PS *58 (1.7)		*passim* (and Diogenes Laertius)	p. 79
P *66 (1.8)		*Phil.* 54	p. 88
P *96 (1.11)		*Rep.* 3. 405[7]	p. 122

[6] Milton gives the source as *Phaedrus* where Downham had simply said, '*Atque hanc distributionem Plato videtur primus attigisse.*'

[7] Milton's translator in the Columbia edition, Allan H. Gilbert, here makes a serious mistake. Quoting Downham, Milton writes: '*Hoc argumento Plato miseras civitates auguratur, quae medicorum et judicum multitudine indigeant, quia multum quoque et intemperantiam et injustitiam in ea civitate versari necesse est.*' The translation given is: 'By means of this argument Plato conjectures that "those states are wretched which lack a multitude of physicians and judges, since necessarily much intemperance and injustice will be practised in such a state." ' Clearly Plato says the very opposite in the *Republic* 3. 405, and Milton's '*multitudine indigeant*' must mean 'need a multitude.'

Passage	Date	Source	Quoted
S [P]*140-2 (1.16)		*Crito* 44	p. 164
P *150 (1.18)			p. 177
S *166 (1.18)			
P *200 (1.21)		*Laws* 3, *Phaedo* 92	p. 209
S *204 (1.21)			p. 212
S *228 (1.25)		(Aristotle)	p. 242
P *228-30 (1.25)		?*Phil.* 16-8, ?*Statesm.* 287	pp. 243-4
P *238 (1.27)		*passim* and *Meno* 72-7	pp. 249-50
P *240 (1.27)		*Statesm.*	p. 251
P *286 (1.33)		*Rep.* 5. 473	p. 290
P *308 (2.3)		*Crat.* ?431	p. 324
P **334 (2.4)			p. 365[8]
P *470 (2.17)		*Phil.* 16	p. 472
P *474 (2.17)		?*Phaedr.*, ?*Statesm.*	p. 428
P **494 (Praxis)		?*Tim.*	p. 47
P.R.	1671		
S 3.96-9		*passim*; esp. ?*Apol.* 29-31, 36-42; ?*Crito*, ?*Phaedo*	Agar 35
P 4.244-7			Agar 37
S[P] *4.272-8		?*Apol.* 20-3	
SP 4.293-5		*passim*	Agar 38
?*On Worthy Master Shakespeare*, C. E. 18. 361	?		
P **15-8		*Tim.* 39	

---

[8] Downham had written, *'ut Poeta pro Homero aut Virgilio: philosophus pro Aristotele: orator pro Demosthene aut Cicerone.'* Milton inserts Plato as one for whom *philosophus* may stand: *'ut poeta pro Homero aut Virgilio, Philosophus pro Aristotele aut Platone et similia.'*

CHAPTER II

'Academics Old and New'

B Y THE SEVENTEENTH CENTURY the influence of Plato had so permeated European thought that few books Milton knew or might have known were untouched by it. The Bible itself, that rock on which he built his life, owes something to the Academy, if, as scholars tell us, the 'Logos' of St. John and St. Paul's doctrine of love have Platonic origins. At any rate, apart from the Bible, European literature can show little that owes no debt to Plato. Without writing the history of Platonism or noting every author in whose work Milton was likely to meet it, we may try to place him in the Platonic tradition. The seventeenth century continued the interest in Plato that the Florentine Academy had revived. Milton, abreast of his time, shared its best enthusiasms; and the zealous study of Plato that marked his age, his country, and his university, provided at least one channel through which the ancient philosophy reached him.

But Milton knew the tradition independently. He evidently studied ancient writers who throw light on the origins and development of Plato's doctrines, and he shows a marked preference for those who were closest to Platonic thought. For example, take the lists of reading commended in his Tractate *Of Education*. The most important of these is for the course in ethics, since the aim of the whole program is ethical and religious:

The end, then, of learning is to repair the ruins of our first parents by regaining to know God aright, and out of that knowledge to love Him, to imitate Him, to be like Him, as we may the nearest by possessing our souls of true virtue, which, being united to the heavenly grace of faith, makes up the highest perfection. (Ainsworth, p. 52.)

And again:

I call therefore a complete and generous education that which fits a man to perform justly, skilfully, and magnanimously all the offices, both private and public, of peace and war. (*Ibid.*, p. 55.)

Now the course in ethics is to be divided into two parts; first:

To season them and win them early to the love of virtue and true labor . . . some easy and delightful book of education would be read to them; whereof the Greeks have store, as Cebes, Plutarch, and other Socratic discourses. (*Ibid.*, p. 56.)

And later:

By this time, years and good general precepts will have furnished them more distinctly with that act of reason which in ethics is called *proairesis;* that they may with some judgment contemplate upon moral good and evil. Then will be required a special reinforcement of constant and sound indoctrinating to set them right and firm, instructing them more amply in the knowledge of virtue and the hatred of vice; while their young and pliant affections are led through all the moral works of Plato, Xenophon, Cicero, Plutarch, Laertius, and those Locrian remnants; but still to be reduced in their nightward studies wherewith they close the day's work, under the determinate sentence of David or Solomon, or the Evangels and Apostolic Scriptures. (*Ibid.*, p. 58.)

This avowed preference for 'Socratic discourses' on education together with the almost exclusively Platonic list of 'moral works' is highly significant in a writer of Milton's studied effects. And apparently he prescribes what was, at least in part, his own teaching practice; for according to Edward Phillips, his pupils read 'Plutarch's *Placita Philosophorum* and Περι Παιδων Ἀγογιας [*sic*].' (See Helen Darbishire's edition of the *Early Lives of Milton*, p. 60.) What light does all this throw on his Platonism?

First, Socrates was for Milton, even more than for many readers of Plato, a figure of unusual interest. From the early Fourth *Elegy* he remains a model of excellence even till *Paradise Regained*, where Jesus praises him as 'next memorable' to Job. All the extant writings of the Socratics won Milton's interest, the fragment of Aeschines (referred to in C.E. 11. 166) as well as Cebes' *Pinax* and the works of Xenophon and Plato. But it is to Xenophon next after Plato that a student of Socrates must turn.

According to Professor Saurat (*La Pensée de Milton,* p. 274), Milton was as much interested in the Socrates of Xenophon as in the Socrates of Plato. Professor Saurat refers us to the *Commonplace Book* for proof; but since neither Socrates nor Plato nor Xenophon appears in the *Commonplace Book,* we must suppose him to mean the *Accidence Commenced Grammar,* where Plato and Xenophon are linked as contemporaries (6. 329), and again as disciples of Socrates (6. 349). Actually there is only one point on which Milton uses Xenophon as a separate authority on Socrates. We are told in *Animadversions* (3. 161):

The heathen Philosophers thought that virtue was for its own sake inestimable, and the greatest gain of a teacher to make a soul virtuous; so Xenophon writes of Socrates, who never bargained with any for teaching him.[1]

The opinion Milton held on the relation of the three is best shown in a passage in his *Logic,* where he condenses

---

[1] See Xenophon's *Apology* 26 and *Memorabilia* 1. 2. 1-8; 1. 6. 11-13.

George Downham's commentary on the logical works of Peter Ramus. Now usually he kept very close to his original; but here Downham had written:

Doctrina Platonis et doctrina Socratis non possunt in quantitate comparari, nisi prius constet doctrinam utrique adjungi. (P. 289.)

Milton makes one change in the illustration: for Socrates he substitutes Xenophon:

Platonis doctrina et Xenophantis ante adjuncta utrique erat, quam comparata. (11. 150.)

It is a proper change. We have little certain knowledge of the doctrine of Socrates himself; what we know is the writings of two of his pupils. To what conclusions the comparison of Plato and Xenophon led Milton, his references show: Socrates appears in his pages as the figure Plato made the most interesting in the Dialogues.[2] And Xenophon is often merely an emphatic line drawn under Plato.

But Milton often associates Plato with others besides Socrates; with Pythagoras for example. Thus in the Tractate:

The course of study hitherto briefly described is, what I can guess by reading, likest to those ancient and famous schools of

---

[2] Thus the testimony of the oracle as Milton gives it in the Sixth *Prolusion* and *Paradise Regained* corresponds with Plato's *Apology* 21 rather than Xenophon's *Apology* 14. See also Milton's *Def. Sec.* (8. 192). With the reference to Socrates' profession of ignorance in the Seventh *Prolusion* (12. 280) compare especially Plato's *Apology* 21-3. The accusation of Socrates as given in *Tetrachordon* (4. 70) agrees with Plato's *Apology* 18. The refutation of sophists mentioned in the *Reason of Church-Government* (3. 202) as an activity of the 'Socratic school' suggests Plato rather than Xenophon. Similarly Milton's other allusions to Socrates, in *Pro Se Def.* (9. 176), *Ap. Smect.* (3.293, 318), and *Def. Sec.* (8. 74), all suggest the account of Plato rather than that of Xenophon.

Only one reference (in the Sixth *Prolusion* 12. 218) suggests a source in Xenophon (*Banquet* 2. 10) or Diogenes Laertius (2. 36-8).

Pythagoras, Plato, Isocrates, Aristotle, and such others. (Ainsworth, p. 61.)

The 'school of Pythagoras' is mentioned again in *Areopagitica* (4. 393), and with like respect. In the early Prolusion *De Sphaerarum Concentu* (12. 150) Aristotle is *'Pythagorae et Platonis aemulus et perpetuus Calumniator,'* while Plato wisely followed Pythagoras, *'Deum illum Philosophorum,'* in affirming the harmony of the spheres. May we not explain this enthusiasm for Pythagoras less by the fragmentary remains of Pythagorean writings than by Plato's debt to the school? Diogenes Laertius and Cicero had stressed the Pythagorean cast of Plato's thought.[3] Milton would be aware of it, and the respect he invariably pays to the 'Samian master' shows one basis for his sympathy with Platonism.

Most pre-Socratic thought apparently seemed to him, as to Plato, insignificant until joined with Pythagorean and Socratic teachings, for he shows no interest in it.[4] He does esteem the early Greek law-givers to the point of including them in his program of education,[5] and thus indicates sympathy with still another formative element in the thought of Plato.

The importance and respect accorded to Plato's various teachers reappears in the treatment Milton accords those who drew from Plato. He puts the 'Locrian remnants,' that is, the treatise *On the Soul of the World,* on the reading

---

[3] See Diogenes, *Life of Plato* 8; and Cicero, De Finibus 5. 87; *Tusculan Disputations* 1. 32; and *De Republica* 1. 10.

[4] Thus Milton's Jesus agrees with Satan that Socrates was the first pagan philosopher. See *P.R.* 4. 272-7, 293-4. A single reference to Protagoras occurs in *Areopagitica* (4. 299); otherwise Milton does not mention the pre-Socratic philosophers.

[5] *Of Ed.* (4. 285). Cf. *Republic* 10. 599 and *Timaeus* 20. For other references to Lycurgus and Solon in Plato, see *Phaedrus* 258, 278, and *Symposium* 209.

list of his academy and similarly commends Plutarch, Cicero, and 'Longinus.' Cicero especially was a favorite. From the early letters and *Prolusions* through the *Logic,* he is a constant authority, familiarly alluded to and quoted. And while his importance in the schools may in part account for the familiarity, the tone of these citations can be explained only by basic agreement. Milton explicitly calls him 'Academic' (11.138), cites a quotation of his from Plato (11.286), and frequently adds his words to support Platonic theory.[6] He appears with Plato again in the Tractate among authorities on rhetoric. Indeed it is a highly Platonic rhetoric that Milton wished to have taught 'out of the rule of Plato, Aristotle, Phalereus, Cicero, Hermogenes, Longinus' (Ainsworth, pp. 59-60). The list begins with Plato, whose treatment of the art is singularly unlike that of the usual rhetorician; it includes, besides Cicero, who tried to reconcile rhetoric with the doctrines of the Academy, the essay of Demetrius of Phalerum with its many quotations from Plato and frequent praise of his style; and it ends with the treatise that, more than any other work on the subject, applies to the art of persuasion the spirit and canons of Plato's teaching. The epistle of 'Longinus' *On the Sublime* might stand as a Platonic discourse on rhetoric. Cicero, we may think, lent Milton support for the view that rhetoric may be taught out of 'the rule of Plato,' and 'Longinus' confirmed him in it.

Taken as a whole, the lists in the Tractate suggest that Milton's view of education was 'Socratic,' his concept of rhetoric largely 'Academic,' and his ethical theory almost entirely Platonic. He evidently was aware of what he omitted from the course in ethics, for having named only Socratic and Platonic authors, he concludes with the reminder that these are still to be supplemented with the 'de-

---

[6] See, for example, *Logic* (11.22); *D.D.D.* (3.441); *Tetrach.* (4.157-8); *Def.* (7.166-8, 304-6).

terminate sentence' of Holy Scripture. Diogenes Laertius, to be sure, would present varieties of ethical opinion; yet even he emphasizes rather than moderates the Academic bias of the 'moral works' to be taught; for Diogenes gave Platonism preferential treatment. (See especially the *Lives* 3. 47.) Despite the inclusion, then, of the *Lives and Opinions of Eminent Philosophers,* the question remains: Why did Milton not allow Epicurean, Stoic, and, most important, Peripatetic, to speak for themselves? With Stoic and Epicurean, the answer is surely that Milton cared little for what they might say. He invariably refers to Epicureanism and Stoicism with contempt; and though he respects Lucretius, Seneca, and Chrysippus, it is not for the distinctly Epicurean or Stoic parts of their moral teaching. But the same explanation will not hold for the silence imposed on Aristotle. Clearly, in order to place Milton in the Platonic tradition we must understand his opinion of Plato's first great pupil.

On the whole, he thought decidedly well of 'Aristotle, our chief instructor in the universities' (6. 136), and turned to his authority early and late. Once while still at Cambridge, he took issue with his 'chief instructor' for disagreeing with Pythagoras and Plato on the music of the spheres, and called him their *'aemulus et perpetuus Calumniator'* (12. 150), just as later he made sport of the Aristotelian misreading of the Platonic Idea. These disparaging remarks both involve a comparison favoring Plato. Otherwise Aristotle is usually treated with respect, even in *De Doctrina Christiana* where Milton makes some effort to disentangle the interwoven threads of Aristotelian and scholastic theology. (See especially 14. 48; 15. 8.) Again in his *Logic,* following Downham and Ramus, Milton often cites Aristotle as evidence and authority. More important, the Aristotelian *Poetics,* which in the Tractate *Of Education* Milton placed first among the readings on 'that sublime art,' is a basis for the prefatory note to *Samson Agonistes*.

We may conclude that Milton did not underestimate Aristotle, and recognized him as one of 'the best interpreters of nature and morality,' but none the less rejected the Aristotelian way of thought. Why, we learn from a passage in the *Doctrine and Discipline of Divorce*. Here Milton deals with an apparent disagreement between Plato and Aristotle, not jestingly as in the Second *Prolusion* and the verses *De Idea Platonica,* but seriously. He writes:

> It is the constant opinion of Plato in *Protagoras* and other of his dialogues, agreeing with that proverbial sentence among the Greeks, that 'no man is wicked willingly'—which also the Peripatetics do rather distinguish than deny. (3. 464. Cf. *Nicomachean Ethics* 7. 1-10.)

Milton recognized what many students forget, that Plato taught Aristotle for long years to the apparent satisfaction of both, and that the writings of master and pupil disagree far less than those of the militant Platonists and Aristotelians of later generations. On Milton's page, the two often appear together in support of the same doctrine, and their agreement is not forced. The emphasis is right; in general, Aristotle does 'rather distinguish than deny' Platonic teachings. And where Aristotle 'distinguished,' Milton often accepted the refinement.

But where he denied, Milton was cautious. In ethics Aristotle denied too often, at any rate, denied the most important point; and hence the omission in the Tractate and the contempt shown for his moral system in *Paradise Regained* 4. 297-8:

> Others in virtue plac'd felicity,
> But virtue join'd with riches and long life.

These are, of course, the Peripatetics; and the doctrine condemned is central to their ethical system.

Among the ancients, then, Milton gave special attention

34

to those who present elements of the Platonic philosophy—
Socratics, ancient law-givers, Pythagoreans—and those who
show his pervasive influence—Cicero, Plutarch, 'Longinus.'
How did he regard the Neoplatonists whom his contemporaries revered as true interpreters of the Platonic tradition?
We have seen in Chapter 1 that he associated Hermes
Trismegistus with Plato both in the verses *De Idea Platonica* and in *Il Penseroso*. He may even have accepted the
philosophical genealogy sanctioned by Ficino:

> Eo tempore quo Moyses natus est, floruit Athlas . . . ; cuius
> nepos fuit Mercurius Trismegistus. . . . Primus igitur theologiae
> appellatus est auctor. Eum secutus Orpheus, . . . Aglaophamus,
> . . . Picthagoras, . . . Philolaus . . . Divi Platonis nostri praecep-
> tor. Itaque una priscae theologiae undique sibi consona secta ex
> theologis sex miro quodam ordine conflata est, exordia sumens a
> Mercurio, a Divo Platone peritus absoluta. (See *Hermetica*, ed.
> and trans. by Scott, 1. 31.)

Perhaps, as Agar observes, Milton later came to see how
foreign the *Hermetica* is to the true Platonic spirit, and yet
something of Hermetic mysticism remains even in *Paradise
Lost*. The demonology which *Il Penseroso* associates with
Hermes (rightly) and Plato (wrongly) reappears not only
in the 'attendant Spirit' of *Comus* ('daemon' in the manuscript), the 'Genius of the shore' in *Lycidas* 183, and the
'Angelus unicuique suus' of the first poem *Ad Leonoram*,
but at the end of the sonnet on his blindness and even in
Paradise Lost 4. 677-8:

> Millions of spiritual Creatures walk the Earth
> Unseen, both when we wake, and when we sleep.

These are the Hermetic

> Daemons that are found
> In fire, air, flood, or under ground,
> Whose power hath a true consent
> With Planet, or with Element. (*Il Penseroso* 93-6.)

Probably Milton, like his contemporaries, knew the work of Michael Psellus in Ficino's translation, *De Daemonibus,* and other similar writings. C. S. Lewis has shown in *A Preface to Paradise Lost* (pp. 105-11) how largely the 'Platonic' theories then current explain Milton's angels.

But the age studied more sober Platonists as well, the Neoplatonists, pagan, Jewish, and Christian, who had kept something, if not the whole, of Plato's doctrines alive in Europe during the centuries when little more than *Timaeus* was known. (See A. E. Taylor, *A Commentary on Plato's Timaeus,* pp. 2-3.) To scholars of the Renaissance, newly familiar with Plato but long familiar with the Neoplatonists, they seemed valid interpreters of Plato's thought. Plotinus especially was to influence the general understanding of Plato; for Ficino, who set the style in Platonism, translated and commented on the *Enneads* as a proper sequel to the Dialogues. And hence Coleridge jests that the Cambridge Platonists should rather be called 'Plotinists.' Like Dr. Whichcote, who 'set young students much on reading the ancient philosophers, chiefly Plato, Tully, Plotin,' Henry More, chief of the Cambridge group, studied the 'Platonic writers, Marsilius Ficinus, Plotinus himself, Mercurius Trismegistus, and the mystical divines.' John Tulloch, in *Rational Theology . . . in the Seventeenth Century,* speaks thus of the Cambridge Platonists:

They betray no suspicion of the enormous interval of thought betwixt Plato and Plotinus, still less of any growth or development of thought in Plato himself. . . . Plotinus is the chief favorite. . . . The suspicion that Plotinus and Proclus, while building upon the Platonic basis, may have had little or none of the spirit of the master-builder, never disturbed them. (2.479-81.)

The judgment here expressed is rather harsh. Let us say rather that the age was more concerned with the mystical part of Plato—and surely we must grant that Plato is partly mystic—as developed and magnified by Plotinus and his students, than with the severely rational part which we often consider the whole of Platonism. We need not, however, stay longer with Plotinus and his disciples; for Milton, in a period which thought the *Enneads* the very echo of Plato, pays almost no attention to pagan Neo-platonists. His few references to Porphyry and Proclus indicate little admiration for their views, and Plotinus he does not even mention.

At the same time, however little interest he may have expressed in Plotinus, Milton had much in common with the Cambridge group. In a study of the *Platonic Tradition in Anglo-Saxon Philosophy* (pp. 29-31), Muirhead lists among their major doctrines: (1) the belief that Heaven and Hell are states of soul rather than places; (2) the identification of Reason with God; (3) an insistence that true freedom dwells only in reason and in the control of life by reason; and (4) the conviction that faith and reason, far from being at odds, are fundamentally alike, and lead to the same persuasions. We recognize these as views held by Milton. Parallels between the Cambridge Platonists and Milton have been demonstrated by Elbert N. S. Thompson,[7] Marjorie H. Nicolson,[8] and Ernst Cassirer;[9] and further investigations are sure to reveal other similarities, for there is much in Milton's writing that cannot be called by any name but Neoplatonism.

A closer tie between Milton and contemporary Platonists may be their common interest in the writers who first attempted to reconcile Plato with Holy Writ; Philo Judaeus, for example, who began the system of Biblical exegesis which made of the text a peg from which to suspend Plato's

---

[7] See 'A Forerunner of Milton,' *MLN*. 32 (1917). 479-82.
[8] 'The Spirit World of Milton and More,' *SP*. 22 (1925). 433-52.
[9] *Die Platonische Renaissance in England*, p. 23.

doctrines.[10] Milton took Philo as an authority, or at least recognized his repute with the age, for he justifies an argument in his first *Defensio* thus:

Another solid authority, Josephus' contemporary Philo Judaeus, one very studious in the law of Moses, upon the whole of which he wrote an extensive commentary, when in his book concerning the creation of the king he interprets this chapter of the law, releases the king from the law no otherwise than as an enemy may be said to be so released. (7. 78-9.)

He goes on to quote a few words in Greek, and then continues with a Latin translation of the passage. Evidently he knew Philo well.

Far more important to him was Augustine, in whose work Platonic thought, already adapted to Christianity by Clement and Origen, became its very handmaid. With Protestants Augustine was especially popular; he presented a doctrine convenient to oppose to the Thomism dominant in the Roman Church, just as the Platonic theories upon which he had based his doctrine were a useful answer to the Aristotelian theories on which Thomas had built. With Protestant Milton he was a favorite, the most often quoted and consistently respected of the Churchmen. And Augustine's Christian Platonism is doubtless the chief link between Milton and other Platonists of the time, especially the group at Cambridge. Here is much the same union as they and Milton make between Platonic and Biblical precept, the conversion of Platonic ethics and cosmology to the divine order of the universe, the identification of the radiant Idea of the Good with the unapproachable light of God, the interpretation of every major Christian doctrine—save the most important, that of the Man Divine—in the terms of Platonism and Neoplatonism. Augustine's scale of being, or the successive emanations which descend like a ladder

[10] See, for example, Philo, *Special Laws* I. 327-9.

from God, is Neoplatonic, though it derives from the Dialogues. Similarly the constant figure of God as light, of truth as illumination, comes through Plotinus, and perhaps Manicheism, though ultimately from the Allegory of the Cave in the *Republic*. But the emphasis on these doctrines in Augustine and the later Church is assuredly closer to the spirit of Plotinus than to Plato.

Here, then, in the Christian use of Neoplatonism, rather than in the works of Plotinus, Porphyry, and Proclus themselves, we may find the source of Milton's Neoplatonic-sounding phrases on light (*e.g., P.L.* 3. 1-6) and the scale of being (*P.L.* 5. 469-79).

Augustine and such Augustinian scholastics as Scotus Erigena also help to explain Milton's use of the cosmological and eschatological myths of Plato, although they took the myths from Neoplatonists and he directly from Plato. The ordering of the world out of elementary chaos, the figure of God as father of the created universe, of formless space as the mother, the institution of the dance-like planetary changes to serve man's reckoning of time and draw his mind by contemplation to the worship of their maker; all these cosmological theories from Plato's *Timaeus* constantly recur in Milton's writing, though either barely suggested in the Bible or totally foreign to it. Their use, justified by the precedent of Christian Neoplatonists, serves to expand the poetic brevity of the Bible. Even when Milton speaks of the soul's native star (as in *Damon* 123) Christian tradition gives him warrant. Dante too used this Platonic myth, and long before Dante it had become a part of Christian lore.

So also with the accounts of the after-life in *Phaedo, Gorgias,* and the *Republic*. References to Hell and Heaven are few and brief in the Bible, and no mention at all of Purgatory is to be found there. In Protestant fashion Milton has no Purgatory in the hereafter, but for the rest adopts Plato's myths to supplement Scripture. Again, Christian precedent is behind him, and the habit of Christian Platonists in the age is with him. Even when he slips on a very few occasions into suggesting that the soul enjoyed a previous existence, as in *Ad Patrem* 30-1, the Christian mysticism of the time supports him.

On all these counts it seems reasonable to modify Agar's conclusions about the relation of Milton to traditional Platonism. Milton, says Agar,

the first in Europe so far as I have discovered, read and studied Plato with a mind freed from the influence of the Alexandrians and their Renaissance disciples, and so attained to an understanding of the dialogues. (P. 31.)

We recognize the change that Agar marks from the kind of Platonic material Milton used in his earlier poems to the kind he used in his prose and later poetry. In *Comus* Milton was still dealing chiefly with the supra-terrestrial doctrines of the Neoplatonists. These remain in *Paradise Lost;* but here, and yet more in *Paradise Regained* and *Samson Agonistes,* the more strictly ethical parts of Plato assume a major importance, while demonology and accounts of the creation are subordinated to the primary questions of human happiness. Yet this change in Platonic materials does not distinguish Milton's from all other Platonism of the age. Apart from the group at Cambridge, there were many who studied Plato; and some among them surely pentrated to his meaning. His main doctrines are not hard to grasp; to say they are is to charge Plato with an obscurity of which he is not guilty.[11]

---

[11] One example may suffice. In his *Discourse on the Light of Nature* 6 (quoted by E. T. Campagnac in *The Cambridge Platonists,* pp. 245-7), Nathanael Culverwel takes right reason as the natural law graven in the heart of man, and cites the argument in Plato's *Gorgias* to support his view in very much the same way as Milton does in *D.D.D.* (3. 458, 500-1) and *Eikon.* (5. 121).

It is Agar's view that, in passages like *Paradise Lost* 12. 82-104,

Milton takes a number of Plato's fundamental conceptions, such as the identity of virtue and reason, the tripartite division of the soul, the analogy between the soul and the State, and uses them to explain the condition of man. These ideas did not come from Spenser, or Ficino, or Margaret of Navarre. They are foreign to the spirit of Renaissance Platonism, and represent an aspect of the philsopher to which that period was indifferent. (P. 31.)

The statement is only partly true: these Platonic doctrines are not peculiar to Milton.[12] Nor was the spirit of Renaissance Platonism foreign to him.

To be sure, we find no references to the Florentine Academy in Milton's writing, except for one passing allusion to Bembo (3. 236). But Milton doubtless knew something of its work. Probably he used Ficino's translation of Plato, if not his commentaries. And in his visit to Italy, he may have heard talk at the various academies about their Florentine model. While in Florence, he wrote to Benedetto Buommattei, asking,

who among all the host of authors can justly claim the second place after the acknowledged masters of the Florentine tongue, who excels in tragedy, who writes lively and elegant comedy, who shows acuteness or depth of thought in letters or dialogues, and who has a noble style in historical writing. (Tillyard, p. 18.)

Some Florentine Platonists would be named in such a list, and would again be among the writers whose works Milton had shipped from Italy when he set off for his return to England.

But however much or little Milton read of Florentine Platonism, he inevitably met it in English writers. Under

---

[12] On the identity of reason and virtue, see note 11 above; cf. Spenser, *Faerie Queene* 2. 11. 1-2; and for the whole concept of rational freedom see Muirhead's analysis of the doctrines of the Cambridge Platonists, as given above.

Ficino's direction the Florentine Academy had turned its interest in Plato into a cult, which quickly spread. It reached Oxford, chiefly through Thomas Linacre; captured the interest of Colet, Erasmus, More, and Eliot; and with Erasmus' teaching at Cambridge became the philosophy that was to dominate Sidney, Spenser, and a whole generation of English poets.

When Sir John Cheke taught 'Cambridge and King Edward Greek,' he taught very largely the Greek of Plato and added the Latin Platonism of Ficino.[13] So too with Erasmus, Ascham, and More. All were under the spell of Plato, and it was Ficino who cast the Platonic spell upon them all. The matter is too generally agreed upon to need further comment.[14] What interests us is to see with what sympathy and approval Milton always speaks of these transmitters of Italian Platonism, especially Erasmus. Perhaps Bacon too may be linked with the group since, like Giordano Bruno, Ramus, and Galileo, he brought a kind of Platonism to oppose the contemporary Aristotelianism.[15] The interest Milton took in this latter group squarely contradicts Agar's view. And through the Elizabethan poets, his tie to Renaissance Platonism is even stronger. In Sidney, for example, we find a temperament, at once Platonic and Protestant, very like Milton's own.

But obviously the strongest tie is with Spenser, whom Milton acknowledged as his 'original' (18. 381). Scholars

[13] See Einstein, *The Italian Renaissance in England*, p. 345.

[14] For a succinct account of the introduction of Platonism into England see Kurt Schroeder, *Platonismus in der Englischen Renaissance vor und bei Thomas Eliot*, pp. 1-21.

[15] Against Bacon's vehement condemnation of Plato in *Temporis Partus Masculus* and some few other passages, may be set many favorable comments, among them the suggestion, in *Novum Organum* 1. 105, that Plato alone had glimpsed the true scientific method of induction. See also *Novum Organum* 2. 226; and *The Advancement of Learning* 3. 4 and 5. 4.

have begun to show how far the *Faerie Queene* was a model for *Paradise Lost*[16]; and like study will reveal a like use in *Comus* and *Paradise Regained*. Milton declared 'our admired Spenser' (3. 166-7) a 'better teacher than Scotus or Aquinas' (4. 311); and what Spenser taught, when not strictly Platonic, is the Platonism of Ficino, associated, as in Ficino himself, with matter drawn from Aristotle and Christianity.

As Augustine links Milton with the Christian mystics of his age who favored the Neoplatonism of Plotinus, so Spenser links him with contemporaries who drew their Platonism from Ficino. Agar rightly distinguishes Milton's purer understanding of Plato from much of the mystic and fanciful interpretation popular at the time. Yet in so far as Milton gave his admiration to Augustine and Spenser, we cannot think all the interpreters of Plato who preceded Milton alien to him. Indeed, he used Neoplatonic teachings as they did, and was no more sedulous than they to draw sharp lines between Platonism, Neoplatonism, and Christianity. The only distinction we can make between Milton and others in their reading of Plato comes simply to the inevitable difference between the clearer insight of a keener mind and the more confused impressions of the less gifted. The emphasis in Milton's use of Plato is certainly more on what is reasoned and analytic, less on the mythical and exuberant, than in other Platonists of the Renaissance; but they all use both aspects of the Dialogues. Only he, having greater power of analysis and reason, is more aware of the same powers in Plato.

---

[16] See especially Edwin Greenlaw, 'A Better Teacher than Aquinas,' *SP*. 14 (1917). 196-217; and 'Spenser's Influence on *Paradise Lost*,' *SP*. 17 (1920). 320-59.

CHAPTER III

'Himself a True Poem'

MILTON's enthusiasm for the Platonic teaching left its mark on his theory of poetry. Even before he began his careful study of the Dialogues he had used Platonic myth and figure to adorn his verse, like most poets of the Renaissance. And again like them, he had recognized the poet in Plato. Thus he concluded his lines *De Idea Platonica* by addressing Plato:

But you, the unfading glory of the Academy—if you were the first to introduce such monsters [the Ideas] to the schools—surely you will recall the poets exiled from your State, for you are the greatest fabler of them all; or, founder though you be, you must yourself go forth. (MacKellar, p. 143.)

The lines show too that from the first Milton recognized in Plato's words on poetry a paradox. And though he came to think it only a seeming paradox, in coming to terms with the apparent inconsistency he gained, like the Platonists Sidney before and Shelley after him, a view of poetry that Plato often teaches. The paradox may indeed have been designed to that end. At any rate, Milton worked out a solution to the riddle.

To be sure, the view of poetry he thus came to hold was current in the Renaissance. But so too was Platonism. And we are here concerned with the direct impact of one great mind upon another, an impact that we know occurred, however it was prepared for in advance or later strengthened

45

by the influence of all the Platonists from Aristotle on down. In any event, it was far from common even in the Renaissance for a poet to say as Milton did:

> He who would not be frustrate of his hope to write well hereafter in laudable things ought himself to be a true Poem, that is, a composition and pattern of the best and honorablest things. (*Ap. Smect.* 3. 303.)

The definition of a true poem as a 'composition and pattern of the best and honorablest things' is extraordinary, and so too the assertion that a poet can communicate only what he himself is, and should therefore himself be such a composition of the good and honorable. Had Milton fed only on the Platonic critics of his age, he would not have thus identified poet, poem, and moral excellence.

What then is the paradox that had this influence on him? Simply, that Plato, himself a poet and an admirer of the poetic gift, condemned poetry. In other terms, it is the composite of the two things that every one knows Plato said about poetry: that poets are the inspired oracles of the gods and that poets ought to be banished from a perfect State. The two assertions are in the most obvious manner contradictory; if Plato held the one view, he could not in all piety have held the other. At any rate, he had somewhat more to say about poetry.

'Is not the test by which we always distinguish one art from another,' asks Socrates in the *Republic* 1. 346, 'its possession of different powers? And does not each of these arts give us a distinctive, and not a common, benefit?' To our knowledge, Plato never had his Socrates define the 'different powers' and 'distinctive benefit' of poetry. But everywhere he insisted that the true function and true form of an art are interchangeable, and that since the form is properly determined by the function, the function may not be abused without damage to the form. Further, when he banished poetry from his ideal State, he gave as chief reason its damaging effect on the audience, thus stating decisively—if in negative terms—that the ultimate function of poetry, as of every activity, must be to make men better. What Plato did, in effect, was to question the right of an art to exist in opposition to the end of all other human activity, the happiness that, according to him, is won only through the wisdom synonomous with virtue.

What then of the poet's divine inspiration? If his words are to be judged by the same measure as all the more prosaic utterances of lawyer and schoolmaster, that is, by the measure in which they inculcate the habits of thought that promote harmonious living, what sense can there be in calling his words divinely inspired? No sense at all in calling the words so, but much in so naming the gift; for in exiling poets lest they corrupt his citizenry, the Platonic Socrates paid them an unusual tribute inasmuch as he credited them with the power of swaying others to share their views. But, however inspired he thought the poetic capacity, he did not think that ended the matter. On the contrary, when he chose to dismiss the poets as irrelevant, in the *Apology* for example, he called them inspired madmen; but when he had them up for the test, in the *Republic* and the *Laws,* he asked how sanely they were using their inspiration.

The word that solves the riddle of Plato's statements on poetry is *teaching*. The poets could teach—that he never questioned; their persuasive power was god-given. But did they know that they were teachers, and to what they should persuade? And here he did question—with what effect Milton bears witness.

Milton, who saw how much a poet Plato himself was, at first refused to take the condemnation of poetry seriously. He much preferred the doctrine of poetic inspiration. And little wonder! Here is the vindication of the poet's vision and rapture. He is told that his Utopian fancies are nearer to reality than other men's humdrum reasonings, and that the capacity to see and speak those fancies is divine. What ardent maker of verses will deny the compliment? To Milton, fresh from rereading *Phaedrus*, the language of divine inspiration was highly acceptable. Thus he writes to his close friend Diodati in the letter previously quoted:

Though I know not God's intent toward me in other respects, yet of this I am sure, that he has imbued me especially with a mighty passion for Beauty. Ceres never sought her daughter Proserpine (as the legend tells) with greater ardor than I do this Idea of Beauty, like some image of loveliness; ever pursuing it, by day and by night, in every shape and form ('for many forms there are of things divine') and following close in its footprints as it leads. . . . What am I thinking about? you ask. So help me God, of immortality. What am I doing? Growing wings and learning to fly; but my Pegasus can only rise on tender pinions as yet, so let my new wisdom be humble. (Tillyard, p. 14.)

He is as inspired as the best of them, and as certain that the realm his Pegasus will climb to is the realm of Beauty Absolute.

Earlier too, in his Sixth *Elegy*, he had spoken of the poet as an oracle:

But the poet who tells of wars, and of heaven under Jove to manhood grown, of pious heroes, and of demigods, the leaders of men—who sings now of the sacred decrees of the gods above, and now of that deep realm guarded by the barking dog—he indeed must live sparely, after the manner of the Samian master, and herbs must supply his harmless fare. Let only the crystal-clear water in a beechen bowl stand near him, and let him drink temperate draughts from the pure spring. More than this, his youth must be chaste and free from sin, his manners strict, and his hand without stain, even like you, O priest, when in sacred vestment and gleaming with the waters of cleansing you rise as augur to face the angry gods. . . . Truly the bard is sacred to the gods; he is their priest, and both his heart and lips mysteriously breathe the indwelling Jove. (MacKellar, pp. 99-101.)

And similarly in *Ad Patrem:*

Scorn not the poet's song, a work divine, which more than aught else reveals our ethereal origin and heavenly race. Nothing so much as its origin does grace to the human mind, possessing yet some sacred traces of Promethean fire. (*Ibid.,* pp. 143-5.)

But though these passages recall the accounts of poetic inspiration in *Ion* (534) and *Phaedrus* (244-7), they tell less about how the poet is to achieve his sublime function than does the letter to Diodati. In the Sixth *Elegy* Milton sets mysterious hurdles for himself; in the letter he has at least to pursue the Idea in every shape and form. In *Ad Patrem* the 'poet's song' is by its very nature 'a work divine'; in the letter its divinity has to be won.

And even so, the letter to Diodati bespeaks the young Platonist, and it took an older, wiser student of the Dialogues to write *Paradise Lost, Paradise Regained,* and *Samson Agonistes.* Much that had been satisfactory to the youth at Horton became inadequate to the man in middle life watching his country in civil turmoil. Like any thoughtful man, he was aware of the contradiction between what humanity might be and what it is; and circumstances did not permit him to remain half aware. The strife in England forbade unconcerned pursuit of the seemingly remote path of artistic achievement. If the world was awry, men of vision must set it right. And who were the men of vision if not such as he? It was as visionary power that he had thought his poetic talent divine, and because it was to give him sight beyond men's actual lot, insight into what their lot might and should be, that he had sought the Idea of Beauty. His first duty, then, was to lend his eyes to the State. So Milton chose to do.

But the choice meant a departure from his once-chosen path, if only because a man cannot at the same time be doing two distinct kinds of work. Either poetry must become his pleasant avocation in leisure hours, or he must cease to be an active poet. If Milton had thought poetry a mere personal indulgence, he could have been content; or if he had thought it the most important activity of human life, he could have ignored the troubles of politics for the nobler calling. But Milton thought neither the true role of poetry.

Yet poetry could hardly be an occupation for men living in a settled and perfected state of society; for the times are always somewhat out of joint, and the tasks of civic life endless even when they are not tasks of military performance. The institutions which men in their occasional spurts of vision create, and in their long centuries of folly pervert, are always in some need of correction. When would a poet ever be freed by the stability of society to be a poet? Yet a poet Milton felt himself to be, and only at second best a statesman or political theorist. Somehow he must reconcile with the more obvious duty the career to which he had first pledged himself.

The *Reason of Church-Government* records how Milton made that reconciliation. What he there says is relevant to our search, because Plato's theory of poetry gave him the argument by which he could assign to poetry the rank of means, not end, and still justify himself as a poet. Let us consider the relevant passages step by step.

The work starts with a principle from Plato's *Laws,* which Milton intends to apply to the matter in hand:

In the publishing of human laws, which for the most part aim not beyond the good of civil society, to set them barely forth to the people without reason or preface, like a physical prescript, or only with threatenings, as it were a lordly command, in the judgment of Plato was thought to be done neither genrously nor wisely. His advice was, seeing that persuasion certainly is a more winning and more manlike way to keep men in obedience than fear, that to such laws as were of principal moment there should be used as an induction some well-tempered discourse, showing how good, how gainful, how happy it must needs be to live according to honesty and justice; which being uttered with those native colors and graces of speech, as true eloquence, the daughter of virtue, can best bestow upon her mother's praises, would so incite, and in a manner charm the multitude into the love of that which is really good as to embrace it ever after, not of custom and awe, which most men do, but of choice and purpose, with true and constant delight. (3. 181.)

The principle, Milton hastens to add, is not Plato's alone; he finds this 'point of so high wisdom and worth' in the Mosaic law, as well as in the *Laws* of 'the wisest of the heathen.' Plato thus has the sanction of consistency with Holy Writ; or, as we might say, the important point is not that it was Plato who said this, but that what he said is true.

This doctrine, that persuasion is a better instrument than force for the improvement of men, becomes the basis of Milton's further argument in the *Reason of Church-Government* on the place of the Church and of Churchmen in political life, and later the basis of his arguments on government, marriage, education, and censorship. The doctrine, that is to say, becomes central to his thought; it is of the highest importance in his theory of poetry.

The Second Book of the *Reason of Church-Government* begins with the declaration that the man of knowledge would indeed be happy if his knowledge did not carry with it the burden of spreading the truth he knows, and that in the face of men's frequent hostility to truth. Lest his reader ask, 'What truth?' Milton prevents the question by distinguishing between understanding of fact ('that knowledge that rests in the contemplation of natural causes and dimensions, which must needs be a lower wisdom, as the object is low') and the knowledge which we might call insight ('of God, and of his true worship, and what is infallibly good and happy in the state of man's life, what in itself evil and miserable, though vulgarly not so esteemed'). The distinction is much the same as Plato made between the realms of Becoming and Being, or as we might make between the studies of physics and ethics. The point to note is that Milton and Plato attribute much greater importance to ethical than to physical knowledge.

Now since this burden of education is imposed on the philosophical mind, Milton—though he may seem 'too inquisitive or suspicious' of himself and his doings—feels that such ability as God has entrusted to him was intended to be used on just such occasions as this present dispute on Church-affairs. Otherwise his conscience might say through the rest of life:

> Thou hadst the diligence, the parts, the language of a man, if a vain subject were to be adorned or beautified; but when the cause of God and his Church was to be pleaded, for which purpose that tongue was given thee which thou hast, God listened, . . . but thou wert dumb as a beast; from henceforward be that which thine own brutish silence hath made thee. (3. 232-3.)

Briefly, Milton feels that not to enter this controversy on the gravest of human concerns would condemn him to think poetry, what many do think it, the 'vain adorning and beautifying of vain things.' If he chooses, then, to write with his 'left hand,' knowing himself in such controversy to be inferior to himself in his native medium of poetry, it is because a poet's right concerns are not with vanity, but with things of the highest seriousness. And on this point he may permit himself to expatiate.

Thus we come to Milton's *apologia* for poetry, which begins, appropriately enough, with an account of his own poetic training, significant in its emphasis on the discipline which a poet must undergo, on the 'labor and intent study' which he must take to be his 'portion in this life' even if given the strong propensity of nature.' The career of the poet, we are to understand, cannot be lightly undertaken; nor was it by Milton. His regard is to God's glory 'by the honor and instruction' of his country; his purpose, 'not to make verbal curiosities the end (that were a toilsome vanity), but to be an interpreter and relater of the best and sagest things among mine own citizens.' (Observe how that *best and sagest* prefigures the definition of poetry in the *Apology for Smectymnuus* as 'a pattern of the best and honorablest things.')

After enumerating the poetic types and subjects through which such an aim might be fulfilled, Milton goes on to argue that such is the aim, not simply of the poet Milton, but of poetry, that this function of interpreting and relating the best and sagest things' is not arbitrarily assigned by him, but proper to the talents which we call poetic.

Before we quote in its entirety the next passage, in which Milton pretty well condenses his whole theory of poetry, let us remind ourselves of the argument with which the *Reason of Church-Government* opened, that persuasion is a better educational instrument than force. Now if man is to be persuaded to goodness, clearly the poet, who shares with the orator the talent for persuasive utterance, may take his place beside lawgiver, educator, and spiritual adviser, beside all who seek to improve human life—if the poet understands his own powers and the use to be made of them. Thus Milton:

These abilities, wheresoever they be found, are the inspired gift of God, rarely bestowed, but yet to some (though most abuse) in every nation; and are of power, beside the office of a pulpit, to inbreed and cherish in a great people the seeds of virtue and public civility, to allay the perturbations of the mind, and set the affections in right tune; to celebrate in glorious and lofty hymns the throne and equipage of God's almightiness, and what He works, and what He suffers to be wrought with high providence in his Church; to sing the victorious agonies of martyrs and saints, the deeds and triumphs of just and pious nations doing valiantly through faith against the enemies of Christ; to deplore the general relapses of kingdoms and states from justice and from God's true worship. Lastly, whatsoever in religion is holy and sublime, in virtue amiable or grave, whatsoever hath passion or admiration in all the changes of that which is called fortune from without, or the wily subtleties and refluxes of man's thoughts from within; all these things with a solid and treatable smoothness to paint out and describe—teaching over the whole book of sanctity and virtue through all the instances of example, with such delight to those especially of soft and delicious temper, who will not so much as look upon truth herself unless they see her elegantly dressed; that whereas the paths of honesty and good life appear now rugged and difficult, though they be indeed easy and pleasant, they would then appear to all men both easy and pleasant, though they were rugged and difficult indeed. (3. 238-9.)

For Milton too, it seems, the reconciling word is teaching. And for good reasons, not least among them that the source of this passage is in Plato's *Laws*. There, in a discussion of poetry, the Athenian Stranger had come upon the problem that led Socrates in the *Republic* to outlaw poets, and had resolved it by a more limited—and yet more rigorous because more seriously intended—censorship. The problem is this, Will they, won't they, poets do teach. The solution is let them be told what they must teach. And hence the Athenian Stranger lists the kinds of poem to be composed.

It will be most fitting to address the gods in hymns and strains of praise and prayer commingled; and, after the gods, then should be offered prayers and praises in like manner to the demigods and heroes, as severally befits them. . . . Thereafter we may at once proceed without demur to the following regulation:

All citizens who have brought to an end a life of honorable toil, of bodily or spiritual achievement, and been obedient to the laws, shall be considered fitting objects of our praises. . . . But those who are still living it is not safe to honor with hymns and panegyrics; it is not safe till a man has finished his course, and reached a noble end. . . .

Delight is common to all styles of composition. What counts is whether a man has been reared, from childhood up to the age of firm good sense, in music that is sane and orderly; if so, he is repelled whenever he hears the opposite kind, and calls it vulgar; whereas if he has been reared on music of the common sugary sort, he declares that its opposite is frigid and unpleasing. Accordingly, as I was saying, in respect of the pleasure or dissatisfaction either type affords, neither takes precedence of the other; the real superiority lies herein, that one type always makes those who are reared in it better, while the other makes them worse. (*Laws* 7. 801-2. Cooper, pp. 400-2.)

The passages from Plato and Milton are alike, especially in their lists of approved subjects. Where Plato has (1) hymns and praises of the gods, Milton makes only the change required by monotheism; for (2) the pagan demigods and heroes to whom prayers and praises are to be addressed, Milton substitutes Christian saints and martyrs; (3) the private citizens, the individuals of Plato's City-State, who are to be the subjects of eulogy give way to the just and pious nations' of Milton's more cosmopolitan scheme; and (4) where Plato would have no man celebrated before his death, lest he lapse from virtue, Milton thinks the very lapses 'from justice and God's true worship' become fit subjects if properly deplored.

Such a parallel comes neither by accident nor by servile imitation. Milton has taken to mind what the Athenian said, has weighed its worth, added what he found wanting, and canceled what he thought amiss. He dismisses with the words 'though most abuse' the whole condemnation of unlicensed poetic practice which occurs just before the passage here quoted from the *Laws* and ends with the words 'Taken as a whole, the poets are not so very capable of discerning what is good and what is not.' He changes Plato's legislation. The Athenian would decree that:

No poet shall write any poem that conflicts with what, in accordance with the public standard, is right and lawful, beautiful and good; nor show his compositions to any private individual until they have been submitted to the appointed judges in these matters, and to the guardians of the law, and been officially approved. (*Laws* 7. 801. Cooper, p. 400.)

For Milton, not the legislator's edict, but the nature of poetry suggests whatsoever is 'holy and sublime' as fit for poets 'to paint out and describe.' And finally, where Plato still doubtful of the poet's ability to keep this high aim declares that either the good or the bad may become delightful through habit, Milton puts it positively as the poet's native function 'to inbreed and cherish . . . the seeds of virtue and public civility.' Plato says this can be the effect of a poetry properly guided by law; Milton asserts that it is the effect proper to poetry.

But obviously he can assert no such thing in the face of what actual poets often do, which Plato had considered before deciding that they need legislative restraint. Milton may dispense with the suggested restraint, but cannot blink the fact. He puts his stress therefore on the nature of poetry, 'though most abuse'; and of the abuses speaks no more gently than Plato.

The passage in the *Reason of Church-Government* goes on:

And what a benefit this would be to our youth and gentry may be soon guessed by what we know of the corruption and bane which they suck in daily from the writings and interludes of libidinous and ignorant poetasters, who having scarce ever heard of that which is the main consistence of a true poem, the choice

56

of such persons as they ought to introduce, and what is moral and decent to each one, do for the most part lap up vicious principles in sweet pills to be swallowed down, and make the taste of virtuous documents harsh and sour.

This being true, perhaps the Athenian law-giver was right after all, and the State should concern itself with poetry. At least Milton feels it necessary to add:

But because the spirit of man cannot demean itself lively in this body without some recreating intermission of labor and serious things, it were happy for the commonwealth if our magistrates, as in those famous governments of old, would take into their care, not only the deciding of our contentious law-cases and brawls, but the managing of our public sports and festival pastimes; that they might be, not such as were authorized a while since, the provocations of drunkenness and lust, but such as may inure and harden our bodies by martial exercises to all warlike skill and performance; and may civilize, adorn, and make discreet our minds by the learned and affable meeting of frequent academies and the procurement of wise and artful recitations, sweetened with eloquent and graceful enticements to the love and practice of justice, temperance, and fortitude, instructing and bettering the nation at all opportunities, that the call of wisdom and virtue may be heard everywhere, as Solomon saith. . . . Whether this may not be, not only in pulpits, but after another persuasive method, at set and solemn paneguries, in theatres, porches, or what other place or way may win most upon the people to receive at once both recreation and instruction, let them in authority consult.

There can be no question that Milton had been reading the *Laws*. Though 'Solomon saith' in *Proverbs* (i. 20-1), 'Wisdom crieth without; she uttereth her voice in the streets; she crieth in the chief place of concourse, in the openings of the gates'; it was Plato's Athenian Stranger who gave edicts on how she might best use her voice, naming the administrators, the occasions, and the public assemblies in which she was to be heard, almost exactly as Milton names them.

The details of those edicts need not be retold here; for far more significant than any borrowing of details is Milton's acceptance, with modification, of the principles involved. With modification, be it noted, because while the Athenian would have the wrong kind of poetry forbidden by statute, Milton urges only that the right kind be encouraged by 'them in authority.' Why he rejected the negative decree we shall better understand when we come to his treatment of Plato's censorship in *Areopagitica*.

Here, in the *Reason of Church-Government*, Milton has applied the declaration of Plato, that persuasion is superior to force, more thoroughly than Plato himself ever attempted to do. Not by force of censorship, but by persuasion to civic duty, the State shall set the poet to a right use of his inspired abilities. Milton himself intends to encourage poets by the persuasive force of his example. Now that he is satisfied with the poet's high mission, he has absolved himself from the suspicion of vanity, of remoteness from the important issues of life, or of concern with such poetry as may be 'raised from the heat of youth or the vapors of wine, like that which flows at waste from the pen of some vulgar amorist, or the trencher fury of a rhyming parasite.' He now may 'covenant with any knowing reader' to produce at some future time just such poetry as he has described as poetry proper—granted always that 'by devout prayer' he may continue to receive the divine inspiration and that by 'industrious and select reading, steady observation, insight into all seemly and generous arts and affairs' he perseveres in training that inspiration into the ways of art. The time is not yet, because the effects of poetry are ultimate and the immediate effects of rhetoric are at present needed, but the path of his return to poetry has been cleared of the last conscientious doubt.

Plato having offered the alternatives of poetry in the service of morality or no poetry at all, Milton, though he denied the alternative, accepted the duty, and having accepted, fulfilled it to the letter in *Paradise Lost, Paradise Regained,* and *Samson Agonistes.* Poetry has now a function other than, yet not unconnected with, the revelation of the Beautiful, a work to be done in the realms of true doctrine and social good as well. Milton therefore may still think of himself as a poet; and while he continues to write pamphlets because of immediate necessity, he may bide his time with no sense that the pull in him towards poetry is a pull away from his responsibilities as man and citizen. He has found his own bent justified by the same philosopher who had described the pursuit of Ideal Beauty.

On the didactic function of poetry, Milton and Plato are thus agreed. But what of the didactic effect of bad poetry? If Plato was right to count poetry among the instruments of teaching, how can Milton deny the ill done by those poets who are 'not so very capable of discerning what is good and what is not'? As we have seen, he makes no attempt to deny the evil, but abjures the means by which Plato's Utopian polities would prevent it. We have, in other words, still to consider *Areopagitica,* which seems a flat repudiation of all that Plato had to say on poetry, inasmuch as it repudiates the censorship prescribed in the *Laws* no less than the dismissal of poets in the *Republic.* Indeed, Milton rightly fixes his attention on the *Laws* as the serious utterance which advocates of censorship might cite:

Plato, a man of high authority indeed, but least of all for his Commonwealth, in the book of his *Laws,* which no city ever yet received, fed his fancy with making many edicts to his airy burgomasters, which they who otherwise admire him, wish had been rather buried and excused in the genial cups of an Academic night sitting. By which laws he seems to tolerate no kind of learning but by unalterable decree, consisting most of practical traditions, to the attainment whereof a library of smaller bulk than his own Dialogues would be abundant; and there also enacts that no poet should so much as read to any private man what he had written, until the judges and law-keepers had seen it and allowed it. (4. 316.)

What follows then for Milton, who 'otherwise admired' Plato? Not simple defiance, but an attempt to extricate some ground of agreement:

But that Plato meant this law peculiarly to that common-wealth which he had imagined, and to no other, is evident. Why was he not else a law-giver to himself, but a transgressor, and to be expelled by his own magistrates, both for the wanton epigrams and dialogues which he made, and his perpetual reading of Sophron, Mimus, and Aristophanes, books of grossest infamy; and also for commending the latter of them, though he were the malicious libeler of his chief friends, to be read by the tyrant Dionysius, who had little need of such trash to spend his time on? But that he knew this licensing of poems had reference and dependence to many other provisos there set down in his fancied republic, which in this world could have no place; and so neither he himself, nor any magistrate or city, ever imitated that course, which, taken apart from those other collateral in-junctions, must needs be vain and fruitless.

Obviously the insistence that Plato is really of Milton's party may be mere polemic. It is well in pushing an argument to reinterpret the authorities your opponent may cite, and to make them, if you can, sanction your own view. But why drag Plato in at all unless you acknowledge his author-ity? Or why not, if Plato's name can be hurled against you, hurl back Aristotle's? Instead, Milton elaborates the discus-sion in *Areopagitica*—because, we surmise, he wanted to agree with Plato if he could. He goes on to show that the laws of censorship in the Dialogues are not rightly under-stood apart from their context:

If we think to regulate printing, thereby to rectify manners, we must regulate all recreations and pastimes, all that is delightful to man. No music must be heard, no song be set or sung, but what is grave and Doric. There must be licensing dancers, that no gesture, motion, or deportment be taught our youth, but what by their allowance shall be thought honest; for such Plato was provided of.

But 'provided of,' Milton reminds us, as a poet for a mythical realm, not as a legislator for an existing community. And here he uses the most severe words of all:

To sequester out of the world into Atlantic and Utopian polities, which can never be drawn into use, will not mend our condition, but to ordain wisely as in this world of evil, in the midst whereof God hath placed us unavoidably. (4. 318.)

Now if Milton had thought Plato a mere 'Utopian' who 'fed his fancy with making many edicts to his airy burgomasters' (an 'escapist' to use our term), we should have to revise our whole preceding argument, and say that after he had written *The Reason of Church-Government* Milton came to see how wrong the whole Platonic theory of poetry was. Milton was not one to approve the sentimental turn of mind which takes refuge in impossible phantasy. But then, no more was Plato; and Milton knew it. Indeed, he knew perfectly well that Plato knew what a Utopia is for, and he states the knowledge with every mark of assent, though not in *Areopagitica*. In the *Apology for Smectymnuus* he had praised

that grave and noble invention which the greatest and sublimest wits in sundry ages, Plato in *Critias,* and our own two famous countrymen, the one in his *Utopia,* the other in his *New Atlantis,* chose, I may not say as a field, but as a mighty continent wherein to display the largeness of their spirits by teaching this our world better and exacter things than were yet known or used. (3. 294.)

Utopias, then, have their practical bearing. So too may a Utopian censorship; but *Areopagitica* would hardly have been the work in which to stress the point. Yet even here Milton asserts—and surely admirers of Plato will agree—that an intelligent reader gains from the ideal States of Plato not an impossible set of legal prohibitions, but a way of regarding human life and of testing the worth of human aims. Milton ends the argument by pointing to what in the *Laws* (and doubtless the *Republic* too) best merits attention:

> Nor is it Plato's licensing of books will do this [that is, mend our condition], which necessarily pulls along with it so many other kinds of licensing as will make us all both ridiculous and weary, and yet frustrate; but those unwritten, or at least unconstraining, laws of virtuous education, religious and civil nurture, which Plato there mentions as the bonds and ligaments of the commonwealth, the pillars and the sustainers of every written statute, these they be which will bear chief sway in such matters as these, when all licensing will be easily eluded. (4. 318.)

But what precisely are these 'unwritten, or at least unconstraining, laws of virtuous education' and the rest, to which Milton would allow 'chief sway in such matters as these'? They seem to this student of the *Laws* very nearly the same as those of censorship, or rather simply their converse. When the Athenian Stranger discusses the kinds of music the State will encourage, he implicitly, and explicitly too, rejects every other. Milton seems to have led us to a paradox of his own every bit as puzzling as Plato's. For the great difference would seem to be that Milton would have censorship by encouragement, and specifically in the realms of 'education, religious and civil nurture'; Plato, by encouragement and discouragement both, and throughout all realms of life. And how slight a difference that comes to a few minutes of thought would have led Milton to see—if he had believed that Plato meant his censorship to be a legal prescription at all. He did not; he thought the explicit legalities a challenge rather than a prescription, and right

62

as a challenge where they would be wrong as a prescription. He took this transfer of censorship from external law to internal education to be in the spirit of Plato's intention, and on the need of such censorship agreed with Plato. The poet is to keep himself at his proper work, and the reader to guard himself against the mistakes of wrong poetry.

How the principle would work we may see in *Paradise Regained,* when just after Satan's magnificent encomium of classical literature, to the distress of a good many readers, Jesus replies censoriously:

Think not but that I know these things; or think
I know them not, not therefore am I short
Of knowing what I ought: he who receives
Light from above, from the fountain of light,
No other doctrine needs, though granted true;
But these are false, or little else but dreams,
Conjectures, fancies, built on nothing firm. . . .
     Who therefore seeks in these
True wisdom, finds her not, or by delusion
Far worse, her false resemblance only meets,
An empty cloud. However, many books
Wise men have said are wearisome; who reads
Incessantly, and to his reading brings not
A spirit and judgment equa: or superior,
(And what he brings, what needs he elsewhere seek)
Uncertain and unsettl'd still remains,
Deep verst in books and shallow in himself.

                (4. 286-92, 318-27.)

Intolerable as the doctrine sounds, and especially intolerable from Milton, who could not have written even these lines if he had not himself read the pagan classics, Jesus' speech has a meaning, and Milton agreed with it. If you have the perfect in a Platonic Republic or by a direct and complete participation in the divine mind, of what use can the imperfect be to you? Moreover, how can you be in need of it? But, of course, if you do not have the perfect revelation of truth, or perfect poems, or a perfectly working life for all the members of your State, the answer must be different. Milton can use and does need the classics, as Plato needed and could use Sophron, 'Mimus,' and Aristophanes. And yet we do well to keep in mind what the perfect truth and the perfect poem would be, if only as a standard by which to judge what in the imperfect is to be assimilated and what in it the assimilating mind should reject. The meaning of Plato's censorship, as Milton took it, like the meaning of Jesus' speech on classical learning is: Be wary if you read, even warier if you write.

For both Milton and Plato, then, poetry is doctrine whether true or false, with a fearful power of influence Plato seems to stress the fearful side, Milton the power; and yet both see the same duty and the same danger. For both the poet is a teacher, not because they thought poorly of poetry, but because they thought astonishingly well of teaching. When Milton says 'what religious, what glorious and magnificent, use might be made of poetry both in divine and human things' (Ainsworth, p. 60), he ascribes a didactic function to art as surely as Plato did.

But when Milton says that poets can teach, and therefore should teach wisely, he no more means than Plato did that the poet is to be for ever conning over the maxims of copy-book morality. 'Teaching over the *whole* book of sanctity and virtue' is his phrase. If we think of a small book and an unimaginative preceptor, Milton is hardly at fault He meant all virtue by 'virtue,' not temperance alone, and by 'sanctity' the wholeness and health which are the prerequisites to, if not indeed the essence of, a full and joyous life. He meant by poetry's teaching what Wordsworth meant by 'truth carried alive into the heart by passion'; by 'sanctity and virtue,' Sidney's 'ending end of all earthly learning'; and by the 'whole book' of it, Shelley's 'very image of life expressed in its eternal truth.'

De Quincey would have it that the cookery-book teaches while *Paradise Lost* moves. Yet the cookery-book moves the gourmand; and *Paradise Lost* taught De Quincey, by moving him to think Milton's thought and affirm Milton's values—as far as De Quincey could. Neither Plato nor Milton ever said that the poet must remember to add a moral to the story. Indeed, Milton quoted Plato as objecting to the acceptance of moral commonplaces from 'custom and awe, which most men do,' and insisting that the good to be really good must be deliberately chosen 'with true and constant delight.' They thought the whole story a continuous revelation of morality, good or bad; that what the heart affirms the mind too will come to believe—and act upon; that, as Milton put it, doctrine and discipline are one. And hence the truth or falsehood cherished by the poet inevitably leaves its impress on his poetry, and his poetry, if it is successful, on his audience; for if the poet makes us sympathize, he inevitably makes us sympathize with better or with worse modes of thought, feeling, and behavior. And if he makes us sympathize wrongly, he works against what all wise men work for, and abuses a power greater than others possess.

Thus the Athenian of the *Laws* argued when he fancied himself addressing the poets:

'Most estimable Strangers,' we shall say, 'we ourselves are the authors of a tragedy, at once the finest and the best we can compose. At any rate our polity has all been framed in *imitation of the best and fairest life*; which, as for us, we hold to be in very fact the truest tragedy. Thus if you are poets, then we too are poets, makers of the self-same things, rivals in your art.' (*Laws* 7. 817. Cooper, p. 417. The italics are mine.)

Milton, far from quarreling with this view of poetry, goes

along with Plato in the last, hardest step of all to the conviction that we can teach others only what we ourselves
are. The poet's task, therefore, is not for every one who
can turn rhymes. Plato's lawgiver had said:

Herein not every one shall be an author; no, first the poet
must not be under fifty years of age; nor, again, shall they
compose who, though they have within themselves the gift of
poetry and music, have never yet performed one noble and
illustrious deed. But they who in themselves are good, and are
honored in the State as artists in the doing of fair deeds, their
poems may be sung even if the natural music should be lacking.
(*Laws* 7. 829. Cooper, p. 418.)

Milton deliberately approves the passage, and rightly connects it with the definition of true tragedy as the 'imitation
of the best and fairest life.'

To be sure, there is no reference to Plato in the Tractate
Of Education when Milton speaks of

that sublime art which in Aristotle's *Poetics*, in Horace, and the
Italian commentaries of Castelvetro, Tasso, Mazzoni, and others,
teaches what the laws are of a true epic poem, what of a dramatic, what of a lyric, what decorum is—which is the grand
masterpiece to observe. (Ainsworth, p. 60.)

But if nothing is said of learning the ultimate function of
poetry from Plato, the earlier study of ethics may have
taken care of that, and the study of rhetoric out of 'the rule
of Plato' may reinforce the teaching. And in any event the
course in poetic theory is to enable the student to perceive
what religious, what glorious and magnificent, use might be
made of poetry both in divine and human things.

That use is not pleasure alone. In *Paradise Lost*, Milton
puts it that

Eloquence the Soul, Song charms the Sense. (2. 556.)

The line expresses the central concept of *Phaedrus*, that
rhetoric is the art of enchanting the soul. And poetry is

66

own sister to rhetoric in enchantment. Aristotle, Horace, and the rest will explain how the art succeeds or fails in casting the spell, but Plato tells what spell is to be cast. Moreover, after all the principles have been given—on epic, dramatic, and lyric poetry, and on decorum—the place to start from has still to be told. Like Plato, Milton thought it best to start from the truth to be expressed, by feeding on

> Thoughts that voluntary move
> Harmonious numbers. (*Paradise Lost* 3. 37-8.)

If the aim is to charm the hearer into the ways of good life, then the poet must begin by nourishing that life in himself. That is the gist of Plato's poetics from *Phaedrus* through the *Laws*. And Milton summarizes the whole Platonic argument when he declares:

And long it was not after, when I was confirmed in this opinion, that he who would not be frustrate of his hope to write well hereafter in laudable things, ought himself to be a true Poem, that is, a composition and pattern of the best and honorablest things, not presuming to sing high praises of heroic men or famous cities unless he have in himself the experience and practice of all that which is praiseworthy.

To be a true poet, a man must live the good life.

CHAPTER IV

The Good Life: Pleasure, Wealth, Fame

W HEN Satan turns Jesus in *Paradise Regained* to behold 'Athens, the eye of Greece,' he uses as bait

> Sage Philosophy. . .
> From Heaven descended to the low-rooft house
> Of Socrates.

Milton has allowed the temptation to begin with the best of pagan thought, the philosophy of 'the wisest of the heathen.' But, heathen still, the Socrates of the Dialogues could guide Milton only within the limits set by Christianity. To be sure, the limits were flexible. With Christian thought Platonized at least since Augustine, the dividing line is hard to fix even in theology. In ethics it becomes imperceptible. And it was in ethics especially that Milton followed Plato's leading, as the summary at the end of this chapter indicates.

Investigators have already shown how deeply Plato affected Milton's views on cosmology and music,[1] and we may guess that studies of his politics and rhetoric would yield similar results. But the chief effect was in the realm of ethical thought. Perhaps, as Agar says, Milton and Plato had 'an affinity of spirit,' though it is hard to de-

---

[1] See Sigmund Gottfried Spaeth, *Milton's Knowledge of Music;* William Fairfield Warren, *The Universe as Pictured in Milton's Paradise Lost;* and Edward Chauncey Baldwin, 'Milton and Plato's *Timaeus,' PMLA.* 35 (1920). 210-7.

cide where temperamental affinity ends and assimilation through study begins. Milton himself thought that study can create dispositions. And since we cannot hope to show how far his Platonic habits of thought were native, how far acquired, we had best be content to say merely how far they were Platonic.

Apparently Milton's own feeling was that the Dialogues gave him warrant for many of his views, and, in at least one particular, for personal habit. The reader will note in the appended table how often he comments on the Socratic jest. Sometimes, indeed, we could wish he had learned from Plato the gentleness that invariably tempers Socratic irony in the Dialogues; for the Miltonic jest cuts beyond the offense; and because his delight in satire often takes him too far for laughter, he is less successful than Plato in making error ludicrous.

But in assimilating the ethics of Plato he was more fortunate. We can watch his mind feeding on the Dialogues in the prose of his middle years, and in his later poetry see the result. The Platonism is no longer tagged in *Paradise Lost, Paradise Regained,* and *Samson Agonistes;* it is Milton's own. And now the influence has its real effect, being no longer in process of assimilation, but absorbed in the life-blood. But even those who deny that the mind can be nourished from without may find interest in marking how far these two sharp-sighted men see alike.

Milton, like Plato, was from early years concerned with the basic human question, what constitutes the good life? Like Plato again, he steadily examined the various aims that engage man's interest. His final choice among them is not Plato's, but in testing them he reveals a system of values remarkably akin to that of the Dialogues. It happens that both Plato and Milton took occasion at least once to sift a number of the goals men aim at, and measure their real contribution to happiness. Plato in the Eighth and Ninth

Books of the *Republic,* and Milton in *Paradise Regained,* test a series of human aims, reject with explanation all but one, and give us the principles by which the one exception is made the essential basis of human well-being. Throughout the writings of both, these goods are often dealt with and similarly judged, but here they are arranged in a scale, by Plato in descending order from best to worst, by Milton from lower to higher in the series of Jesus' temptations. It happens also that the two deal with very nearly the same list. As Plato traced the fall of the soul and the State from the aristocratic search for wisdom, through the timocratic love of fame and the democratic pursuit of wealth and then pleasure, to the final abyss of tyrannical hedonism, so Jesus conquers by renouncing pleasure, wealth, and power with its attendant fame, until at last he confronts the temptation of knowledge. The chance correspondence is important, but not essential. What matters most, what shows the heart of Plato's influence on Milton, is that they make very nearly the same judgment not only of the best, but of the worse and better.

PLEASURE

In Plato's scheme the life of pleasure corresponds to the rule of the lowest faculty of the soul. Appetite, the 'many-headed monster,' has three main desires: food, drink, and sexual gratification. None of these is bad in itself, although as they withdraw the soul from its chief concern they become obstacles to the highest life, that of philosophy. Still the evil is not in appetite, but in its resistance to control; and Plato takes care to distinguish between necessary and unnecessary desires, and between their attendant pleasures, honorable and dishonorable. In so far as every element in the soul seeks its proper object, each seeks pleasure; but while the higher objects afford the most intense delights,

Plato generally restricts the term ἡδονή to what pleases the sieve-like appetites. A life devoted to such gratification is the death of the spirit; for the anarchy of indulgence, although it seems at first to ask equal pleasure for all parts of the soul, eventually leads to the tyrannical destruction of the higher parts. When at length reason and will seek to balk undisciplined appetite, the 'many-headed monster,' which has been strengthened by feeding, kills off every better impulse, and thereafter lives for itself alone.

Whenever Plato allows pleasure to be a good at all, he means not the gratification of the senses however obtained, but what delights the best man, whose pleasure is a good and a test of the good in every other thing. In this sense pleasure and happiness may be identified, and Plato can deny that the tyranny of desire produces any enjoyment whatever. But in its more usual meaning, as the object of sensual appetite, pleasure is, of all possible ends, farthest removed from the highest good. Whatever meaning is given to the term, the kind of life generally called pleasant, that of unrestrained luxury, is the basest life a man may lead. Only when desire yields to reason, when pleasures are chosen by the standard of philosophy, can the senses properly be fed. Such a life we may call one of true enjoyment, but the measure of its joy is not in appetite.[2]

Milton, too, counts the pleasures of appetite the least of goods, and most likely to become a destructive force. His constant censure of Epicurean and Cyrenaic thought, his disdain of idolatrous ritual, and his high praise of temperance, all mark his distrust of the senses. 'Epicurus or that libertine school of Cyrene' for him, as the hedonism of a Callicles or Thrasymachus for Plato, represents the lowest kind of ethical doctrine. Similarly the feeding of the

---

[2] See *Republic* 9. 581-7; *Laws* 5. 732-4; also *Protagoras, Gorgias,* and *Philebus.*

senses in religious service, the pleasures afforded to sight, hearing, and smell, are in his view, no fit accompaniment to worship, but divert the worshiper from serious contemplation of God to idolatry. Hedonism is thus the perversion of ethics, and idolatry of religion, for the same reason: they pamper what they should restrain. In *Of Reformation* Milton argues against the Roman Catholic service:

Faith [needs] not the weak and fallible office of the senses to be either the ushers or interpreters of heavenly mysteries, save where our Lord himself in his sacraments ordained. (3. 1-2.)

He uses the imagery of *Phaedrus* to describe the effect that sensuous pleasures have had upon religious rites:

The Soul by this means of over-bodying herself, given up justly to fleshly delights, bated her wing apace downward; and finding the ease she had from her visible and sensuous colleague the body in performance of religious duties, her pinions now broken and flagging, shifted off from herself the labor of high soaring any more, forgot her heavenly flight, and left the dull and droiling carcass to plod on in the old road and drudging trade of outward conformity. (3. 2-3.)

We need not follow the polemic against religious formalism. Milton's position there is but the counterpart of his ethical doctrine on sensual pleasures, and we readily see that for him, as for Plato, loss of the wings of the soul is the invariable consequence of indulging the 'low inclinations of the senses.'

Comus is Milton's first hedonist. Corresponding to the Lady's virtue of chastity or the rule of reason, the vice of Comus is 'luxury' or the rule of pleasure. The image of men turned into beasts comes from Homer and Spenser, but Milton is Platonic in linking the transformation with sensual enjoyments. The court of Comus is the court of the 'many-headed monster' in both the Homeric and Platonic senses. Travelers wander into his realm and drink of his 'orient liquor,'

> which as they taste
> (For most do taste through fond intemperate thirst)
> Soon as the Potion works, their human count'nance,
> Th' express resemblance of the gods, is chang'd
> Into some brutish form. . . .
> And they, so perfect is their misery,
> Not once perceive their foul disfigurement,
> But boast themselves more comely than before,
> And all their friends, and native home forget
> To roul with pleasure in a sensual sty. (66-77.)

Of the uncontrolled delight in meats and drinks, the Lady says:

> If every just man that now pines with want
> Had but a moderate and beseeming share
> Of that which lewdly-pamper'd Luxury
> Now heaps upon some few with vast excess,
> Nature's full blessings would be well dispens't
> In unsuperfluous even proportion. (767-72.)

Thus the social as well as the individual effects of hedonism are the antithesis of good. So Plato held, and made the tyranny of appetite the lowest order not only for the soul but for the State.

But obviously the basest of pleasures is not that about which Comus and the Lady argue. Milton makes clear that the final degradation of the soul comes not from over-indulgence in food and drink, but

> when lust
> By unchaste looks, loose gestures, and foul talk,
> But most by lewd and lavish act of sin,
> Lets in defilement.

Then at length,

> The soul grows clotted by contagion,
> Imbodies, and imbrutes, till she quite lose
> The divine property of her first being. (462-8.)

In *Comus* Milton rejects pleasure as a good without any hesitation. But *Comus,* as we have said before, stems more from Spenser than from Plato.

In *Paradise Lost* there is a more Platonic distinction between necessary and unnecessary desires, pleasures right and wrong. Belial, a magnified Comus, comes last among the fallen angels,

> than whom a Spirit more lewd
> Fell not from Heaven, or more gross to love
> Vice for itself. (1. 490-2.)

His was the worship when

> Ely's Sons . . . fill'd
> With lust and violence the house of God.
> In Courts and Palaces he also Reigns
> And in luxurious Cities, where the noise
> Of riot ascends above their loftiest Tow'rs,
> And injury and outrage: And when Night
> Darkens the Streets, then wander forth the Sons
> Of Belial, flown with insolence and wine. (1. 495-502.)

Belial is thus the arch-hedonist, and Milton elsewhere describes 'the brood of Belial, the draff of men, to whom no liberty is pleasing but unbridled and vagabond lust' (3. 370).

But although pleasure taken as an end produces the monstrous Belial, pleasure subject to reason is not evil. Hence the large part accorded to sensual enjoyment in the Garden of Eden. Even the angelic hierarchy are not without senses and their delights, for hear Raphael's exposition of the manner of their enjoyment:

> What he [God] gives
> (Whose praise be ever sung) to man in part
> Spiritual, may of purest spirits be found
> No ingrateful food: and food alike those pure
> Intelligential substances require

> As doth your Rational; and both contain
> Within them every lower faculty
> Of sense, whereby they hear, see, smell, touch, taste,
> Tasting concoct, digest, assimilate,
> And corporeal to incorporeal turn.
> For know, whatever was created, needs
> To be sustain'd and fed; of Elements
> The grosser feeds the purer. (5. 404-16.)

The pleasures of sense, like the senses themselves, are of God's making, and are appointed to be the due satisfaction of natural desire. Only the perversion of values whereby the purer feeds the grosser results in the Comus-like perversion of incorporeal to corporeal. Milton's treatment of the love of Adam and Eve repeats this doctrine; the use of body is for spirit, of bodily delight for spiritual growth. Conversely, to separate bodily pleasure from, or magnify it above, spirit is to turn what God created good into evil. If we understand Milton's hierarchy of goods and his insistence that they be rigorously kept in order, we shall have no difficulty in reconciling the varied treatment of sensual pleasure in *Paradise Lost*. Nor shall we make the mistake, common among recent interpreters, of supposing that Milton exalts the goods of the body into an equality with goods of the soul.

The theme of Milton is constantly the theme of Plato:

> Nothing is so native to men as pleasure, pain, and desire; they are, so to say, the very wires or strings from which any mortal nature is inevitably and absolutely dependent. We have therefore to commend the noble life, not only as superior in comeliness of repute, but further as superior, if a man will but taste it and not decline it in the days of his youth, in that on which we are all set, life-long predominance of pleasures over pains. (*Laws* 5. 732 e-733 a.)

Since the central issue of *Paradise Regained* is the winning of happiness, we may look there for Milton's more explicit judgment of the goods men have made their end. To be sure, all Satan offers must be temptation, and the dramatic fiction therefore allows Milton to discuss only false goods. Within the frame of the debate, he can show the true *summum bonum* only by implication and by denial of the lesser goods. Pleasure is the first of them to be ruled out. Belial's suggestion even Satan at once dismisses:

> Belial the dissolutest Spirit that fell,
> The sensuallest, and after Asmodai
> The fleshliest Incubus . . . thus advis'd.
>   Set women in his eye and in his walk,
> Among daughters of men the fairest found; . . .
> Such object hath the power to soft'n and tame
> Severest temper, smooth the rugged'st brow,
> Enerve, and with voluptuous hope dissolve. . . .
>   To whom quick answer Satan thus return'd.
> Belial, in much uneven scale thou weigh'st
> All others by thyself. (2. 150-74.)

Jesus, who had already refused the satisfaction of simple hunger, was not likely to fall prey to lower appetites. In Biblical phrase, he had said:

> Think'st thou such force in Bread? is it not
>   written . . .
> Man lives not by Bread only, but each Word
> Proceeding from the mouth of God? (1. 347-50.)

The interpretation later given to this denial of hunger turns on the Platonic opposition of body and soul:

> Though hunger still remain: so it remain
> Without this body's wasting, I content me, . . .
> Nor mind it, fed with better thoughts that feed
> Mee hung'ring more to do my Fathers will. (2. 255-9.)

If Satan hopes to trap Jesus through 'Lawful desires of Nature,' he is defeated before he starts. He has been Platonist enough, as distinguished from Belial, to recognize that unnecessary and ignoble pleasures tempt only the most degraded; he is also Platonist enough to see that pleasures of sight and smell are more likely to win a noble mind than the pleasure of taste alone. The banquet he provides is therefore not for the mere gourmand, but for the aesthete. But Jesus replies to the whole offer:

> Thy pompous Delicacies I contemn. (2. 390.)

Satan has offered him all at once the most pleasant satisfaction for all honorable desires, but offered them in opposition to better goods. And Satan recognizes which of the goods Jesus has spurned, and which of the Platonic virtues he has demonstrated, observing:

> Thy temperance invincible besides,
> For no allurement yields to appetite. (2. 408-9.)

The temptation of pleasure comes again in connection with other goods, but still without the one good which makes the virtue of every other; and Jesus again rejects the lure:

> Nor doth this grandeur and majestic show
> Of luxury, though call'd magnificence,
> More than of arms before, allure mine eye,
> Much less my mind. (4. 110-3.)

And like Plato on the Syracusans, he condemns the people

> grown . . .
> Luxurious by thir wealth, and greedier still,
> And from the daily Scene effeminate. (4. 141-3.)

To those who set pleasure highest in the scale of goods Milton made one constant answer, the query in which Jesus speaks his utter scorn of the vulgar concern with the stomach:

> And with my hunger what hast thou to do? (2. 389.)

Neither Milton nor the Jesus of his *Paradise Regained* denies the need or the pleasure that would attend its satisfac-

78

tion, but there are more important principles of choice than the impulse of desire. The happy life will include satisfaction for every need; Jesus will banquet, when the temptations are over, on 'Celestial Food, Divine, Ambrosial,' will enjoy what is due to palate, eye, and ear—but not until he has put last things last. And pleasure is last in Milton's as in Plato's scale.

WEALTH

In the *Republic* Socrates ranks wealth as an object of pursuit intermediate between sensual pleasure and power. Like other goods popularly thought to be the means to happiness, wealth is itself neither good nor bad; but the undue importance usually given to it vulgarizes the soul, and its frequent use for a life of self-indulgence makes it a source of corruption. Of these principles Plato is convinced throughout the Dialogues. The good man will neither need nor desire, and is therefore not likely to obtain, great riches; while to the unjust man they are a positive evil, aiding him to accomplish his self-perversion. Since even honest gain if too zealously pursued taints the soul, and since the zealous pursuit of gain often leads to dishonesty, riches can hardly occupy the man bent on finding happiness. Yet Plato holds no ascetic ideal of poverty, but freely admits the deliberalizing effects of extreme want. The proper state is one of limited needs duly satisfied in order that a man may proceed to his proper tasks. And hence the careful regulations of wealth in the *Laws,* and the communism imposed upon the ruling class in the *Republic.* Let men be freed from the cares of poverty, and secured against the vices of luxury, thinks Plato, and they may then direct their attention to more humane concerns. He is thus at one with Ruskin in distinguishing between wealth and 'illth,' but even more decisively rejects popular notions of value.

For both, the test is usefulness for human good; but for Plato material prosperity cannot ever be of real benefit, and as it is far more likely to divert men from what is really beneficial, wealth must be spurned in the search for happiness.[3]

Like most high-minded men, Milton feels a similar scorn for the popular interest in money-making. If there is little that is distinctively Platonic in this feeling, still his agreement with Plato is complete. He dwells very little on the question of riches, thinking it a vulgar concern, and quickly turns his attention to more important matters. In an early letter, he compliments Thomas Young on being able to

reign peacefully over [his] little estate, and, despising fortune, triumph over wealth, ambition, pomp, luxury, and all that common men admire and gape at. (Tillyard, p. 9.)

The distinction between what the herd admires and the wise man's interest is repeated in *Ad Patrem:*

Go, gather wealth, fool, whoever you are, that prefer the ancient treasures of Austria, and of the Peruvian realms. But what more than learning could my father have given, or Jove himself had he given all but heaven? (Mac Kellar, p. 149.)

Here Milton believes, like Plato, that exaggerated interest in money is a perversion of the natural yearning for good, and opposed to the desire for knowledge.

In the anti-Prelatical writings, where Milton turns his attention to the economy of the Church, he necessarily becomes more concerned with the effects of wealth and its pursuit. And now his judgments become more recognizably Platonic. We need not repeat in detail his accusations against a money-loving clergy; a passage from the *Apology for Smectymnuus* will show their doctrinal basis:

Therefore must the ministers of Christ not be over-rich or

---

[2] See especially *Republic* 8. 549-55; *Laws* 5. 742-4.

-great in the world, because their calling is spiritual, not secular; because they have a special warfare, which is not to be entangled with many impediments, . . . and lastly because a middle estate is most proper to the office of teaching. (3. 364.)

Milton demands of the clergy what Plato demanded of his philosopher-kings: both groups, dedicated to a life of service, are to be freed from worldly concerns, not by embracing the life of poverty, but by being maintained in a 'middle estate,' untroubled by need, and unimpeded by wealth.

In *Eikonoclastes*, Milton restates the effect of wealth upon the clergy:

When ministers came to have lands, houses, farms, coaches, horses, and the like lumber, then religion brought forth riches in the Church, and the daughter devoured the mother. (5. 233.)

Thenceforth and with increasing emphasis, he connects wealth with the vices of luxury as surely as Plato held that a plutocracy was but one short step from the pleasure-seeking life of a democracy. In his first *Defensio*, he traces the corruption of the Church:

Afterwards, the Church, which he [Constantine] had vastly enriched, began to fall in love with offices, absolute rule, and secular power, and then the Christian religion went to wrack. First luxury and sloth, and then a crew of all the heresies and vices, as if their dungeons had been set open from behind, trooped over into the Church; thereupon envy, hatred, and discord overflowed everywhere, and at last they . . . were as much at variance and strife as the bitterest enemies. (7. 257-9.)

Finally, the *Means to Remove Hirelings* treats at length of the need to exorcise from the Church every last taint of acquisitiveness by prohibiting regular pay to ministers. Much in the vein of Plato's remarks on the Sophists who taught for money, Milton writes:

The corruption of teachers, most commonly the effect of

hire, is the very bane of truth in them who are so corrupted. (6. 46.)

Even more like the Platonic notion that philosophers must rule, and not for salary, is the assertion to Parliament:

Till which grievances be removed, and religion set free from the monopoly of hirelings, I dare affirm that no model whatsoever of a commonwealth will prove successful or undisturbed. (6. 45.)

The phrasing echoes the famous 'great wave' of the *Republic* 5. 473:

Unless philosophers bear kingly rule in cities, or those who are now called kings and princes become genuine and adequate philosophers, and political power and philosophy are brought together, . . . there will be no respite from evil, my dear Glaucon, for cities, nor, I fancy, for humanity.

And Milton echoes the conviction of Plato that from wealth flows ill, not good, that the just man, group, or nation will not be concerned with acquiring riches, and that riches could be useful to none but the just. Very close indeed to the account of civic degeneration in the *Republic* are these words from *Eikonoclastes:*

For wealth and plenty in a land where justice reigns not is no argument of a flourishing State, but of a nearness rather to ruin or commotion. (5. 154.)

The experience of cupidity in Church and State apparently taught Milton how prevalent and vicious was the money-hunting that he had once dismissed as merely perverse, for in his later poetry wealth receives more explicit treatment, and denunciation. Mammon he describes in *Paradise Lost* as

> the least erected Spirit that fell
> From heav'n, for ev'n in heav'n his looks
> and thoughts

> Were always downward bent, admiring more
> The riches of Heav'n's pavement, trodd'n Gold,
> Than aught divine or holy else enjoy'd
> In vision beatific. (1. 679-84.)

The principle of judgment is Platonic: he who concentrates upon the lesser good forgets the highest. And the admonition that follows shows how completely Milton had come to associate wealth with corruption:

> Let none admire
> That riches grow in Hell; that soil may best
> Deserve the precious bane. (1. 690-2.)

Later in the poem Michael comments on a part of the historical panorama he is presenting:

> For a while
> In mean estate live moderate, till grown
> In wealth and multitude, factious they grow. (12. 350-2.)

We are reminded of the change recounted in the *Republic* (2. 372-4) from the primitive State with its simple needs to the luxurious 'State at fever-heat' in which a military class is first required.

For Milton's most explicit judgment of wealth, as of every other good, we must turn to *Paradise Regained*. There Satan on finding that Jesus can resist the life of pleasure tries him with the temptation that Plato had thought a degree less base. Associating wealth with the power to which it may be a means, he argues:

> Great acts require great means of enterprise. . . .
> Money brings Honour, Friends, Conquest, and Realms. . . .
> Therefore, if at great things thou wouldst arrive,
> Get Riches first, get Wealth, and Treasure heap,
> Not difficult, if thou hearken to me,
> Riches are mine, Fortune is in my hand;
> They whom I favour thrive in wealth amain,
> While Virtue, Valour, Wisdom sit in want.

Jesus at once answers:

> Yet wealth without these three is impotent,
> To gain dominion or to keep it gain'd,
> Witness those ancient Empires of the Earth,
> In highth of all thir flowing wealth dissolv'd;
> But men endu'd with these have oft attain'd
> In lowest poverty to highest deeds. . . .
> Extol not Riches then, the toil of Fools,
> The wise man's cumbrance if not snare, more apt
> To slacken Virtue, and abate her edge,
> Than prompt her to do aught may merit praise. (2. 412-56.)

His reply is thoroughly Platonic: 'Virtue, Valour, Wisdom' are the true necessities; without them wealth causes its own ruin. So Socrates had argued:

> The excess of wealth, and the neglect of all else but money-making, destroyed oligarchy. (*Rep.* 8. 562.)

Further, against the many who suppose wealth to be the object of the State, Plato's second lawgiver, the Athenian, asserted:

> I can never concede . . . that a rich man is truly happy unless he is also a good man; but that one who is exceptionally good should be exceptionally wealthy too is a mere impossibility. (*Laws* 5. 743 a.)

Ultimately each man must choose among the so-called goods, not only as one surpasses another, but as pursuit of one hinders pursuit of another. With Milton as with Plato there can be no question between wealth and virtue, and Plato's sentence will suffice to state the final judgment both make:

> Purchase for purchase, I shall have made a better bargain in a better cause, if I choose to get rectitude for my soul rather than wealth for my pocket. (*Laws* 11. 913.)

If Plato and Milton are not alone in this belief, still we

do well to remember that some, even among philosophers, have not shared it. Milton at least was conscious of another opinion on the subject, for in *Paradise Regained* he has Jesus remark of one school of thought:

> Others in virtue plac'd felicity,
> But virtue join'd with riches and long life. (4. 297-8.)

The others are clearly of the Peripatetic school, repeating the words of Aristotle:

> He is happy who is active in accordance with complete virtue and is sufficiently equipped with external goods, not for some chance period but throughout a complete life. (*Eth. Nic.* I. 10. 1101a.)

Plato alone among ancient philosophers placed felicity in a virtue neither ascetic like that of the Stoics nor dependent upon good fortune like that of the Peripatetics, but a virtue which of itself would bring all lesser goods by its very independence of them. When Jesus, at the end of his trials, becomes 'heir of both worlds,' gaining wealth far beyond Satan's most lavish offer, Milton surely has it in mind to demonstrate the Biblical maxim of Matthew 6. 33: 'But seek ye first the kingdom of God, and his righteousness; and all these things shall be added unto you.' But he might also take the reward as proof of the Platonic doctrine:

> For surely the gods do not neglect him who will bestir himself to become just. . . . Then at the hands of gods the just man will get some such prizes as these. . . . At the end of every action and partnership, and at the end of life, they [the just] win a good report and carry off prizes at men's hand. (*Rep.* 10. 613.)

The principle, whether taken from the Bible or from Plato, is the same; and Milton, a Christian Platonist, holds it firmly. Wealth, far from being the chief good or even its necessary support, is a hindrance to man's true object; and only when scorned for itself, can it be appropriately and in due measure added to adorn the happiness which must be sought elsewhere.

FAME

Milton gives to 'fame' much the same meaning and value as Plato gives to τιμή; both occasionally use other words for the concept.[4] By derivation, 'fame' simply means report, and τιμή worth; ordinarily, however, both words signify high esteem, one of the goods chiefly desired by mankind. In Plato's scheme this desire is next to the highest, which is of wisdom and virtue. Indeed, the yearning for honor is the least perverted expression of a universal longing for eternal happiness, the root of every desire. Those who are dominated by love of τιμή are the ambitious, the φιλότιμοι, ranking in worth just below the best men who control this love by a higher, the φιλόσοφοι. Still, ambition itself can control lower appetites, and not the desire but its dominion over the higher love is wrong; for all men want what the φιλότιμοι want, not only as all want everlasting happiness, which these think to obtain by honor, but as all want a fair reputation. The great difference is that the φιλόσοφος wishes to deserve esteem; the φιλότιμος primarily regards the esteem, whether or not it is duly earned. In consequence, while to the lover of wisdom only the opinion of wise and good men is important, the lover of honor cares little about the source of his praise. And hence the philosopher desires and secures a truer and more perfect honor than he who seeks honor alone. True fame lies not simply in high esteem, but in the merited esteem of good judges, or even in merit whether it is recognized or not. In this last sense of τιμή, the Athenian of the *Laws* can affirm:

Honor, I take it, is a thing divinely good, and can be conferred by nothing that is evil. (*Laws* 5. 727 a.)

[4] See Ast, *Lexicon Platonicum* under δόξα and φήμη as well as τιμή. The various terms used by Milton appear in the present section.

This conception of τιμή reappears in every detail in Milton's treatment of fame. To what extent Milton himself shared the universal longing for good repute the autobiographical portions of his verse and prose amply reveal. Commentators have exaggerated his desire as idiosyncratic; Milton recognized it as human, in himself because in all mankind. As early as the year 1632 or 1633, he admitted the existence of

a desire of honor and repute and immortal fame seated in the breast of every true scholar. (12. 324.)

The fame desired is immortal, as Plato held, and the men to whom the desire is imputed are a class better than most.

But while still an undergraduate at Christ's College Milton had recognized an even more desirable state:

To have no thought of glory when we do well is above all glory. (Tillyard, pp. 117-8.)

The higher spirits are more tempted by praise, while the highest overcome the temptation. Because Milton keenly feels this superiority, he denies with emphasis the charge of writing for renown:

But I was not eager for fame, who is slow of pace; indeed, if the fit opportunity had not been given me, even these things would never have seen the light; little concerned, though others were ignorant that I knew what I did. It was not the fame of every thing that I was waiting for, but the opportunity. (8. 113.)

Like Plato, he thus comes to have what seems a varying, but is in fact a steady, view of honor. The esteem won from the ignorant many becomes despicable in *Paradise Lost:*

Thus Fame shall be achiev'd, renown on Earth,
And what most merits fame in silence hid. (11. 698-9.)

They who care for such renown, the φιλότιμοι at their worst, eventually come to wish, as Nimrod wished, simply to

> get themselves a name, lest far disperst
> In foreign Lands thir memory be lost,
> Regardless whether good or evil fame. (12. 45-7.)

But as there is worthless praise, the ignorant acclaim of undeserving men, there is also a glory more properly desirable, the deserved regard of the judicious; and this praise Milton could wish to have.

In his first Academic Exercise at Cambridge he was already aware that his audience must be few if they were to be fit:

> The approval of these, few though they be, is more precious to me than that of the countless hosts of the ignorant, who lack all intelligence, reasoning power, and sound judgment. (Tillyard, pp. 53-4.)

He asks in the *Reason of Church-Government* to be 'heard' only, if it might be, by the elegant and learned reader' (3. 234)—because here fitness to judge depends upon a knowledge comparable to the learnedness of the subject. But where erudition and elegance are not demanded by the occasion, Milton's fit audience is composed of the morally even more than of the intellectually eminent. In 1659, presumably at the time when he was composing *Paradise Lost*, he wrote to Jean Labadie:

> It is my conviction that the only real fame I can claim is the good opinion held of me by good men. (Tillyard, p. 47.)

The sentence is an accurate condensation of Plato's scattered remarks on τιμή.

From this distinction between proper and improper judges, it is but a step to the notion that truest fame is the opinion of the truest judge, God. Here a Christian element enters the concept which thus far exactly reproduces that of Plato, but only the character of the judge alters, not the character of the judgment; for Plato, like Milton, held the final decision on human worth to be beyond human wisdom, and the true honor divine. Thus in *Comus*, the glory awarded is Plato's own notion of τιμή with nothing supra-Platonic in the lines but the word 'faith':

> Heav'n hath timely tri'd their youth,
> Their faith, their patience, and their truth.
> And sent them here through hard assays
> With a crown of deathless Praise. (969-72.)

Again the eloquent passage in *Lycidas* contains no element opposed to Plato's view. The 'Dorick' singer begins:

> Alas! What boots it with uncessant care
> To tend the homely slighted Shepherd's trade,
> And strictly meditate the thankless Muse?
> Were it not better done as others use,
> To sport with Amaryllis in the shade,
> Or with the tangles of Neaera's hair?
> Fame is the spur that the clear spirit doth raise
> (That last infirmity of Noble mind)
> To scorn delights, and live laborious days.

According to Plato also, the desire of fame can stir men to unwonted toil. Wise Diotima explains the impulse, and specifically names poets among those most affected by it:

Marvel not then at the love which all men have of their off-spring; for that universal love and interest is for the sake of immortality. . . . Of that, Socrates, you may be assured;—think only of the ambition of men, and you will wonder at the sense-lessness of their ways, unless you consider how they are stirred by the love of an immortality of fame. They are ready to run all risks, greater far than they would have run for their children, and to spend money and undergo any sort of toil, and even to die, for the sake of leaving behind them a name which shall be eternal. . . . I am persuaded that all men do all things, and the better they are the more they do them, in hope of the glorious fame of immortal virtue; for they desire the immortal.

Those who are pregnant in the body only, betake themselves to women and beget children—this is the character of their love; their offspring, as they hope, will preserve their memory and give them the blessedness and immortality which they desire in the future. But souls which are pregnant—for there certainly are men who are more creative in their souls than in their bodies—conceive that which is proper for the soul to conceive or contain. And what are these conceptions?—wisdom and virtue in general. And such creatures are poets and all artists who are deserving of the name inventor. (*Symposium* 208-9.)

Ambition can thus cast out every lower desire as Socrates affirms in the *Republic* (9. 581) and elsewhere. And still the hope of praise is an infirmity, though the last since least erroneous: the φιλότιμος is just below the φιλόσοφος, since the nobler mind is naturally more susceptible to the error nearest the true way. (Cf. *Phaedrus* 256 and *Republic* 6. 491-2.) But the desire, even when of merit as well as of acclaim, is still in error, as life itself, the test of ethical truth, demonstrates:

> But the fair Guerdon when we hope to find,
> And think to burst out into sudden blaze,
> Comes the blind Fury with th' abhorred shears,
> And slits the thin-spun life.

Why, then, the toil of virtue if the reward is uncertain, the singer asks, much as Glaucon and Adeimantus had asked of Socrates (*Rep.* 2. 358-68); and he receives a Socratic answer:

> Fame is no plant that grows on mortal soil,
> Nor in the glistering foil
> Set off to th' world, nor in broad rumour lies,
> But lives and spreads aloft by those pure eyes,
> And perfet witness of all judging Jove;
> As He pronounces lastly on each deed,
> Of so much fame in Heav'n expect thy meed.

Only the 'perfet witness' can pronounce true praise or blame, the everlasting honor is in the deed itself, recognition is therefore desirable and meaningful only from the knowing judge, and he will assuredly grant it.

Compare this concept of fame with that of others, and its Platonism shows clear. Virgil's notion, for example, which Milton, following Downham, carefully dissected in his *Logic* (11. 274-8), is merely 'broad rumour,' here rejected as inadequate. Closer to Milton's view is the discussion in Cicero's *Dream of Scipio;* but even that passage, though in the Academic strain, resembles Milton's less completely than the scattered reflections of Plato. Plato and Milton, unlike Cicero and Virgil, grant that the human need for recognition is an integral part of the desire for happiness and that every human need if kept in due proportion can be itself right and rightly satisfied. Τιμή is not to be discarded because virtue is more desirable, but rather to be transmuted into the image of virtue, to lose its infirmity and become the strength and solace of the noble mind. When the various desires follow truth, says Plato, they each enjoy 'the truest pleasures that they are capable of receiving' (*Rep.* 9. 586-7). Wherefore the Athenian Stranger maintains:

When I bid men honor their own souls next to the gods, our sovereign lords, and the powers under them, the counsel I give is right. Yet not a man of us, I may say, honors his soul aright, though he dreams he does. Honor, I take it, is a thing divinely good, and can be conferred by nothing that is evil. . . . Honor, we hold, is, in sum, to follow after what is better, and for what is worse but may be amended, e'en to make it good as best may be. (*Laws* 5. 727-8.)

Worth and honor are thus ultimately identical since they are identical with the happiness of man. The proper distinction is between true and false notions of honor. If there is a difference between the views of Milton and Plato, it is the higher importance in Milton of the 'perfet witness,' in Plato of the inner consciousness of worth.

Paradise Regained repeats every element of the doctrine in *Lycidas,* but more fully and with a more complete opposition of heavenly to earthly glory. As the treatment is enlarged, Milton's shift of emphasis becomes clearer, while his essential agreement with Plato remains. From the first, Jesus desires high achievements. He recollects how, as a boy,

> my Spirit aspir'd, victorious deeds
> Flam'd in my heart, heroic acts. (1. 215-6.)

And his mother encouraged him, even as Plato or Milton would:

> High are thy thoughts
> O Son, but nourish them and let them soar
> To what highth sacred virtue and true worth
> Can raise them, though above example high. (1. 229-32.)

Satan immediately recognizes the 'timocratic' character in Jesus:

> But he whom we attempt is wiser far
> Than Solomon, of more exalted mind,
> Made and set wholly on the accomplishment
> Of greatest things. (2. 205-8.)

Knowing this, Satan rejects the advice of Belial that he tempt Jesus with sensual pleasures, and counters:

> With manlier objects we must try
> His constancy, with such as have more shew
> Of worth, of honour, glory, and popular praise. (2. 226-8.)

Many a philosophical nature has been deluded by Satan's very first argument:

> All thy heart is set on high designs,

> High actions; but wherewith to be achiev'd?
> Great acts require great means of enterprise. (2. 410-2.)

History records their names and Plato explains their fall from the first high purpose.

> Then consider how many and how great are the causes of destruction to those rare souls. . . . One you will be extremely surprised to hear. Each of those very qualities which we praised as belonging to the philosophic nature destroys the soul possessing them and draws it away from philosophy—I mean courage, temperance, and the rest. . . . Or do you fancy that great crimes and unmixed wickedness come from a feeble nature and not rather from a noble nature ruined by education? (*Rep.* 6. 491.)

Knowing his own powers, knowing what such powers can win, Jesus would seem fair prey to the next of Satan's arguments for fame:

> These God-like Virtues wherefore dost thou hide?
> Affecting private life, or more obscure
> In savage Wilderness, wherefore deprive
> All Earth her wonder at thy acts, thyself
> The fame and glory, glory the reward
> That sole excites to high attempts the flame
> Of most erected Spirits, most temper'd pure
> Aetherial, who all pleasures else despise,
> All treasures and all gain esteem as dross,
> And dignities and powers all but the highest. (3. 21-30.)

Ever the sophist, Satan has mixed his little lie into the truth. 'Fame *is* the spur,' but not the sole one. It does excite the 'noble mind,' but not the *'most* erected.' The ambitious do 'scorn delights,' but so do others. Jesus refutes this sophistry by first distinguishing between the two kinds of fame:

> What is glory, but the blaze of fame,

> The people's praise, if always praise unmixt?
> And what the people but a herd confus'd,
> A miscellaneous rabble, who extol
> Things vulgar, and well weigh'd, scarce worth
>   the praise?
> They praise and they admire they know not what;
> And know not whom, but as one leads the other;
> And what delight to be by such extoll'd,
> To live upon thir tongues and be thir talk,
> Of whom to be disprais'd were no small praise?
> His lot who dares be singularly good.
> Th' intelligent among them and the wise
> Are few, and glory scarce of few is rais'd. (3. 47-59.)

This is what Socrates had repeated in the Dialogues, and the Athenian of the *Laws* had said. The confused opinion of the rabble is not fame, while the judicious are too few to grant renown. Only one right hope of esteem can remain:

> This is true glory and renown, when God
> Looking on the Earth, with approbation marks
> The just man, and divulges him through Heaven
> To all his Angels, who with true applause
> Recount his praises. (3. 60-4.)

Again Milton has shifted from the Platonic emphasis on inner merit to the Christian emphasis on heavenly glory. But 'the just man' who wins 'true glory and renown' is Plato's. Milton gives us assurance on this point: the first illustration of this true glory is Biblical Job, but the second is Socrates,

> Poor Socrates (who next more memorable?)
> By what he taught and suffer'd for so doing,
> For truth's sake suffering death unjust, lives now
> Equal in fame to proudest Conquerors. (3. 96-9.)

Plato was right. Remember that, in discussing how the

94

philosophical nature deteriorates into the ambitious, he had made Socrates prefigure his own martyrdom; the last inducement against philosophical pursuits was the practical argument of 'dishonor, fines, and death' (*Rep.* 6. 492). And Socrates ended the discussion by asserting that the philosophical nature, if it is to be saved at all, must be 'saved by the power of God.' Jesus is the philosopher saved by divine power, as Job and Socrates were saved for pursuit of the real praise. The question and answer to Satan are:

> Shall I seek glory then, as vain men seek
> Oft not deserv'd? I seek not mine, but his
> Who sent me, and thereby witness whence I am. (3. 106-8.)

Again the Christian change is struck in Plato's tune, and yet once more repeated:

> Yet so much bounty is in God, such grace,
> That who advance his glory, not thir own,
> Them he himself to glory will advance. (3. 142-4.)

Jesus, however, apparently thinks Socrates among those who sought to advance the glory of God; and Milton consequently would seem to make no distinction between Plato's insistence on inner worth and his own insistence on the heavenly reward of worth.

At any rate, the semi-Platonic sophistry of the tempter is refuted by the wholly Platonic philosophy of Jesus. Whether or not a supra-Platonic line completes the argument, it does complete the adventure, for Milton is not content to leave his philosopher with the τιμή of unregarded merit, but at the last gives him the express honor of hearing an angelic choir sing:

> Queller of Satan, on thy *glorious* work
> Now enter, and begin to save mankind.
>   (4. 634-5, italics mine.)

PLATONIC DOCTRINES CITED BY MILTON
ETHICS

Plato heads the list of 'moral works' to be studied in an academy. *Of Ed.* (4. 284.)

Love

Alcibiades' love of Socrates is associated with seeking the other half of one's soul. *Eleg.* 4. 23-4.

Socratic doctrine taught Milton to reject the yoke of desire *Eleg.* 7, Postscript.

Milton learned the doctrine of true love from Plato and Xenophon. *Ap. Smect.* (3. 305.)

The myth of love's birth in the *Symposium* agrees with the Mosaic account. *D.D.D.* (3. 398.)

The myth of Aristophanes in the *Symposium* erroneously suggests that man and woman are equal. *Tetrach.* (4. 76.)

Knowledge

Socratic ignorance is coupled with the caution of the sceptics. *Prolus.* 7 (12. 280.)

The learned conferences of Plato would be worth hearing *Prolus.* 7 (12. 262-4.)

The Sophists, who taught for hire, were refuted by the Socratics. *Church-Gov.* (3. 202.)

Socrates in the Dialogues often refutes Sophists. *Ap. Smect* (3. 293-4.)

Those who could not refute Socrates blamed his persuasive power. *Tetrach.* (4. 70.)

Socrates died for the sake of truth. *P.R.* 3. 96-9.

Socrates rightly professed ignorance, and was therefore the wisest of the heathen. *P.R.* 4. 293-4.

Virtue

Every man has a guiding genius in his conscience. *Ap. Smect.* (3. 318.)

Admonition and reproof purify the soul according to Plato *Church-Gov.* (3. 264.)

Both destiny and will must combine to make men virtuous according to Academic doctrine. *D.D.D.* (3. 441.)

Men err involuntarily, as Plato says in *Protagoras* and elsewhere. *D.D.D.* (3. 464.)

Fame

Socrates won true fame through his virtue. *P.R.* 3. 96-9.

Amusement

Socrates often indulged in jests. *Prolus.* 6 (12. 218, 238.)

Plato's Dialogues are like mimes, and Plato enjoyed the humor of mimes. *Ap. Smect.* (3. 293-4.)

There is much jesting in the Dialogues. *Pro Se Def.* (9. 176, 180-2.)

Plato indulged in fables and 'smooth conceits.' *P.R.* 4. 295.

POLITICS

Plato, the 'wisest of the heathen,' is an authority on law. *Church-Gov.* (3. 181-2.)

The Ideal State

Plato rightly thought slight changes in custom a danger to the State. To Buommattei (12. 32.)

Plato's mythical island in *Critias* teaches us better notions of government. *Ap. Smect.* (3. 294.)

The censorship of the *Republic* is unnecessarily severe. *Tetrach.* (4. 157-8.)

The presentation of Utopian states as in the *Republic* is useless, and the censorship there favored is erroneous. *Areop.* (4. 316-7.)

Plato's 'laws of virtuous education' are the true safeguard of his ideal State. *Areop.* (4. 318.)

Law

Laws should have an explanatory preface, as Plato says in the *Laws. Church-Gov.* (3. 181-2.)

According to the *Laws* 4, there should be no contradictory statutes. *D.D.D.* (3. 458-9.)

Law and nature really agree, as Socrates shows in *Gorgias*. *D.D.D.* (3. 500-1.)

The Ruler

According to Plato and others the good of the State constitutes the good of the king. *Of Ref.* (3. 39.)

Plato calls magistrates the servants of the Law in the *Laws* and the Eighth *Epistle. Def.* (7. 158, 166-8, 304-6.)

Plato, one of the wisest men, praised Lycurgus for limiting the king's power. *Def.* (7. 348-50.)

Education

Plato's system of education is the proper basis of his ideal State. *Areop.* (4. 318.)

'Socratic discourses' are to be used as books on educational theory in the proposed academies. *Of Ed.* (4. 281.)

The proposed academy is like that of Plato, and should prevent defects in the State. *Of Ed.* (4. 287.)

Marriage

In the *Laws* 6, Plato affirmed that offspring were desirable, and related the institution of marriage to the good of the State. *Tetrach.* (4. 81.)

Liberty

Plato recommended the works of Aristophanes, although these seem to be the kind he would have censored. *Areop.* (4. 299.)

In the Eighth *Epistle,* Plato advocated a just mixture of law and liberty. *Def.* (7. 350.)

THEORIES OF ART

Plato was provided with 'grave Doric' arts to substitute for those he banned from the *Republic. Areop.* (4. 317.)

Poetry

The myth in *Phaedrus* has given Milton an image of his own poetic hopes. To Diodati (12. 26.)

Rhetoric

Rhetoric is to be taught from the 'rule of Plato' and others. *Of Ed.* (4. 286.)

For the proper use of jests, see *Ethics: Amusement.*

Music

Plato rightly followed Pythagoras in maintaining the doctrine of the harmony of the spheres. *Prolus.* 2 (12. 150.)

METAPHYSICS

Plato is a most skilful interpreter of nature. *Prolus.* 2 (12. 150.)

The Cosmos

Milton will 'unsphere' Plato to learn where the souls of the dead dwell. *Il Pens.* 87-96.

The Ideas

Aristotle looks for the Platonic Idea in the wrong way. *Idea Plat.*

Milton seeks the Idea of the Beautiful described in *Phaëdrus.* To Diodati (12. 26.)

CHAPTER V

The Good Life: Knowledge

LIKE Plato, Milton rejects pleasure, wealth, and power with its attendant fame, as the chief means to happiness. Only one good remains in the Platonic scheme, knowledge or wisdom, between which terms Plato makes little distinction. Philosophy is the love of the rational element of the soul; its object, truth, becomes knowledge in possession and wisdom in action. For Plato wisdom as the function or virtue is always the immediate effect of knowledge, which is the form of truth in the mind. As such, knowledge is the ultimate goal of all men's striving, if they but knew it; for the happiness universally sought is eternal possession of the good, and the good by its very nature can be possessed only by being known. Further, knowledge by producing wisdom produces all virtue—justice, fortitude, and temperance being so many aspects of the single habit of choice that results from vision of truth. And hence philosophy is the real pursuit of happiness, and knowledge the *summum bonum.*

Not every kind of knowledge, however. According to *Charmides* 174, 'the crown of happiness' is bestowed by the 'science of good and evil.' The Idea of the Good, mystically presented in the *Republic* as an object of knowledge higher than justice and the other virtues, means at one time the source of all truth imaginatively seen in its unity, at another the ethical concept of perfect virtue. In general, throughout the Dialogues, ethical knowledge is the highest, the ultimate truth, and every other learning is subordinated as a tool of this science or a discipline preparatory to it. Since ethics and politics are for Plato merely the individual and social aspects of a single body of principles, the architectonic science of the good appears now as the 'kingly art, having supreme authority' (as in *Euthydemus* 291), now as the guide of personal life.

For this reason the kings of the *Republic* are to be philosophers, and the guardians of the *Laws* are to have special instruction in the 'one idea' which is the single principle in virtue and the good, and, even more important, a training in theology not required of most citizens. (See the *Laws* 12. 965-6.) In Plato's thought, as seldom outside of some Christian writings, knowledge of God, of truth, and of the good become one and inseparable. And because he regards the whole of human life as a unit, and the guiding of it to proper ends as a single task, he rigorously subordinates every other activity, intellectual or productive, to the principal activity, and every other knowledge, of theory or craft, to the architectonic knowledge of philosophy.

And hence the seeming inconsistency of various passages in the Dialogues. At one time natural science is derided as well-nigh useless, but at another receives remarkably thorough attention. Here poets are banished from the Republic, there taken as the 'fathers to us of all knowledge.' But however the particular judgment varies with the occasion, a constant principle remains: Keep first things and the knowledge of them first. Where a subordinate learning impedes, dispense with it; where it can be the instrument of a higher, retain it. There is much mockery of useless knowledge in the Dialogues, but no knowledge is ever condemned in itself; it is useless when given undue importance or employed for a wrong end. Only one kind of knowledge may exist for its own sake, and that is the kind that never professes to: the ethical knowledge represented as the pursuit of Socrates, and figured in the various dialogues as the Absolute Beauty, the Good, or the 'one idea' in all the virtues.

True knowledge, and Plato refuses to call any other sort knowledge at all, is thus the chief good, intellectually as it satisfies the desire of reason for truth, ethically since it corresponds to and produces the ruling virtue of the soul, and politically because in application to the social life of man it begets the highest order of civilization. If Aristotle disliked Plato's 'Universal Good' because it could mean many things, Plato apparently liked it for that very reason: the Idea of the Good can unite in symbol all the varied aspects of the happiness which man attains through knowledge.

With Milton the highest good for man is a synthesis of elements even more diverse than entered into the concept of Plato, but again unified, as was Plato's by a single principle. The principle is no longer Platonic, but Plato took Milton far on his way toward a distinctively Christian goal for men. He had only to cap the Platonic ideal in order to change the highest good from the philosophical life praised in the Dialogues to the 'more abundant' life of Christianity. Augustine had said of the Platonists, in *The City of God* (8.5), *'Nulli nobis quam isti proprius accesserunt.'* And Ficino had written to his fellow-Platonist, Giovanni Pico della Mirandola: *'Philosophica ingenia ad Christum perveniunt per Platonem.'* Milton felt the same. We find in his ethic nothing subtracted from Plato's, but only something added.

For Milton, as in the Dialogues, knowledge far surpasses the other goals men set themselves, as more fully satisfactory to the whole of human nature. The glorification of philosophy in his Cambridge exercises already resembles Plato's, especially the Seventh in Defense of Knowledge, with its rejection of Ignorance as 'the life of a beast.' The wise lady of the *Symposium* may have taught the matter for his argument:

God would indeed seem to have endowed us to no purpose, or even to our distress, with this soul which is capable and indeed insatiably desirous of the highest wisdom, if he had not intended us to strive with all our might toward the lofty understanding of those things, for which he had at our creation instilled so great a longing into the human mind. (Tillyard, pp. 107-8.)

And even beyond satisfying the mind, knowledge provides the key to happiness, individual and social:

If then Learning is our guide and leader in the search after happiness, if it is ordained and approved by almighty God, and most conformable to His glory, surely it cannot but bring the greatest blessings upon those who follow after it. . . .

And indeed a single household, even a single individual, endowed with the gifts of Art and Wisdom, may often prove to be a great gift of God, and sufficient to lead a whole State to righteousness. (*Ibid.*, pp. 108-9.)

And hence in the letter to Gill, July 2, 1628, the disapproval of those who

take their flight to theology before ever they are fledged, almost untrained and uninitiated in literature and philosophy alike. (P. 8.)

These are the 'blind mouths' of *Lycidas,* who

> scarce themselves know how to hold
> A Sheep-hook, or have learn'd aught else the least
> That to the faithful Herdman's art belongs!

With Milton, the charge of ignorance is as damning as with Plato.

Similarly, in defending knowledge against the groundless accusations of the uninitiate, they are at one. As the younger brother in *Comus* puts it:

> How charming is divine Philosophy!
> Not harsh and crabbed as dull fools suppose,
> But musical as is Apollo's lute,
> And a perpetual feast of nectar'd sweets,
> Where no crude surfeit reigns. (475-80.)

The last phrase looks forward to Adam's speech of gratitude for the instruction Raphael has given him:

> [Fruits] satiate, and soon fill,
> Though pleasant, but thy words with Grace Divine
> Imbu'd, bring to thir sweetness no satiety. (8. 214-6.)

Thus Plato had opposed the pleasures of learning to those of sense, and Milton twice adopts the opposition in order to magnify knowledge in the scale of human good.

Milton, who took 'intent study' as his 'portion in this life,' spoke of the joy he himself felt in 'beholding the bright countenance of truth in the quiet and still air of delightful studies' (*Church-Gov.* 3. 241). To be sure, men innumerable have found learning a delight, and if this were the whole or even a separable aspect of Milton's theory, we should hardly call it Platonic. But in Milton and Plato we find the same emphasis on the charm of study coupled with the same critical scrutiny of its use. Both insist on the constant devotion of subordinate learnings to a higher end, and reserve for that end the term 'knowledge.' The true knowledge satisfies reason, promotes virtue, and serves the common weal. Hear Milton, then, on false learning:

> Finally, the supreme result of all this earnest labor is to make you a more finished fool and cleverer contriver of conceits, and to endow you with a more expert ignorance. . . .
>
> For the rest, even were I silent, it is amply clear to you how little these trivialities contribute to morality or purity of life, which is the most important consideration of all. From this obviously follows my final point, namely that this unseemly battle of words tends neither to the general good nor to the

honor and profit of our country, which is generally considered the supreme purpose of all sciences. (Tillyard, p. 71.)

And note in this same attack on the scholastic philosophy, his concept of useful learning:

But let not your mind rest content to be bounded and cabined by the limits which encompass the earth, but let it wander beyond the confines of the world, and at the last attain the summit of all human wisdom and learn to know itself, and therewith those holy minds and intelligences whose company it must hereafter join. (*Ibid.*, p. 72.)

We are reminded of Plato here in the reminiscence of the Delphic 'Know thyself' which Socrates took as his maxim,[1] and again when the test of learning is made its use, not in a narrowly 'pragmatic' sense, but for the humane happiness by which every supposed good is to be measured. By this test, many kinds of knowledge are found wanting, and Milton condemns them always in the same terms:

These studies promote neither delight nor instruction, nor indeed do they serve any useful purpose whatsoever. (Tillyard, p. 68.)

The word by which Milton expresses his contempt of false learning is 'sophistry.' It is Plato's word, and we know from the *Reason of Church-Government* (3. 202), and from the *Apology for Smectymnuus* (3. 293-4), that Milton associated it with Plato. In the Third *Prolusion,* where he first spoke his dislike of scholastic philosophy, Milton was already identifying waste and abuse of study with false teaching, deriding the 'warty controversies of the sophists' (C.E. 12. 159),[2] and characterizing the 'moulders of sophis-

---

[1] Compare Milton's definition of 'a true knower of himself' as one 'in whom contemplation and practice, wit, prudence, fortitude, and eloquence' meet. (*Church-Gov.* 3. 186.)

[2] In this passage and the one on the next page, the Columbia translation shows the point more clearly than Mrs. Tillyard's.

tries' in the manner of Plato as 'inclined by some innate tendency to quarrels and dissension, prating fellows moreover, and such as detest and ever turn away from sound and wholesome wisdom' (Tillyard, p. 70). Thenceforth Milton constantly drew an ever clearer line between knowledge and the 'Lernaean swamp of sophisms, contrived for shipwreck and destruction' (C.E. 12. 277); until in the *Reason of Church-Government* he finally declares that the 'thorny lectures of monkish and miserable sophistry . . . [have] stopped and hindered all true and generous philosophy from entering' (3. 273).

This opposition of 'sound and wholesome wisdom' to its deceptive semblance is Plato's own; and for Milton, his opponents in theology and politics adequately fill the role assigned in the Dialogues to the tribe of Sophists. Pretenders to learning, ignorant of all correct doctrine, eager for pay, careless of the true end of instruction, they represent the very antithesis of the scholars whose company Milton wished to join, and their fancied erudition the opposite of the studies that foster life. But however sternly Milton and Plato reject 'the foreign, the superfluous, the useless,' in learning, and however harsh their constant censure of the 'dangerous deceiver' with his 'sly shuffle of counterfeit principles,' they both retain the conviction that pursuit of knowledge is the activity for which man was intended. And although difficult, the pursuit is the avenue to happiness.

The concept Milton held of the knowledge worth this toil and of its use in rendering man happy appears throughout his works. Oliver Morley Ainsworth has collected a number of relevant excerpts in his edition of the Tractate *Of Education,* and Ida Langdon's study of *Milton's Theory of Poetry and Fine Art* bears upon the problem. But for our present purpose, a single passage from the *Reason of Church-Government* will suffice:

How happy were it for this frail and, as it may be truly called, mortal life of man, since all earthly things which have the name of good and convenient in our daily use, are withal so cumbersome and full of trouble, if knowledge yet, which is the best and lightsomest possession of the mind, were, as the common saying is, no burden; . . . for not to speak of that knowledge that rests in the contemplation of natural causes and dimensions, which must needs be a lower wisdom as the object is low, certain it is that he who hath obtained in more than the scantest measure to know anything distinctly of God, and of his true worship, and what is infallibly good and happy in the state of man's life, what in itself evil and miserable, though vulgarly not so esteemed, he that hath obtained to know this, the only high valuable wisdom indeed, . . . cannot but sustain a sorer burden of mind and more pressing than any supportable toil or weight which the body can labor under; how and in what manner he shall dispose and employ those sums of knowledge and illumination which God hath sent him into this world to trade with. (3. 229.)

The constituents of 'the only high valuable wisdom' which Milton here names are precisely those set for the advanced training of the guardian class in the *Laws*. Knowledge of 'natural causes and dimensions' is, as Plato thought it, a 'lower wisdom.' The higher is not easy to win, and when won, becomes a responsibility to its possessor. Like Plato, Milton is fully aware of the debt imposed on the few who can win the knowledge that constitutes the happiness of all men. Always with the consciousness of 'gifts of God's imparting' must go the 'fear lest they be reckoned many rather than few' (3. 282); always the philosopher must conceive of himself 'as a member incorporate into that truth' (3. 284) which he has won. The Platonic view that philosophers must take upon themselves the burdens of society, not resting in contemplation, but returning to instruct and guide the benighted dwellers in the Cave; this view, which has seemed to many an inconsistency in Plato, is precisely Milton's understanding of the function of knowledge.

If Milton or Plato had supposed that the highest truth resides in any knowledge but that of good and evil, we might find them less unwilling to accept contemplation divorced from practice as the great source of happiness. Plato is often thought to have done this very thing, but hardly by so careful a student as Milton. The entire design of the *Republic* is to show the proper relation of reason, will, and appetite, not merely in the individual, but in the organically unified State. The *Laws,* again, is deeply concerned with the practical life of the body politic. And the glorified Socrates of the Dialogues consistently engages in the social work of stinging his fellow-citizens to learn and practice the good life. Plato nowhere praises a reclusive contemplation at the cost of social benefit. He could not and still retain his belief that ethical studies are the knowledge in which human happiness is rooted. And similarly Milton, accepting ethics as the architectonic science, must regard true knowledge and practice as one; or to use his own terms, he cannot regard 'discipline' as anything but 'the execution and applying of doctrine home' (3. 6).

Thus far we have found a marked similarity between Milton's view of knowledge and the belief of Plato that philosophy is the highest good for man. Their rejection of sophistical learning is merely the negative aspect of a high faith in true knowledge rightly used. Milton moves from an early enthusiasm for studies to a conviction, more pronounced in his later writings, that the noblest study, unlike inferior kinds, bears within itself what is needed for individual and social well-being. But he has a test for 'sound doctrine' that Plato could not have, the explicit revelation of truth by God. And emboldened by possessing an indubitable standard, he can judge and condemn realms and modes of thought with a finality that we shall not find in the Dialogues. Yet his judgments, although determined by another principle, resemble those of Plato, since he had assimilated Platonic teaching to the essential doctrines of Christianity

Both *Paradise Lost* and *Paradise Regained*, where Biblical influence is dominant, retain the Platonic views of knowledge that permeate Milton's less theological writings In the first description of Adam we are reminded of the end which Plato set as man's chief good:

> For contemplation hee and valour form'd.

There is throughout the poem high praise of philosophy, by implication and often by negation, as when Milton describes the fallen angels in debate:

> Of good and evil much they argu'd then,
> Of happiness and final misery,
> Passion and Apathy, and glory and shame,
> Vain wisdom all, and false Philosophy. (2. 562-5.)

What Milton says of empty and erroneous thought must not be taken as his judgment of a serious inquiry into ethical truth. We are to remember in every encounter with the fallen angels that they are Sophists all. Milton does his best to warn us, using terms much like the Platonic account of false rhetoric; Satan's words bear

> Semblance of worth, not substance. (1. 529.)

And Belial owes at least one sentence in the description of him to Plato's character of the Sophists:

> A fairer person lost not Heav'n; he seem'd
> For dignity compos'd and high exploit:
> But all was false and hollow; though his Tongue
> Dropt Manna, and *could make the worse appear*
> *The better reason,* to perplex and dash
> Maturest Counsels: for his thoughts were low. (2. 110-5.)

He is the archetype of false rhetorician, but all the Satanic troop are members of one family.

In *Phaedrus*, we remember, Socrates distinguished the subjects wherein deception is possible as the disputable class of things, such topics as justice, goodness, love, or, briefly, the realm of ethics. Now merely because Milton, like Plato, recognizes this as the field for Sophists, we are not to suppose he thinks it their property. Before he himself could write *Paradise Lost* Milton had to probe the very questions discussed by his sophistical fallen angels,

> Providence, Foreknowledge, Will, and Fate,
> Fixt Fate, free will, foreknowledge absolute. (2. 559-60.)

Only, whereas they 'found no end, in wand'ring mazes lost,' he did reach solutions, having presumably avoided their mazes of self-deception. Those who have rejected the source of all Truth could hardly discuss such questions without error; he, having started from the right point in his inquiry, could complete it satisfactorily.

Commentators generally find it hard to allow the counsel Raphael gives to Adam on the quest for knowledge:

> Be lowly wise:
> Think only what concerns thee and thy being. (8. 173-4.)

But this again is a corollary to the Platonic principle of Milton's ethics: the secondary is always dangerous when not subordinated to the primary. We have the clue to his meaning in the Argument prefixed to Book 8:

Adam inquires concerning celestial Motions, is doubtfully answer'd, and exhorted to search rather things more worthy of knowledge.

Knowledge is still good, though its various branches are more and less worthy of pursuit. We must reckon with the time and circumstances of Raphael's admonition if we are not to misinterpret. We know from *Areopagitica* that Milton sympathized with Galileo, who dared think 'in astron-

omy otherwise than the Franciscan and Dominican licensers
thought.' And Raphael cannot be a mere licenser, setting
bounds to a scientific curiosity on the part of Adam. Look
back at the answer Uriel made to Satan, who disguised his
intent in visiting the new world as

> Unspeakable desire to see, and know
> All these [God's] wondrous works, but
> chiefly Man.

The 'Regent of the Sun' and 'sharpest-sighted Spirit of all
in Heav'n' applauded the desire

> which tends to know
> The works of God, thereby to glorify
> The great Work-Master;

and thought that it

> leads to no excess
> That reaches blame, but rather merits praise.
> (3. 662-97.)

Milton himself in earlier years had praised a like interest:

The more deeply we delve into the wondrous wisdom, the mar-
velous skill, and the astounding variety of its [the universe's]
creation (which we cannot do without the aid of Learning), the
greater grows the wonder and awe we feel for its Creator and
the louder the praises we offer Him, which we believe and are
fully persuaded that He delights to accept. (Tillyard, p. 108.)

Recall the argument in the *Laws* on this same question
Plato has the Athenian make astronomy a study of the
guardian-class, and then affirm:

It is currently said that it is wrong—indeed, positively blas-
phemous—to prosecute inquiry or busy ourselves with the quest
for explanation where the Supreme God and the universe as a
whole are concerned—though the very opposite should seem to
be our right course. (7. 821.)

The reason for this view is given more fully in *Timaeus:*

Sight, then, as I hold, is the cause of our chiefest blessing, inasmuch as no word of our present discourse of the universe could have been uttered, had we never seen stars, sun, nor sky. As it is, the vision of day and night, months and circling years, equinoctials and solstices, has created number, given us the notion of time, and moved us to search out universal nature; hence we have derived philosophy, than which no greater boon has been, nor ever shall be, bestowed by heaven on mortality. This, then, I say is the chief blessing of eyesight. . . . God invented it and bestowed it on us that we might perceive the orbits of understanding in the heavens and apply them to the revolutions of our own thought that are akin to them, the perturbed to the imperturbable, might learn to know them and compute them rightly and truly, and so correct the aberrations of the circles in ourselves by imitating the never-erring circles of the god. (47.)

Noting that Plato praises astronomical study for giving knowledge of the gods, and thereby improving human nature, we can better understand why Uriel praises in the dissembling Satan, and Raphael discourages in Adam, a curiosity about the same sphere of learning. The 'divine Historian' has already merited thanks from Adam for having

> allay'd
> The thirst I had of knowledge, and voutsaf't
> This friendly conversation to relate
> Things else by me unsearchable, now heard
> With wonder, but delight, and, as is due,
> With glory attributed to the high
> Creator. (8. 7-13.)

But Adam's fond inquiry is next,

> How Nature wise and frugal could commit
> Such disproportions,

making all Heaven revolve about 'the sedentary Earth.'

And still Raphael reaffirms the notions Plato held about this study:

> To ask or search I blame thee not, for Heav'n
> Is as the Book of God before thee set,
> Wherein to read his wond'rous Works, and learn
> His Seasons, Hours, or Days, or Months, or Years.
>
> (8. 66-9.)

So far astronomy is useful; but the remainder of Adam's inquiry Raphael disparages:

> God to remove his ways from human sense,
> Plac'd Heav'n from Earth so far, that earthly sight,
> If it presume, might err in things too high,
> And no advantage gain. . . .
> Heav'n is for thee too high
> To know what passes there; be lowly wise:
> Think only what concerns thee and thy being. (8. 119-74.)

Milton, we see, is still insisting upon the hierarchy of learnings, and still measuring study against study by the human advantage to be gained. The precept, 'Be lowly wise,' reminds us of the Platonic letter he had written years before to Diodati. Seeking by the guidance of *Phaedrus* for the Idea of the Beautiful, he was then meditating flight into the high realms of poetry; but having found the wings of his Pegasus as yet too tender, he made his maxim *'Humile sapiamus.'* In knowledge as in art the first step must be humbly made, and Adam may not yet be ready for the astronomical rung in the ladder of science. Blake and Wordsworth and Whitman would certainly have agreed with Raphael that Adam can do better at this stage than become a learned astronomer. Moreover, this speech of Raphael sends us back to an earlier passage in *Paradise Lost*:

> So little knows
> Any, but God alone, to value right

> The good before him, but perverts best things
> To worst abuse, or to thir meanest use. (4. 201-4.)

Adam still good and happy can accept the doctrine as Plato and Milton accepted it; a useless knowledge is no knowledge at all. He can even apologize for his ill-timed question:

> But apt the Mind or Fancy is to rove
> Uncheckt, and of her roving is no end;
> Till warn'd, or by experience taught, she learn
> That not to know at large of things remote
> From use, obscure and subtle, but to know
> That which before us lies in daily life,
> Is the prime Wisdom; what is more is fume,
> Or emptiness, or fond impertinence,
> And renders us in things that most concern
> Unpractis'd, unprepar'd, and still to seek. (8. 188-97.)

As in the Tractate *Of Education* and throughout Milton's writings, so here, in Paradise on the point of being lost, the proper study of mankind is ethics. Raphael will gladly help Adam inquire 'into the ways of God with Man.' This is of course the inquiry of *Paradise Lost* itself, and Milton points the analogy by using the very words with which he had concluded his first invocation of the Muse. The Eighth Book with its discourses on knowledge good and and evil prepares us to see the real error in the later choice of the forbidden fruit; for God has not deprived Adam of the right to know. When Adam named the animals as they passed, he understood

> Thir Nature, with such knowledge God endu'd
> My sudden apprehension. (8. 353-4.)

This understanding of the lower orders of creation was useful to him who was to be their master. In every way Milton assures us before the fall that the fruit offered no knowledge at all, and could produce nothing either necessary or useful to man's happiness. The point would seem too obvious for

statement did not readers again and again miss the inten
tion of Milton's account. Some would even have us think
the fall a necessary prelude to the highest happiness; but
they are deceived, like our original parents, by the argu
ment that good can be known only by experience of evil.

Undeceived, Milton does his best to warn the reader
Nor may we accept the interpretation of those who put the
burden of this, to them strange, view of knowledge on
its Biblical source. Milton chose the plot of his epic poem
with great care, after much deliberation; and the theory o
knowledge involved in the fall is central to the story. More
over, Milton deliberately elaborates this part of the fable
and, since he could not find material for the elaboration in
his primary source, uses the philosophy he thought closest
to Scriptural teaching in order to emphasize the wrong view
of knowledge which causes man and woman to lose their
happiness. From Plato he takes the principle by which
Raphael warns Adam:

> Knowledge is as food, and needs no less
> Her Temperance over Appetite, to know
> In measure what the mind may well contain,
> Oppresses else with Surfet, and soon turns
> Wisdom to Folly, as Nourishment to Wind. (7. 126-30.)

If Plato made knowledge itself the measure of temperance
Milton converts this highest principle of the Platonic ethics
into one yet higher. For Plato the end of man is to know
and enjoy knowledge for ever; for Milton it is to glorify
God and for ever enjoy Him. Thus Adam in his state of
innocence thanks the archangel:

> Well hast thou taught the way that might direct
> Our knowledge, and the scale of Nature set
> From centre to circumference, whereon
> In contemplation of created things
> By steps we may ascend to God. (5. 508-12.)

There is a knowledge by which man ascends to comprehension of his Maker. So, too, thought Plato; but in the Christian Maker there is a purpose for man that Plato did not comprehend. Love is the final standard of conduct in the Christian view, love of God with its necessary and inseparable companion, love of neighbor. As the highest virtues in the Platonic scale, wisdom and its companion, justice, are displaced by the Christian virtues, so knowledge, the food of reason, must yield to faith, the food of love, as the most desirable of goods. Eve and Adam after her break faith in disobeying God's commands, reverse the scale of values, thinking to raise knowledge above trust, and thus fall from love and wisdom, faith and knowledge, all at once. As Plato had made the science of good and evil and its attendant virtue of wisdom the keystone of all happiness, upon which the right use of every other good depends, so Milton places the trustful acceptance of God's will and its attendant virtue of love. Remove the keystone, according to either scheme, and the entire structure of human well-being topples to the ground. Exactly as Plato had held that a courage and temperance not founded in knowledge were not courage and temperance at all, for Milton a knowledge not rooted in faith is only the false semblance of knowledge.

Elsewhere, in his treatise *De Doctrina Christiana*, Milton explicitly states the relations between faith and knowledge, love and wisdom, which are the essential teaching of *Paradise Lost*:

Christian doctrine is comprehended under two divisions: *Faith, or the knowledge of God; and Love, or the worship of God....* Obedience and love are always the best guides to knowledge.... It must be observed, that Faith in this division does not mean the habit of believing, but the things to be habitually believed. (14. 23-5.)

Man was made in the image of God, and had the whole law of nature . . . implanted and innate in him, . . . which is suf-

ficient of itself to teach whatever is agreeable to right reason
that is to say, whatever is intrinsically good. (15. 115-7.)

This death [from sin] consists, first, in the loss, or at least in
the obscuration to a great extent, of that right reason which
enabled man to discern the chief good, and in which consisted as
it were the life of the understanding. . . . It consists, secondly,
in that deprivation of righteousness and liberty to do good, and
in that slavish subjection to sin and the devil, which constitute,
as it were, the death of the will. (15. 207.)

Evil works downward in Plato's view: destroy the virtue
of reason, and the virtues of will and appetite will die.
Similarly Milton, going a step beyond Plato, keeps to the
same way of thought: if the highest good, faith, is destroyed,
reason cannot know, the will choose, nor appetite enjoy, in
right and happy fashion. What further explanation do we
need to perceive the consistency of Milton's view of knowledge? Test by this standard the sophistical words of the
tempter, who—be it remembered—did *not* taste the apple:

> O Sacred, Wise, and Wisdom-giving Plant,
> Mother of Science, Now I feel thy Power
> Within me clear, not only to discern
> Things in thir Causes, but to trace the ways
> Of highest agents, deem'd however wise. (9. 679-83.)

And test again the arguments by which he would persuade
Eve to be

> Deterr'd not from achieving what might lead
> To happier life, knowledge of Good and Evil;
> Of good, how just? of evil, if what is evil
> Be real, why not known, since easier shunn'd?
> God therefore cannot hurt ye, and be just;
> Not just, not God. (9. 696-701.)

The lie of a Sophist must always approach the truth if it is
to be convincing; and Milton here allows to Satan the half
truth which is the contradiction of the whole. Too many

readers confuse Satan's lie with the truth Milton speaks in *Areopagitica:*

> Good and evil we know in the field of this world grow up to-gether almost inseparably; and the knowledge of good is so involved and interwoven with the knowledge of evil, and in so many cunning resemblances hardly to be discerned, that those confused seeds which were imposed on Psyche as an incessant labor to cull out and sort asunder were not more intermixed. It was from out the rind of one apple tasted that the knowledge of good and evil as two twins cleaving together leapt forth into the world. And perhaps this is that doom which Adam fell into of knowing good and evil, that is to say of knowing good by evil. (4. 310-11.)

Like lesser men, Milton may stretch a point in the effort to persuade; but still there is distinction enough between his argument and Satan's to warrant our belief that Milton did not allow the tempter to speak the truth. First of all, the 'knowing good by evil' is in Milton's phrase a 'doom which Adam fell into,' in Satan's a guide to 'happier life.' Secondly, the situation has been completely reversed: Adam, instructed by God, possessed the useful knowledge; we, ignorant since the fall, must seek what Adam lost, and must therefore seek it upon new conditions. We have no advantage in the necessity imposed upon us of learning good through evil, and Milton does not call it an advantage, but simply a necessity. And finally, if Milton admits that from 'one apple tasted . . . the knowledge of good and evil . . . leapt forth into the world,' he is not among those who rejoice in the twin-birth of such knowledge as fallen Adam can win.

At any rate, throughout *Areopagitica* Milton speaks from the very premise that Satan suppresses in his argu-ment: not the knowledge itself, but the use of it is all-important. The syllogism might have ended differently, had Satan said with Milton:

The knowledge cannot defile . . . if the will and conscience be not defiled. (4. 308.)

Conversely, if the will and conscience be defiled, the knowledge cannot 'lead to happier life'; for if Milton compares knowledge to 'meats and viands, some of good, some of evil substance,' and thinks God 'left arbitrary the dieting and repasting of our minds,' trusting man 'with the gift of reason to be his own chooser,' he yet agrees with Raphael, not Satan, that knowledge 'needs no less her temperance over appetite.' The sum of Milton's argument in *Paradise Lost* is as it is in *Aeropagitica:*

How great a virtue is temperance, how much of moment through the whole life of man. (4. 309.)

Chosen for a wrong purpose, on false grounds, and at the cost of a higher good, the apple produced no knowledge save that of

Good lost and Evil got,
Bad Fruit of Knowledge, if this be to know. (9. 1072-3.)

What else do we expect? As C. S. Lewis points out, the apple is merely an apple. It is not a condensed encyclopedia. Its sole virtue was as a pledge; and the pledge broken, Adam and Eve win no knowledge at all in the sense of understanding, but only the experience of misery. The fatal *double entendre* catches many a reader off-guard.

But to know evil by doing and suffering it is not true knowledge, as repentant Adam is only too eager to admit. In his speech to Michael, the problem begins to be resolved:

Greatly instructed I shall hence depart,
Greatly in peace of thought, and have my fill
Of knowledge, what this Vessel can contain;
Beyond which was my folly to aspire.

> Henceforth I learn, that to obey is best,
> And love with fear the only God. (12. 557-62.)

And the final resolution comes in Michael's reply, the final words of superhuman understanding that end the converse of mankind with Heaven:

> This having learnt, thou hast attain'd the sum
> Of wisdom; hope no higher, though all the Stars
> Thou knew'st by name, and all th' Ethereal Powers,
> All secrets of the deep, all Nature's works,
> Or works of God in Heav'n, Air, Earth, or Sea; . . .
>   only add
> Deeds to thy knowledge answerable, add Faith,
> Add Virtue, Patience, Temperance, add Love,
> By name to come call'd Charity, the soul
> Of all the rest: then wilt thou not be loath
> To leave this Paradise, but shalt possess
> A Paradise within thee, happier far. (12. 575-87.)

They miss the point who think that Milton sets Adam's degenerate state above the state of innocence. Michael compares not the paradise within, which Adam has already lost, with that which he yet may find, but the external Eden with the inner; for the final consequence of the fall is this disjoining of inner and outer state. Happiness may yet be won in this life, but no longer with the circumstantial ease of a state where knowledge of good was not twin-born with knowledge of evil. Look to the end of Michael's words, and see how much 'happier far' the inner state is now to be, when all mankind shall live,

>   though sad
> With cause for evils past, yet much more cheer'd
> With meditation on the happy end. (12. 603-5.)

The happy end, moreover, is now to be attained only by a labor 'above heroic, though in secret done.' We must turn to *Paradise Regained* for the view Milton ultimately took of the relations between happiness and knowledge.

Lest we lose our way in the subtle controversies of *Paradise Regained*, let us repeat the 'sum of wisdom' from Michael's final instruction of Adam. Though man knew all the secrets of physics and astronomy, he could know no more than this, that obedience and love are the source of every other human good. Love is 'the soul of all the rest'; without it, knowledge, like pleasure, wealth, and far-famed power, crumbles to worthlessness. There are no separate goods for man. Happiness can grow in one soil only; in every other the seeds of every lesser joy become sterile.

What then becomes of the Platonic view that knowledge is the chief good? In *Paradise Regained* we shall find it, as in *Paradise Lost* but more clearly, taking the place of fame as the 'last infirmity of noble mind.' Jesus, the Everyman of the poem, recalls that in his youth

> all my mind was set
> Serious to learn and know, and thence to do
> What might be publick good; myself I thought
> Born to that end, born to promote all truth,
> All righteous things: therefore above my years,
> The Law of God I read, and found it sweet,
> Made it my whole delight, and in it grew
> To such perfection, that ere yet my age
> Had measur'd twice six years, at our great Feast
> I went into the Temple, there to hear
> The Teachers of our Law, and to propose
> What might improve my knowledge or their own. (1. 202-13.)

The arch-sophist is clever to reserve knowledge for the final temptation. But even before we hear Jesus and Satan in debate, we are aware that knowledge is not the main end, and therefore not the main source of strength, for this man. Unlike Adam, where knowledge fails him he can say:

> Perhaps I need not know;
> For what concerns my knowledge God reveals. (1. 292-3.)

From the first, he declares that God provides

> In pious Hearts, an inward Oracle
> To all truth requisite for men to know. (1. 463-4.)

Satan hazards a reference to the first fall, assuring Jesus that the food he offers

> no knowledge works, at least of evil. (2. 371.)

And we are convinced that Milton did not think the knowledge won by Adam worth its price. This time Satan will not offer so obviously poor a bargain. But first he flatters the intellectual pride of his opponent, as the Sophist always flatters the instinct on which he plans to work:

> I see thou know'st what is of use to know,
> What best to say canst say, to do canst do;
> Thy actions to thy words accord, thy words
> To thy large heart give utterance due, thy heart
> Contains of good, wise, just the perfect shape. (3. 7-11.)

Satan is preparing to use a seeming Platonism as his final bait. And yet even here Milton makes apparent the sophistry of the tempter. If Jesus already possesses 'of good, wise, just, the perfect shape,' what further need he know?

Perhaps Milton overemphasizes the sophistical nature of the antagonist, and yet the Satan of *Paradise Regained* fools as many as the Satan of *Paradise Lost,* for the 'Rhetoric that sleeks the tongue' of Jesus' tempter is persuasive. Satan begins his argument with words so close to Milton's own in the early prolusions and poems, that we listen amazed:

> Be famous then
> By wisdom; as thy Empire must extend,
> So let extend thy mind o'er all the world,
> In knowledge, all things in it comprehend. (4. 221-4.)

The second step adds the lie that turns the whole to false-hood:

> All knowledge is not couch't in Moses' Law,
> The Pentateuch or what the Prophets wrote,
> The Gentiles also know, and write, and teach
> To admiration, led by Nature's Light;
> And with the Gentiles much thou must converse,
> Ruling them by persuasion as thou mean'st,
> Without thir learning how wilt thou with them,
> Or they with thee hold conversation meet? (4. 225-32.)

The offer of universal knowledge and with it the power of universal persuasion is ever the mark of the Sophist in Plato; and if we need another sign, Satan gives it in his next maxim:

> Error by his own arms is best evinc't. (4. 235.)

Socrates did not think so in spite of Anytus, Polus, and the rest, and Jesus is not more likely to admit that anything but truth can conquer falsehood.

So much for the grandiose pretenses of the temptation. But what of the knowledge itself that Jesus rejects? Let us take, as sample of it, the best:

> To sage Philosophy next lend thine ear,
> From Heaven descended to the low-rooft house
> Of Socrates, see there his Tenement,
> Whom well inspir'd the Oracle pronounc'd
> Wisest of men; from whose mouth issu'd forth
> Mellifluous streams that water'd all the schools
> Of Academics old and new, with those
> Surnam'd Peripatetics, and the Sect
> Epicurean, and the Stoic severe;
> These here revolve, or, as thou lik'st, at home,
> Till time mature thee to a Kingdom's weight;
> These rules will render thee a King complete
> Within thyself, much more with Empire join'd. (4. 272-84.)

This is the very rule over oneself, the very kingship of

philosophy, that Plato called the highest good, and Socrates is made first teacher of this wisdom. Milton evidently has added the scene to the traditional account of the temptation in order that *Paradise Regained* may represent the whole procedure by which man may win happiness.

But what exactly is the temptation that Jesus here overcomes? We must look to the answer he makes:

> Think not but that I know these things; or think
> I know them not, not therefore am I short
> Of knowing what I ought: he who receives
> Light from above, from the fountain of light,
> No other doctrine needs, though granted true. (4. 286-90.)

The Neoplatonic image of light that Milton uses had been fused with Manichean thought and popularized in the Christian schools by Augustine and his followers; and we may well turn to Augustine for help with the doctrine here advanced; for Augustine, next to the Bible itself, guided Milton in theology; and Augustine had dealt with this problem alien to Biblical thought. In the *Confessions,* he says of the time he spent in pagan studies: 'I had my back to the light, and my face to the things enlightened' (4. 16). And asking what it profited him to have known these things, he answers: 'Nothing.' Yet Augustine continued to make use of pagan thought long after his conversion, never attempting to rid his mind of all but Biblical and patristic lore. Apparently he distinguished not so much between a Christian and a pagan learning, as between a Christian and a non-Christian use of learning. His maxim was *'nisi crederitis, non intelligeritis':* only he who has faith can understand the truth in any thought, and he who has faith needs no other measure of truth.

The notion was not peculiar to Milton in the seventeenth century, however odd it may now seem. Ralph Cudworth, another Christian Platonist, explains it at some length:

Knowledge indeed is a thing far more excellent than riches, outward pleasures, worldly dignities, or anything else in the world besides holiness, and the conformity of our wills to the will of God; but yet our happiness consisteth not in it, but in a certain Divine temper and constitution of soul which is far above it.

But it is a piece of corruption, that runneth through human nature, that we naturally prize truth more than goodness, knowledge more than holiness. We think it a gallant thing to be fluttering up to heaven with our wings of knowledge and speculation; whereas, the highest mystery of a divine life here, and of perfect happiness hereafter, consisteth in nothing but mere obedience to the Divine will. Happiness is that inward sweet delight that will arise from the harmonious agreement between our wills and God's will. There is nothing contrary to God in the whole world, nothing that fights against him but self-will. . . . It was by reason of this self-will that Adam fell in Paradise; that those glorious angels, those morning stars, kept not their first station, but dropped down from Heaven like falling stars, and sunk into the condition of bitterness, anxiety and wretchedness, in which now they are. They all entangled themselves with the length of their own wings, they would needs will more and otherwise than God would will in them; and going about to make their wills wider, and to enlarge them into greater amplitude, the more they struggled they found themselves the faster pinioned, and crowded up into narrowness and servility; insomuch that now they are not able to use any wings at all, but inheriting the serpent's curse, can only creep with their bellies upon the earth.[3]

If the doctrine is hard for those less faithful than Augustine, Cudworth, and Milton to accept, we are not therefore to think them inconsistent in holding it. Milton, far more than most admirers of knowledge, sought it actively, but kept firmly in view what gave knowledge its value.

---

[3] Quoted by Grierson in *Cross Currents in English Literature of the Seventeenth Century*, pp. 227-8, from *The Works of Ralph Cudworth* (1829), Vol. 4, Sermon 1.

So with the stern judgment here. Satan has promised Jesus all knowledge, and then offered the partial and imperfect philosophy of Greece separated from the one source of truth without which all knowledge is vain. If Jesus decries the 'sage philosophy' of Satan's offer as

> false, or little else but dreams,
> Conjectures, fancies, built on nothing firm, (4. 291-2.)

the falsity comes not in the doctrines themselves, but in their lack of firm foundation.

> Who therefore seeks in these
> True wisdom, finds her not, or by delusion
> Far worse, her false resemblance only meets,
> An empty cloud. (4. 318-21.)

And still we must ask, What of him who seeks, like Milton himself, to supplement the higher truth of revelation from these lesser sources? Jesus answers:

> Who reads
> Incessantly, and to his reading brings not
> A spirit and judgment equal or superior,
> (And what he brings, what needs he elsewhere seek)
> Uncertain and unsettl'd still remains,
> Deep verst in books and shallow in himself. (4. 322-7.)

A part of this answer we find elsewhere in Milton, as when he counsels his young acquaintance, Richard Jones:

There is also a well-equipped library; but unless it enables the students to improve their minds by the best instruction, it would deserve the name of 'book repository' rather than of 'library.' (Tillyard, p. 35.)

And again, when he mocks an opponent thus:

A learned man?—you that even unto your old age seem rather to have turned over phrase-books and lexicons and glossaries than to have perused good authors with judgment or profit; so that you prate of naught but manuscripts and various readings and dislocated passages and scribal errors, but show that you have drunk never the least drop of more substantial learning. (7. 67.)

Milton was always aware that the scholar must bring to his book 'a spirit and judgment equal or superior,' lest he fall into the vices of the pedant or, worse still, the Sophist; but would he also grant, what readers of *Paradise Regained* are loath to admit, that what the scholar brings he need not seek in his book? Perhaps Milton is here letting Jesus pay Satan with his own coin; perhaps he plays with the words 'spirit' and 'judgment,' and means that these alone the scholar cannot find in his book, while *food* for the spirit and judgment he may find; or perhaps neither the context nor the words will help us to escape from the apparent meaning that ancient wisdom can be useful only to him who does not need it. For Milton does a strange thing at the end of *Paradise Regained;* he shows that Jesus has won every good that Satan offered him, a banquet, power unlimited, and universal fame, every good indeed that mankind strives for, won them all and with them happiness for all mankind, by refusing each of them separately. Only knowledge is not explicitly named in the reward which his faith earns.

We have reckoned thus far without the superhuman nature of Jesus. If we take the poem as theological rather than ethical, the difficulty disappears. The perfect man, the Man Divine, after all, needs no external help, but communicates directly with the source of truth. But, unfortunately, the ethical meaning then disappears along with the difficulty. Milton intended *Paradise Regained* to show Jesus *winning* over Satan a victory that any man in any time could win. We are not to assume the victory from the beginning as predicated on a mystery, but rather to learn from it that for every man faith is the root and strength of all knowledge, and that for the man who perfects himself in faith all knowledge will rise directly from his communion with God. Once again hear Milton on our understanding and its object:

The very essence of Truth is plainness and brightness; the darkness and crookedness is our own. The wisdom of God created understanding, fit and proportionable to Truth the object and end of it, as the eye to the thing visible. If our understanding have a film of ignorance over it, or be blear with gazing on other false glitterings, what is that to Truth? (3. 33.)

Learning is, after all, a mere tool for purging the sight; the vision of Truth is finally the only knowledge; and since faith alone can attain that vision for understanding, the chief good of mankind lies, not, as Plato thought, in intellectual concepts however lofty, but in union of the whole spirit with its Maker. When reason beholds the Good, Plato would say, every part of the soul has its appropriate satisfaction, and enjoys the happiness of justice. Milton, converting the principle, would rather maintain that, in order to satisfy reason as well as every lesser faculty, the soul must live in God, and thence receive the only knowledge that can lead to happiness.

CHAPTER VI

The Theory of Ideas

WHEN Milton refused to knowledge the place of chief good, he did not discard, but amended, Platonic teaching. A part of that teaching, generally held the most distinctive part, is the much-disputed theory of Ideas. The theory is doubtless basic to all Plato's thought, but is presented in so many ways and attended by so many difficulties that scholars have been far from certain about its meaning. Popularly, the Platonic Idea is conceived of as an eternal archetype, remote from this world, yet productive of the whole corresponding class of earthly things, and related to them as a pattern or stamp to its reproduction or impress. The popular conception has grounds in the Dialogues, but there are grounds for doubting it too. Plato himself suggests the major arguments against Ideas of this kind, in some dialogues makes little or no use of the doctrine, and nowhere explicitly asserts that there is an Ideal pattern for every class of things. In general, when the doctrine of archetypes is presented as indisputable, the Idea is an ethical concept, Justice, Beauty, Goodness, or the like. When questions of an Ideal bed or animal are raised, the matter is left in doubt. For these reasons the theory has seemed to many scholars an attempt to support the universal stability of ethical truth rather than to effect a dichotomy of life into two distinct worlds.

Our aim is to find the meaning and use of the doctrine for Milton, and less to unravel the intricate questions it involves. Milton clearly had pondered them, arguing in his collegiate exercises and later whether 'form' could exist apart from matter; knew from Aristotle down the objections to the theory; and came to his own conclusions about Plato's meaning. According to Herbert Agar the doctrine of Ideas 'does not seem to have influenced Milton's thought, though he makes use of it four times as a convenient method of expression' (p. 18). But the four times Agar lists are not the only times Milton employs the doctrine, and are not merely convenient modes of expression.

Examine first some occurrences of the word 'idea' in Milton's writing (I mark with a star those that Agar has not considered):

 * 1 For who can worthily gaze upon and contemplate the *Ideas* of things human or divine, unless he possesses a mind trained and ennobled by Art and Learning, without which he can know practically nothing of them? (Tillyard, p. 107.)

 2 De *Idea* Platonica quemadmodum Aristoteles intellexit.

 * 3 Neither tresses of gold nor rosy cheek beguiles me thus; but, under a new *form* [*nuova idea*], strange beauty charms my heart. (Sonnet 4, tr. by Smart, p. 150.)

 4 Ceres never sought her daughter Proserpine (as the legend tells) with greater ardor than I do this *Idea* of Beauty [τοῦ καλοῦ ἰδέαν], like some image of loveliness; ever pursuing it, by day and by night, in every shape and form ('for many forms there are of things divine') and following close in its footprints as it leads. (Tillyard, p. 14.)

 * 5 That which is thus moral, besides what we fetch from those unwritten laws and *ideas* which nature hath ingraven in us, the Gospel . . . lectures to us. (3. 197.)

 * 6 If therefore the question were in oratory whether a vehement vein throwing out indignation or scorn upon an object that merits it were among the aptest *Ideas* of speech to be al-

lowed, it were my work, and that an easy one, to make it clear both by the rules of best rhetoricians and the famousest examples of the Greek and Roman orations. (3. 312.)

7 I . . . will forthwith set down in writing, as you request me, that voluntary *idea,* which hath long in silence presented itself to me, of a better education. (Ainsworth, p. 52.)

8 Thence to behold this new created World . . . Answering his great *Idea.* (*P.L.* 7. 554-7.)

* 9 For the foreknowledge of God is nothing but the wisdom of God, under another name, or that *idea* of everything [*illa rerum omnium idea*], which he had in his mind, to use the language of men, before he decreed anything. (14. 65.)

*10 For it is neither impious nor absurd to say, that the *idea* [*ideam*] of certain things or events might be suggested to God from some extraneous source; since inasmuch as God had determined from all eternity, that man should so far be a free agent, that it remained with himself to decide whether he would stand or fall, the *idea* [*idea*] of that evil event, or of the fall of man, was suggested to God from an extraneous source. (14. 79.)

*11 Genus does not properly communicate essence to species (since in itself it is in truth nothing outside the species) but merely signifies their essence, for the notion of what is essential and common to all species is called *genus,* and by the Greeks often *idea* [*idea*], but not separated from things, as they think the Platonic ideas are, which are clouds, according to Aristotle (*Metaphysics* 1. 7; 12. 5), but what in thought and reason is one and the same thing common to many species in each of which in fact and nature it appears singly, as Plato says in the *Meno.* The Stoics, however, as Plutarch reports (*De placitis philosophorum* 1. 10), said that ideas were our notions. (11. 239.)

Without arguing about his correctness, we may learn from these passages how Milton interpreted the doctrine. And first, since he uses the term 'idea' four times out of eleven

133

as distinctively Platonic, in all likelihood he consistently associated it with Plato's usage. Secondly, he dismisses the objection of Aristotle that the Platonic 'Idea,' if a self-sustaining entity apart from all its manifestations, is a mere cloud, and cites Plato's own words to show how it may be distinct from, and yet in particular things. Thirdly, he duly assigns to the Stoics, and not to Plato, the view that ideas owe their existence to human thought. Fourthly, he is sure that some ideas, apparently of an ethical nature, are so far independent of our thinking them as to be innately impressed upon our minds. Fifthly, he believes that an essential common nature manifests itself variously in varied objects, in and through which it must be sought. Finally, and most important for him as a poet, he conceives of the Idea as a pattern in the creative mind, divine or human, according to which a world or treatise or series of events may be shaped. Rightly or wrongly, this is Milton's view of the Platonic doctrine of Ideas, and as such he often uses it in his writing.

But we can hardly limit our discussion to Milton's use of the word 'idea,' since Plato himself had many expressions for the concept. After the centuries of intervening discussion, Milton naturally employs various ways of stating the doctrine. Of his alternate terms, 'form' and 'essence' are most important, *forma* having been the regular Latin translation for Plato's ἰδέα or εἶδος, and *essentia* for οὐσία, the ideal being of an object. Insofar as Aristotle refined the concepts of form and essence without refuting Plato's view, Milton tries to keep his use of the terms consistent with both Plato and Aristotle. Thus in his *Logic* he offers the definition:

Form is the cause through which a thing is what it is. This definition joins those of Plato and Aristotle. For Plato defines form as the cause through which, Aristotle as that which is. (II. 59.)

And again:

That the form can also be the end Aristotle testifies. . . . And Plato in the *Philebus* lays down the essence or form of the thing as the end of generation. (11. 67.)

In using these concepts of an inner form or essence correlative with a function or effect, Milton consistently keeps to his definitions; and hence if he takes his definitions to be Platonic, we may regard the passages written in accordance with them as illustrations of the influence the Platonic theory of Ideas had on his thought.

In this sense, the pamphlets on the Church, on kingship, and on matrimony, are products of Plato's doctrine, for in all of them Milton is concerned with true or ideal form and proper function. See, for example, how he speaks of marriage:

The internal *Form* and soul of this relation is conjugal love arising from a mutual fitness to the final causes of wedlock, help and society in religious, civil, and domestic conversation, which includes as an inferior end the fulfilling of natural desire and specifical increase: these are the final causes both moving the efficient and perfecting the *form*. (4. 101.)

And further:

This gives marriage all her due, all her benefits, all her being, all her distinct and proper being. (4. 106.)

So again in *Colasterion* he asks concerning marriage:

How can a thing subsist when the true essence thereof is dissolved? (4. 262.)

And in *De Doctrina Christiana* he answers:

But if the essential form be dissolved, it follows that the marriage itself is virtually dissolved. (15. 157.)

His treatment of political and religious institutions is the same; only when the thing corresponds to its ideal or proper form and function may it be said to exist at all. A king is not a man born to the office, but he who fulfils the office of a king:

Where the Parliament sits, there inseparably sits the King, there the laws, there our oaths, and whatsoever can be civil in religion. They who fought for the Parliament, in the truest sense fought for all these; who fought for the King divided from his Parliament, fought for the shadow of a King against all these, and for things that were not, as if they were established. (5. 243.)

This use of Plato's figure of a shadow to express unreality in comparison with true existence shows Milton to be speaking the language of the Ideas. Again in castigating prelates, he keeps his 'spiritual eye' on the 'inward beauty and splendor' (3. 191) of the Church, and chides:

Believe it, wondrous doctors, all corporeal resemblances of inward holiness and beauty are now past; he that will clothe the Gospel now intimates plainly that the Gospel is naked, uncomely, that I may not say reproachful. (3. 246-7.)

Of those who changed from 'the simplicity and plainness of Christianity' to idolatrous ritual he says:

The beauty of inward sanctity was not within their prospect. (3. 25.)

These are but samples of a habit of thought constant with Milton, the Platonic habit of regarding, not the outer appearance, but the inner meaning, the 'Idea' of the thing. The reader may turn to almost any page of Milton's prose and later poems and find further examples of the pervasive influence of Plato's doctrine of the Idea as the true being, essence, or form of the varied phenomena of nature and human life.

The theory is far less pervasive in his earlier works than the myths through which Plato taught it. What does he take the Platonic Idea to be in his verses on the subject? A poetic fiction prosaically misinterpreted by Aristotle. The festival of the gods, which in *Phaedrus* is the grand occasion for sight of the Ideas, is far more prominent in the early poems of Milton than the Ideas themselves. There are references to it in his obituary verses for the Bishop of Winchester (41-50), in his Fifth *Elegy* (13-24), *On the Nativity* (147-8), and elsewhere; the clearest is in lines 33-6 of the *Vacation Exercise:*

> Such where the deep transported mind may soar
> Above the wheeling poles, and at Heav'n's door
> Look in, and see each blissful Deity
> How he before the thunderous throne doth lie.

Similarly, the myth which makes a beloved person an embodiment of the Ideas serves Milton as a poetic device in various early poems, perhaps most strikingly in the lines on *A Fair Infant* (53-6):

> Or wert thou Mercy that sweet smiling Youth?
> Or that crown'd Matron, sage white-robed Truth?
> Or any other of that heav'nly brood
> Let down in cloudy throne to do the world some good?

But the fancy for the myth connected with the doctrine of Ideas turns later to a sober understanding of their ethical importance. When Milton came to believe in an essential form of marriage, of kingliness, of religious worship, that determines and gives validity to their occurrence in marriages, kingships, and religious institutions, he came to believe in the essential and universal reality of ethical concepts. On this point Agar writes:

Ethical philosophers, such as Plato and Milton, must by nature look upon the moral world either as a realm of permanent truths which are unaffected by the accidents of mortality, or else as just another realm of flux, a repetition of the disorder and impermanence which dominate the physical world, where nothing is but what is not. These two classes of thinkers will be divided by their opinions, not only of the good and the bad, but of the beautiful and the ugly, the true and the false, and all that concerns philosophy. Agreement on this primary question is at least the basis for a bond of sympathy; and it will not be necessary to prove that here the views of Milton and Plato coincide. The statement that change is *not* the order of the moral world would seem true in the highest degree to both of these thinkers, and in the highest degree important. This statement, however, would be concurred in by a number of philosophers, and would not in itself prove any such affinity as I have been claiming. (Agar, p. 2.)

But we have every reason to believe that Plato's statements of the view were of singular importance to Milton, and of an importance far beyond any other philosopher's. The belief that the moral world is 'a realm of permanent truths' has not been generally shared by those on whom Plato had no influence; for it takes some defense, and Plato's theory of Ideas is among the most solid defenses as yet offered. If Milton was convinced that justice, beauty, and the like are unalterable realities, he made the Platonic 'Ideas' the basis of his conviction. Occasionally his choice of words proves this, as for example in *Comus,* when two Christian virtues and a virtue next of kin to Plato's 'temperance' are hypostasized:

> O welcome pure-ey'd Faith, white-handed Hope, . . .
> And thou unblemish't form of Chastity,
> I see ye visibly. (212-5.)

True, Milton may here be using the Platonic 'form' as a convenient poetic expression; and so again in *Paradise Regained:*

> Thy heart
> Contains of good, wise, just, the perfect shape. (3. 10-11.)

But in prose we may expect him to use only the sober expression that fits his thought; and yet we find the same imagery in the *Reason of Church-Government:*

> Should not he rather now by his own prescribed discipline have cast his line and level upon the soul of man, which is his rational temple, and by the divine square and compass thereof form and regenerate in us the lovely shapes of virtues and graces? (3. 191.)

This passage from the *Reason of Church-Government* is explained by another, already quoted to illustrate Milton's use of the word 'idea.' There he speaks of 'those unwritten laws and ideas which nature hath ingraven in us,' here of the 'lovely shapes of virtues'; and in both places he has in mind the Platonic Ideas, and the Platonic theory that we are born with a knowledge of them. As a Christian, Milton rejects Plato's explanation that we won this knowledge in a previous existence, that is, he rejects the doctrines of metempsychosis and recollection; but he finds a convenient substitute in St. Augustine's theory that God himself imparts knowledge of the eternal Ideas to the human mind. (See, for example, *De Civitate Dei* 11. 10, F-G, I; and *De Diversis Quaestionibus* 46, entitled *De Ideis*.) Indeed, it is partly because Augustine accepted this theory and adapted it to Christianity that Milton found himself spiritually at home in the Platonic system of ethics with its absolutely valid Ideas. By making the Wisdom, Justice, Truth, and Beauty of Plato's scheme identical with the essence of God, and calling all other universals thoughts in the mind of God, Augustine gave the Platonic theory a new support. Formerly an objector could argue that the universal Ideas, since they are not of this world, could *be* nowhere; now, if a Christian, he would have to admit the divine mind as a place not only possible, but appropriate to their existence.

In the universality Milton attributes to moral concepts

we find the main influence of the theory of Ideas on him. But where else could we look? Even the young Milton ridiculed the prosaic habit of seeking eternal archetypes such as an Ideal Man, or seeking them in space and time. The very nature of the Idea is that it is to be sought only with the mind's eye, and only in realms explored by an inner vision. The doctrines of ethical thought are its proper habitat; an eternally valid Justice, Wisdom, Truth, are the proper examples to look for; and these we find so abundant in Milton's poetry and prose that we can scarcely present an exhaustive collection of them. Let a few illustrations suffice.

Take, then, the Platonic affirmation in Milton's Seventh *Prolusion:*

> While the other virtues are easily put to flight, Justice from her throne compels homage, for without her even the most unjust States would soon fall into decay. (Tillyard, p. 114.)

And compare his immediate source in the *Republic* I. 352:

> We have already shown that the just are clearly wiser and better and abler than the unjust, and that the unjust are incapable of common action; nay more, that to speak as we did of men who are evil acting at any time vigorously together is not strictly true, for if they had been perfectly evil, they would have laid hands upon one another; but it is evident that there must have been some remnant of justice in them, which enabled them to combine; if there had not been they would have injured one another as well as their victims; they were but half-villains in their enterprises; for had they been whole villains, and utterly unjust, they would have been utterly incapable of action.

That Justice maintains even unjust organizations only a Platonist could believe, only one who held with Plato that Justice absolute is a reality from which the more and less just derive their phenomenal existence. To this Justice absolute, God affirms Adam's punishment is due:

Die hee or Justice must. (3. 210.)

This is the Justice which Milton calls in the *Doctrine and Discipline of Divorce* 'the queen of virtues' (3. 473), and in the *Tenure of Kings* 'the only true sovran and supreme majesty upon earth' (5. 41). For Milton's English poems Bradshaw lists in his *Concordance* some 121 occurrences of the word 'just' and its derivatives. Milton shows his readers how to interpret the word, in a long discussion in *Eikonoclastes*:

For me, though neither asked nor in a nation that gives such rewards to wisdom, I shall pronounce my sentence somewhat different from Zorobabel, and shall defend that either Truth and Justice are all one, for Truth is but Justice in our knowledge, and Justice is but Truth in our practice; . . . or else, if there be any odds, that Justice, though not stronger than Truth, yet by her office is to put forth and exhibit more strength in the affairs of mankind. . . . Though wicked kings and tyrants counterfeit her sword, as some did that buckler fabled to fall from heaven into the Capitol, yet she communicates her power to none but such as like herself are just, or at least will do justice. For it were extreme partiality and injustice, the flat denial and over-throw of herself, to put her own authentic sword into the hand of an unjust and wicked man. (5. 292-3.)

In this passage, we see two Platonic Ideas, Justice and Truth, contending for supremacy; and while awarding higher rank to one, Milton affirms, as Plato affirmed, that there is a unity behind even the Ideal entities, a single Idea of which these are aspects much as phenomena in turn are aspects of them. In any case, Truth like Justice is for Milton absolute and independent of particular truths, giving to them, not gaining from them, real existence. Thus in his Fifth *Prolusion:*

For invincible Truth has within herself strength enough and to spare for her own defence, and has no need of any other help;

and though she may seem to us at times to be hard-pressed and beaten to the ground, yet she maintains herself ever inviolate and uninjured by the claws of Error. (Tillyard, pp. 84-5.)

This is the Truth for serving which Abdiel is praised:

> Servant of God, well done; well hast thou
> fought
> The better fight, who single hast maintain'd
> Against revolted multitudes the Cause
> Of Truth, in word mightier than they in Arms;
> And for the testimony of Truth hast borne
> Universal reproach, far worse to bear
> Than violence. (6. 29-35.)

This is the Truth which the Jesus of *Paradise Regained* thought himself 'born to promote' (1. 205), and for which Socrates lived and died,

> For truth's sake suffering death unjust. (3. 98.)

Bearing in mind the 'perfect shape' of 'good, wise, just,' in *Paradise Regained* 2. 11, we shall recognize in two passages from the *Reason of Church-Government* and *Areopagitica* the visible stamp of Plato's theory of Ideas. In the first Milton says:

For Truth, I know not how, hath this unhappiness fatal to her, ere she can come to the trial and inspection of the understanding; being to pass through many little wards and limits of the several affections and desires, she cannot shift it, but must put on such colors and attire as those pathetic handmaids of the soul please to lead her in to their queen. . . . And contrary, when any falsehood comes that way, if they like the errand she brings, they are so artful to counterfeit the *very shape and visage* of Truth, that the understanding . . . sentences for the most part one for the other at the first blush. (3. 249.)

And again:

Truth indeed came once into the world with her divine Master,

142

and was a *perfect shape* most glorious to look on; but when he ascended and his Apostles after him were laid asleep, then straight arose a wicked race of deceivers, who . . . hewed *her lovely form* into a thousand pieces and scattered them to the four winds. . . . We have not yet found them all, Lords and Commons, nor ever shall do, till her Master's second coming; he shall bring together every joint and member, and shall mold them into *an immortal feature of loveliness and perfection.* (4. 337-8.)

The 'shape' of Truth in both these passages is not merely a personification, but an instance of the Platonic ἰδέα, the form visible to the inner eye. A sentence in the *Defensio Secunda* suggests that Milton, like Augustine and the Bible, identified at least this one of the absolute essences with God:

God himself is truth; and the more closely any one adheres to truth, in teaching it to mankind, the more nearly must he resemble God, the more acceptable must he be to him. (8. 65.)

But those absolute forms and eternal shapes of moral concepts are so numerous throughout Milton's writings that we cannot undertake to list all their appearances. Let it suffice to prove his acceptance of the doctrine, that he added to the ideal essences which appear in the Dialogues his own Idea of Discipline. So thoroughly Platonic is his conception of it that the passage in *The Reason of Church-Government* might be an excerpt from any of the longer speeches of Socrates:

There is not that thing in the world of more grave and urgent importance, throughout the whole life of man, than is discipline. What need I instance? He that hath read with judgment of nations and commonwealths, of cities and camps, of peace and war, sea and land, will readily agree that the flourishing and decaying of all civil societies, all the moments and turnings of human occasions, are moved to and fro as upon the axle of discipline. So that whatsoever power or sway in mortal things weaker men have attributed to fortune, I durst with more confidence (the honor of Divine Providence ever saved) ascribe either to the vigor or the slackness of discipline. Nor is there any sociable perfection in this life, civil or sacred, that can be above discipline; but she is that which with her musical cords preserves and holds all the parts thereof together. . . . And certainly discipline is not only the removal of disorder, but *if any visible shape can be given to divine things, the very visible shape and image of virtue;* whereby she is not only seen in the regular gestures and motions of her heavenly paces as she walks, but also makes the harmony of her voice audible to mortal ears. (3. 184-5.)

We cannot expect in poetry, or even in prose not of a strictly scientific nature, the same rigorous distinction that philosophers who derive their idealism from Plato maintain between a world of flux and a world of permanent realities. The poet, like Plato himself in his more poetic dialogues, will use the Ideal World to show what in the scope of human affairs moves toward, or accords with, the transcendent reality; and so, too, the writer on practical affairs, like Plato himself in his teaching of ethics and politics, will use the supraterrestrial realm to measure and to explain the phenomena of seeming reality. Thus Milton generally uses the Ideas, and yet occasionally he takes the Platonic duality more emphatically as a cleavage between two worlds. We see it in *Paradise Lost* when he describes that

> Portal, . . . inimitable on Earth
> By Model, or by shading Pencil drawn. (3. 508-9.)

Again, Raphael makes the distinction in teaching Adam:

> What surmounts the reach
> Of human sense, I shall delineate so,
> By lik'ning spiritual to corporeal forms,
> As may express them best, though what if Earth
> Be but the shadow of Heav'n, and things therein

> Each to other like, more than on earth is
>   thought? (5. 571-6.)

As Raphael takes earth to be the shadowy counterpart of heaven, so Michael suggests how man may eventually rise

> From shadowy Types to Truth, from Flesh to
>   Spirit. (12. 303.)

But in general, the 'very visible shape and image of virtue' is the main contribution of the Platonic world of true being to Milton's thought—and not only where a phrase reveals his source, but throughout the moral substructure of his writings. Everywhere in Milton's work, more vaguely in earlier years, more distinctly later, belief in the clearly defined and unalterable nature of moral truth is of the essence of his poetry and prose. Thus the eternal decrees of Justice in *Paradise Lost* illustrate the absolute validity of *principles* as opposed to the fluctuations of occurrence, and so, too, in *Paradise Regained* the triumph of Good through Truth, Wisdom, and Justice. This teaching is the contribution of the 'divine volumes' that Milton celebrated in the *Apology for Smectymnuus*.

In yet another way, quite foreign to Plato, the theory of Ideas entered the substance of Milton's work. Through the pagan Neoplatonists the Ideas become Intelligences as well as intelligibles, and thence by easy steps the angels of Neoplatonic Christians. We know that Milton was familiar with this conversion of the Platonic Ideas, for in his copy of Dante's *Convivio* he marked as worthy of note the section dealing with the transformation:

There were others, like Plato, a most eminent man, who assumed not only that there are as many Intelligences as there are movements of the heaven, but also as many as there are species of things, just as there is one species for all men, and another for all gold, and another for all riches, and so on; and they would have it that as the Intelligences of the heavens are

145

producers of these movements, each one of its own, so these other Intelligences are producers of everything else, and exemplars each one of its own species; and Plato called them 'ideas,' which is equivalent to calling them universal forms and natures. (2. 5, trans. by W. W. Jackson.)

Even before Milton undertook to write of the angelic hierarchies, we see the Platonic Idea in his heavenly creatures in such a passage as this from his Third *Prolusion:*

[Let your mind] learn to know itself, and therewith those holy minds and intelligences whose company it must hereafter join. (Tillyard, p. 72.)

The advice is like that of the Dialogues, except that 'those holy minds and intelligences' have replaced the Ideas. Once this is clear, we may see in the angels of *Paradise Lost* and the fallen angels of both *Paradise Lost* and *Paradise Regained* the Platonic essences transformed into the 'Intelligences of the Heavens.' To trace that metamorphosis is beyond our scope, but we may suggest one of the links in the chain that starts from the Ideas of Beauty, Goodness, Justice, and the like, and ends with the robust figures of Raphael and Michael. The change is in process in the Neoplatonic *Liber de Causis*, a work popular in Dante's time, where the imperishable universals of Plato are in process of becoming heavenly spirits.

But that is a separate tale of philosophical, religious, and literary continuity, while ours is of an immediate transfer and assimilation of a philosophical doctrine by a poet. Or shall we say of a poetical doctrine? In the verses *De Idea Platonica*, Milton had called Plato a poet for creating this very doctrine. And it seems unreasonable to suppose Milton untouched by a theory that had permeated European thought in one way or another from Plato's time to his own, or to think that he could have admired the volumes of Plato and ignored their most distinctive teaching. The Idea did not mean to him precisely what it means to Santayana or Whitehead; but Milton could hardly have entertained the concepts of universal reality or arrived at the vision of human circumstances *sub specie aeternitatis* without which *Paradise Lost, Paradise Regained,* and *Samson* are inconceivable, had he not won from his reading in Plato the view of stability behind apparent flux that is named the theory of Ideas.

CHAPTER VII

The Doctrine of Love

W HEN Milton substituted faith and love for knowledge and wisdom as the keystone of happiness, we
may say that he proceeded from a Platonic to a supra-
Platonic ethics. But Milton himself forces us to modify the
statement. The very passage in the *Apology for Smectymnuus* where he speaks of his debt to Plato asserts that what
he primarily learned from the Dialogues was a theory of
love. Let us once more attend to his now familiar words:

Thus, from the laureate fraternity of poets, riper years and
the ceaseless round of study and reading led me . . . to the
divine volumes of Plato; . . . where, if I should tell you what I
learned of chastity and love, I mean that which is truly so,
whose charming cup is only virtue, which she bears in her hand
to those who are worthy (the rest are cheated with a thick
intoxicating potion, which a certain sorceress, the abuser of
love's name, carries about), and how the first and chiefest office
of love begins and ends in the soul, producing those happy twins
of her divine generation, knowledge and virtue, with such abstracted sublimities as these; it might be worth your listening,
readers, as I may one day hope to have ye in a still time, when
here shall be no chiding. (3. 305.)

Our first question must be, What was the doctrine of
love that thus enchanted Milton? Having found that, and
the use to which he put the doctrine, we shall have to see
why, if knowledge is Love's own child, Milton deliberately
replaced knowledge by love as the chief means to happiness.

Before resolving these questions, it is worth observing that, far beyond the common opinion of him, Milton was a poet of love in the tradition of the Renaissance, as genuinely as constant treatment of its themes could make him. The word 'love' in various forms and compounds occurs some one hundred and eighty times in his English poems alone, and the early Latin and Italian verse is predominantly concerned with *amor* and *amore*. Still, apart from some distinctively Ovidian elegies and *sylvae*, even in his earliest work Milton takes love to be something more than the natural affection between the sexes. Thus in the elegy for *A Fair Infant,* he speaks of 'heav'n-lov'd innocence,' certain that man is not only ruled, but loved, by God. The same sense of God's surpassing care for man reappears in the verses *Upon the Circumcision,* where the poet asks and answers himself on the mediation of Christ:

> O more exceeding love or law more just?
> Just law indeed, but more exceeding love!

But it is not primarily the love of God for man that pervades Milton's writing, though almost always this hovers about his use of the word, purifying and enriching his concept of what human love can be with the assurance that God himself loves and *is* Love. More often Milton is concerned with man's own love, frequently with that love which Michael at the end of *Paradise Lost* teaches Adam is the soul of all other virtues, love—

> By name to come call'd Charity.

The word 'charity' is used only two other times in Milton's English poems; usually 'love' does service for the Christian virtue, as in the lines *On Mrs. Thomason:*

> When Faith and Love which parted from thee never,
> Had ripen'd thy just soul to dwell with God. (1-2.)

And here in the love that 'ripens the just soul' we come very close to the doctrine that Milton professed to have learned from Plato. We must leave the distinction in his thought between Platonic and Christian love until we have first examined Plato's concept.

The two dialogues that deal most extensively with the nature of love, *Phaedrus* and the *Symposium,* were favorites in the Renaissance, especially among poets. Ficino, Pico della Mirandola, and Castiglione placed upon these two works an emphasis so extraordinary that 'Platonic love' speedily came to be the one thing Platonic of which, then as now, the generality heard. In Spenser's *Four Hymns* honoring love and beauty, we find the impress of these Platonizing Italians; and let us at once add, the impress is still recognizably Platonic. However distorted the teaching may have become in lesser minds and lesser hands, those who seriously accepted it did not drive it far from the mark that Plato intended.

The speakers of the *Symposium* in their eulogies of Eros advance varied theories, the more important parts of which are caught up, interwoven, and transformed in Socrates' encomium of love. From Phaedrus' discourse he takes the notion that the lover is moved to virtue, especially in the presence of his beloved. From Pausanias comes the distinction between the heavenly and earthly Aphrodite, the heavenly and earthly love. Eryximachus enlarges the realm of love to include the universe, explaining all sympathetic and antipathetic movements as the effects of love and hate, and further separating love into the true harmony of unlike elements and the false conjoining of destructive forces. From Aristophanes comes the myth of the two halves seeking, through love, reunion into an original whole, a myth destined to become famous in itself, and, through Aristotle's conversion of it, into a definition of the friend as 'another self.' Agathon finally adds the touch of lyric rapture, proclaiming love the best and fairest of things human and the cause of every other good, the original poet and source of all poetry, the delicate young god who brings order out of chaos and peace to the hearts of men.

If Plato intended these speeches to be entirely superseded by that of Socrates, he would hardly have composed them all with the excellence of structure and phrase that has won them a permanent hold on readers. And indeed Socrates' discourse surpasses rather than supersedes the previous accounts of love; for although, in his first insistent questioning of Agathon, he seems bent on destroying the premises of all the former speakers, his own further words belie that intention. In his supposed account of the lore of Diotima he uses the better part of the doctrines we have assigned to their first speakers. But Socrates combines and unifies these diverse reflections by defining love as the desire for eternal possession of the good, that is, as the yearning for happiness. Mythically born of Plenty and Poverty at the feast of Aphrodite, Love seeks the beauty which is good in order to beget the lover's likeness and thereby perpetuate him. In the realm of the common or earthly Aphrodite, this seeking and begetting mean marriage and children; in the realm of the Uranian Aphrodite, the lover ascends as on a ladder from physical beauty to spiritual, until he finally wins sight of Beauty absolute, and there brings to birth the realities of knowledge and virtue which constitute the happiness of man. Love thus defined is the generic longing for every good; its highest species is philosophy, the longing for wisdom or knowledge.

In *Phaedrus* again, love, inspired by visible beauty, gains for the soul the vision of transcendent Ideas; but here that vision is clearly a reward in the after-life. Through the images first of the winged soul, and then of the charioteer, reason, with his two horses of will and desire, Socrates teaches the need of continence if love is to bring happiness. The wing of the soul, fed by the sight of earthly beauty, droops at a lustful touch; the wild horse of desire, uncurbed by reason, and unimpeded by will, can delay by thousands of years the visionary bliss. Again, the highest kind of love is philosophy, the desire of knowledge, even if this must be gained through devotion to a particular person in whom the Idea, the true object of knowledge and therefore of love, manifests itself.

Now Milton specifically explains his understanding of Platonic love as (1) a distinction between love and lust; (2) a process that occurs in the soul; (3) a creator of knowledge and virtue; (4) a thing divine; and (5) an 'abstracted sublimity.' Starting with the last first, we note that the term 'abstracted sublimity' reflects the words of Diotima at the critical turn of her speech from earthly to heavenly love:

These are the lesser mysteries of love, into which even you, Socrates, may enter; to the greater and more hidden ones which are the crown of these, and to which, if you pursue them in a right spirit, they will lead, I know not whether you will be able to attain.[1]

Thus in *Comus*, the Lady refuses to teach her tormentor

> The sublime notion, and high mystery
> That must be utter'd to unfold the sage
> And serious doctrine of Virginity.

Her argument is,

> Thou hast nor Ear, nor Soul to apprehend.

But further,

> And thou art worthy that thou shouldst not know
> More happiness than this thy present lot. (784-9.)

Clearly Milton believes with Plato that the 'high mystery'

---

[1] *Symposium* 210 a. Compare the initiation into 'perfect mysteries' in *Phaedrus* 249 c.

of true love, which here, as in the *Apology for Smectymnuus,* is linked with the doctrine of chastity, brings happiness when understood. This belief sheds light on Milton's other uses of the Platonic teaching.

The first mysterious element in love, as Eryximachus and Socrates after him had explained, is its harmonizing power that pervades and sustains the universe. Milton has in mind this universal power when he speaks in *The Doctrine and Discipline of Divorce* about

> the issues of love and hatred distinctly flowing through the whole mass of created things, and . . . [by God's doing ever bringing] the due likenesses and harmonies of his works together, except when, out of two contraries met to their own destruction, he moulds a third existence. (3. 418.)

Like the speakers in the *Symposium,* he is more concerned with those species of the generic love that directly affect human life. Human love arises, and here Milton cites Plato as an authority, from human need:

> All ingenuous men will see that the dignity and blessing of marriage is placed rather in the mutual enjoyment of that which the wanting soul needfully seeks than of that which the plenteous body would joyfully give away. Hence it is that Plato in his festival discourse brings in Socrates relating what he feigned to have learned from the prophetess Diotima, how Love was the son of Penury, begot of Plenty in the garden of Jupiter. Which divinely sorts with that which in effect Moses tells us, that Love was the son of loneliness, begot in Paradise by that sociable and helpful aptitude which God implanted between man and woman toward each other. (3. 398.)

The need being in the soul, as a sense of imperfection longing to be perfected, it requires for its satisfaction not so much outward acts as inward assurance. With this conviction Milton writes to Diodati:

> I would not have true friendship tried by the test of letters

and good wishes, which may all be feigned; but its roots and the sources of its strength should go deep into the mind, and it should spring from a pure origin, so that, even were all tokens of mutual regard to cease, yet it should endure throughout life, untainted by suspicion or recrimination. For its nurture the written word is less essential than a lively recollection of virtues on both sides. Nor does it follow that, in default of your writing, there is nothing to supply the omission; your integrity writes to me in your stead, and indites true letters on the tablets of my heart; the purity of your life and your love of virtue write to me, your whole character too, far above the common, writes to me and commends you to me more and more. (Tillyard, p. 13.)

And some years later, lamenting Diodati's death, he declares of this harmony of friendship that it is desired and attained only by the noble spirit:

He [Love] does not aim at little souls and the ignoble hearts of the rabble, but, rolling his flaming eyes about, unwearied, he ever scatters his missiles on high through the spheres, and never aims his shot downward. Hence minds immortal and forms divine are inflamed with love. (MacKellar, p. 171.)

In the early Latin poems, and in his Italian sonnets with their Florentine Platonism, Milton had celebrated the perceptible beauty that moves to love and creates new gifts and powers in the lover. Like Phaedrus in the *Symposium*, he asserted that love and nobility of spirit are inseparable:

Truly is he destitute of all worth that is not moved to love by thy gentle spirit; which sweetly reveals itself—bounteous in pleasant looks, and the gifts that are the arrows and bow of Love—there, where blooms thy lofty might. When thou speakest in beauty, or singest in joy, . . . let him who is unworthy of thee guard well the entrance of his eyes and ears. Only grace from above may help him, ere amorous longing lingers in his heart. (Smart, p. 144.)

And again:

Love quickens on my swift tongue the new flower of a foreign speech, as I sing of thee, sweet and noble lady. . . . Love willed it; and I knew at the cost of others that Love never willed aught in vain. (*Ibid.*, pp. 146-7.)

Even while assuring Diodati that it was not physical beauty alone that enchanted him, he exalted the embodiment of the 'Idea' as the object of his love in the terms of Petrarchan Platonism:

Neither tresses of gold nor rosy cheek beguiles me thus; but, under a new form [*nuova idea*], strange beauty charms my heart. (*Ibid.*, p. 150.)

But with the letter he wrote to Diodati in 1637, his tone changes. Now it is no longer physical beauty that draws him, but the inward beauty of the noble soul which, Plato had taught, more truly reflects the perfect Idea of Beauty. The words suggest that Milton has learned Diotima's ultimate lesson: the true love of beauty is philosophy, love of wisdom.

Though I know not God's intent toward me in other respects, yet of this I am sure, that he has imbued me especially with a mighty passion for Beauty. Ceres never sought her daughter Proserpine (as the legend tells) with greater ardor than I do this Idea of Beauty, like some image of loveliness; ever pursuing it, by day and by night, in every shape and form ('for many forms there are of things divine') and following close in its footprints as it leads. And so, whensoever I find one who spurns the base opinions of common men, and dares to be, in thought and word and deed, that which the wisest minds throughout the ages have approved; whensoever, I say, I find such a man, to him I find myself impelled forthwith to cleave. (Tillyard, p. 14.)

In 'every shape and form,' says Milton, but clearly he reckons the impress of beauty on 'thought and word and deed' a higher token of the Beauty absolute than beauty of person. The outer beauty retains its fascination for him, but

156

the inner excellence comes more and more to surpass it in his esteem.

When we turn now to the much misinterpreted tracts on divorce, we shall recognize that Milton is doing little more than apply his Platonic theory of love to the institution of marriage. Agar (p. 34, n. 2) rightly thinks *The Doctrine and Discipline of Divorce* among the most Platonic of Milton's writings. It is the immediate product of his thought on that love whose 'first and chiefest office ... begins and ends in the soul.' Since it is 'the mind from whence must flow the acts of peace and love' (3. 93), there can never be true marriage save where 'the fit union of their souls be such as may even incorporate them to love and amity; but that can never be where no correspondence is of the mind' (3. 477-8). We need not labor the matter; throughout the tracts on divorce, Milton insists to the point of repetition that the essential union is of the soul, and that the true mate is 'another self, a second self, a very self itself' (4. 90). Only union of this kind enables man to rise to 'such a love as Christ loves his Church' (4. 192); all other union, under whatever name, is lust.

The theory of marriage and divorce that dominates these tracts, and asserts itself again in the treatise *De Doctrina Christiana,* depends upon the Platonic dichotomy of the world into two realms: the material, or that which affects the body, and the spiritual, or that which affects the soul. (See 15. 155-79.) Presumably Milton came in his later years to discard this separation, for in *De Doctrina Christiana* he affirms:

Man having been created after this manner, it is said, as a consequence, that 'man became a living soul'; whence it may be inferred (unless we had rather take the heathen writers for our teachers respecting the nature of the soul) that man is a living being, intrinsically and properly one and individual, not compound or separable, not, according to the common opinion, made up and framed of two distinct and different natures, as of soul and body, but that the whole man is soul, and the soul man, that is to say, a body, or substance individual, animated, sensitive, and rational. (15. 39-41.)

The heathen writers whose view is here rejected are clearly Plato and the Platonists.

Earlier, Milton had held the same view as Plato, that the body is not merely distinct from the soul, but a prison to it, and death consequently a release. The doctrine is reflected in *In obitum Praesulis Wintoniensis* 31-8, 41-50; the lines *On the Morning of Christ's Nativity* 13-4; *On Time* 4-8, 14-21; *Comus* 380-4, 419-80; and *On Mrs. Thomason* 3-4. Even in *Samson Agonistes* it is alluded to, if not affirmed:

> Thou art become (O worst imprisonment!)
> The Dungeon of thyself; thy Soul
> (Which Men enjoying sight oft without cause
>   complain)
> Imprison'd now indeed,
> In real darkness of the body dwells. (155-9.)[2]

Apparently even after he had discarded the belief that body and soul are separate entities, he could make dramatic use of it. At any rate, he never completely rejected the teaching of Plato on the relative worth of body and soul.

According to Plato, the body is inferior to the soul, at best its instrument, at worst its prison. And even when Milton adopts the Aristotelian concept of the soul as the form of the body (as in *Doct. Christ.* 15. 36-52), he retains the Platonic belief in the superiority of the soul. Thus of the mediatorial office of Christ's rule he writes:

Herein it is that the pre-eminent excellency of Christ's kingdom over all others, as well as the divine principles on which it is founded, are [*sic*] manifested; inasmuch as he governs, not the

---

[2] Cf. *Samson* 102 and 1572.

bodies of men alone, as the civil magistrate, but their minds and consciences. (15. 299.)

Whatever the strict explanation of the union of soul and body, the soul is always for Milton more important. And hence the persistence of his view that marriage is preeminently a joining of souls, and that love is pre-eminently the desire of the soul for happiness.

The psychology of Plato taught Milton that 'the Soul excels the body' (*Tetrach.* 4. 118), and that love of 'the souls of men . . . is the dearest love' (*Animad.* 3. 107). And the Platonic view of the soul had a further importance for Milton's theory of love. The tripartite division into reason, will, and desire, which is imaged in *Phaedrus* under the figure of the charioteer and his two horses, often recurs in the Dialogues, most significantly in the *Republic* 4. 441-3 and *Timaeus* 69-71. Agar (pp. 12-8) has shown beyond the need of further demonstration that Milton adopted this account of the soul. Reason, in his scheme as in that of Plato, is the noblest faculty and should therefore rule; the will, as the instrument of action, should carry out the decisions of reason; the appetites, as the lowest part of the soul and most closely bound to the body, should willingly obey the commands of the better part. And Milton accepted other doctrines connected with this analysis of the soul: the concept of tyranny as the rule of appetite, and of justice as the harmony of the three elements.

Another corollary of the Platonic psychology had an even more marked effect on Milton's thought. If the upstart reign of appetite is the root of error, it is at the same time its punishment. The worst of doing evil is that the soul becomes evil, goes to war with itself, and can never escape. Thus Milton berates an opponent in his *Pro Se Defensio* (9. 189):

But alas! wretch that you are! You have long been at dreadful variance with yourself! To you, nothing is more intolerable than to be, to dwell with yourself. . . . What raises such commotion within is, that within is a whip, and that Argus tormentor of yours . . . follows you ever . . . to disquiet you with the maddening gad-fly of your heinous crimes!

Vice is a disease that destroys the vicious, as God intimates in *Paradise Lost* when he says that, after Adam's fall, he will have to

> renew
> His lapsed powers, though forfeit and enthrall'd
> By sin to foul exorbitant desires. (3. 175-7.)

Thus Plato had explained evil and its punishment throughout the Dialogues. Evil is a disease, to be cured like a disease.

And hence the irony of the half-truth in Satan's first greeting of his new abode:

> Hail horrours, hail
> Infernal world, and thou profoundest Hell
> Receive thy new Possessor: One who brings
> A mind not to be chang'd by Place or Time.
> The mind is its own place, and in itself
> Can make a Heav'n of Hell, a Hell of Heav'n.
> What matter where, if I be still the same? (1. 250-6.)

The mind can doubtless make a 'Hell of Heav'n' as Satan did—but not, by the very nature of Hell *as* a state of soul, a 'Heav'n of Hell.' 'What matter where' indeed, so long as the Hell-making mind is 'still the same.' According to the eschatological myths of Plato, the soul gains for itself a habitation appropriate to it, and can no more create an external heaven for its inner hell than it can fail to turn every outer good into a further torment for itself. And therefore when Satan thinks to change his fortune by changing his place, he cannot leave behind

> The Hell within him, for within him Hell
> He brings, and round about him, nor from Hell
> One step no more than from himself can fly
> By change of place. (4. 20-3.)

He himself recognizes his self-inflicted doom:

> Me miserable! which way shall I fly
> Infinite wrauth, and infinite despair?
> Which way I fly is Hell; myself am Hell;
> And in the lowest deep a lower deep
> Still threat'ning to devour me opens wide,
> To which the Hell I suffer seems a Heav'n. (4. 73-8.)

He had thought to be free in the abyss, to 'reign secure' (1. 259-63), but security and freedom are not for the soul in which the tyranny of ambition and hatred has upset the rule of reason. As Milton puts it in his sonnet on those who think freedom can be theirs for the snatching,

> Licence they mean when they cry liberty,
> For who loves that, must first be wise and good.

Now he is wise in whom reason maintains harmony; he is doomed by his own folly in whom reason becomes the minister to base aims, and doomed to that ministry as well as by it. Only if he can shake off his self-imposed chains will he ever know release; and no external power can help except by inducing in him a change of desire; for a man is ultimately happy or wretched as he wants the right or wrong things. This is the essential teaching of Plato in ethics and psychology.

Our concern is more with the effect of that teaching on Milton's theory of love. The first effect is his distinction between love and lust. Since the mind is 'the worthiest part of man' (*Tetrach.* 4. 87), love manifests the rule of reason, whereas in lust reason and will surrender to appetite. *Comus* stresses the negative aspect of this theory: lust 'imbrutes' the soul, transforming her to the image of the bestial appetites, while chastity turns the body itself 'to the soul's essence' by 'driving far off each thing of sin and guilt.' Were it not that Milton promised to speak of the 'abstracted sublimities' of love after he had written *Comus,* we might think that poem the fulfilment of his promise, and finding there only the negative doctrine of chastity, might reasonably conclude that Milton's view of love was only the lesser half of Plato's. But we know from the Cambridge Manuscript that Milton included in three separate drafts for a tragedy on the subject of *Paradise Lost* a figure that he called 'Heavenly Love.' Here, then, was the poem in which he intended to teach 'that love which is truly so'; and while the epic poem that he finally wrote is doubtless far from his original plan, *Paradise Lost* as it stands does perform the teaching promised in the *Apology for Smectymnuus.* 'Heavenly Love,' the doctrine of the 'divine volumes' of Plato, is a major theme in the explanation Milton gives of the loss of happiness.

To the reader who is aware of Milton's former intention, the first words on love in *Paradise Lost* begin to speak the influence of Plato:

> Hail wedded Love, mysterious Law, true source
> Of human offspring, sole propriety,
> In Paradise of all things common else.
> By thee adulterous lust was driv'n from men
> Among the bestial herds to range, by thee
> Founded in Reason, Loyal, Just, and Pure. (4. 750-5.)

The 'mysterious Law' is the 'mystery of love' expounded by Diotima; and love is distinguished from lust, as in Plato's treatment, by being founded in reason. Milton repeats the distinction with emphasis when he declares of the relation between Adam and Eve:

> Love unlibidinous reign'd. (5. 449.)

But only when we come to the dialogue in the Eighth Book between Adam and his angelic visitor, do we learn why Milton has been so emphatic in his first description of the love between Adam and Eve. As Adam relates how he asked God for a companion, we begin to hear the subtler themes of Platonic love. The myth of Diotima on the birth of Eros, Milton had said in *The Doctrine and Discipline of Divorce* (3. 398), 'divinely sorts with that which in effect Moses tells us, that Love was the son of Loneliness, begot in Paradise.' Here Adam reflects that 'divine agreement' between Diotima and Moses, explaining to God:

> Thou in thyself art perfet, and in thee
> Is no deficience found; not so is Man,
> But in degree, the cause of his desire
> By conversation with his like to help,
> Or solace his defects. (8. 415-9.)

To which the divine voice answered:

> What next I bring shall please thee, be assur'd,
> Thy likeness, thy fit help, thy other self,
> Thy wish, exactly to thy heart's desire. (8. 449-51.)

And now, with love, son of Plenty and Poverty, 'begot in Paradise,' the struggle to stand firm or fall begins. The beauty of Eve moves Adam as Plato had said beauty moves the lover:

> What seem'd fair in all the World, seem'd now
> Mean, or in her summ'd up, in her contain'd
> And in her looks, which from that time infus'd
> Sweetness into my heart, unfelt before,
> And into all things from her Air inspir'd
> The spirit of love and amorous delight. (8. 472-7.)

Raphael, like a wise Diotima or a wiser Socrates, attempts to instruct Adam in the 'higher mysteries,' not blaming his attachment to Eve, but showing how he may make use of it to gain perfect and lasting happiness:

> What higher in her society thou find'st
> Attractive, human, rational, love still;
> In loving thou dost well, in passion not,
> Wherein true Love consists not; love refines
> The thoughts, and heart enlarges, hath his seat
> In Reason, and is judicious, is the scale
> By which to heav'nly Love thou may'st ascend,
> Not sunk in carnal pleasure. (8. 586-93.)

The argument that Raphael uses is Plato's: the beauty of Eve being external, is a thing inferior to the inner beauty of Adam's wisdom; for Adam has admitted that

> All higher knowledge in her presence falls
> Degraded, Wisdom in discourse with her
> Loses discount'nanc't, and like folly shews. (8. 551-3.)

The Angel answers 'with contracted brow':

> Accuse not Nature, she hath done her part;
> Do thou but thine, and be not diffident
> Of Wisdom, she deserts thee not, if thou
> Dismiss not her, when most thou need'st her nigh,
> By attributing overmuch to things
> Less excellent, as thou thyself perceiv'st. (8. 561-6.)

Adam has begun to sever love from reason, to reverse the scale of values by subordinating wisdom to physical beauty; and Raphael sees at once where his error will lead if not swiftly checked. Love can be the 'scale' to heaven only if it does not forget that its proper object is the possession of lasting good. Now lasting good in Christian thought is God and God alone. And hence Adam's mistake in staying at the first rung of the ladder instead of climbing to the highest is, or is likely to become, the preference of Eve to God. The warning of Raphael temporarily serves to recall Adam to the proper nature of his love for Eve. Their love is not the lustful reign of appetite, but

> Union of Mind, or in us both one Soul;
> Harmony to behold in wedded pair
> More grateful than harmonious sound to the ear. (8. 604-6.)

Further, Adam shows himself a good student by repeating Raphael's lesson; he still keeps himself

> free [to]
> Approve the best, and follow what I approve.
> To love thou blam'st me not, for love thou
> say'st
> Leads up to Heav'n, is both the way and guide. (8. 610-3.)

When Raphael answers the question whether the angels love, we see another trace of the 'heavenly' love:

> Let it suffice thee that thou know'st
> Us happy, and without Love no happiness. (8. 620-1.)

No happiness without love of wisdom was Plato's creed; substituting the omniscient God of Christianity for σοφία, Milton's becomes: without love of God no happiness.

But the lower rungs of the ladder remain as in the Platonic scheme. Personal love, according to Phaedrus in the *Symposium,* inspires the lover to virtue. Thus Adam to Eve:

> I from the influence of thy looks receive
> Access in every Virtue, in thy sight
> More wise, more watchful, stronger, if need were
> Of outward strength; while shame, thou looking on,
> Shame to be overcome or over-reacht
> Would utmost vigour raise, and rais'd unite. (9. 309-14.)

And so long as the affection is one that can 'lead up to Heaven,' Adam may assure Eve that God made them for

> Love not the lowest end of human life.

> For not to irksom toil, but to delight
> He made us, and delight to Reason join'd. (9. 241-3.)

But when the delight of love is no longer 'to Reason join'd,' when Adam dignifies Eve beyond her proper worth, and ceases to desire what reason bids him desire, the scale is upset, and his love is no longer that which 'begins and ends in the soul, producing those happy twins of her divine generation, knowledge and virtue.' This is the catastrophe against which Raphael had given due warning, but at the critical moment Adam forgets the lesson.

The fall of Eve, as is often noted, closely follows the account in *Protagoras* of involuntary error. Misled by the serpent into thinking that she will be happier if she disobeys the command of God, she chooses an apparent good that is really an evil. Similarly Adam errs because he mistakes relative values, but his error is specifically that of irrational love. While Eve was a worthy object, the affection for her could be rational, ennobling, and therefore a step in the ascent to heavenly love. But as soon as love of her becomes a preference of her to God, that is to all good, Adam's love is no longer 'that which is truly so,' but the 'thick intoxicating potion' that 'abuses love's name.' Milton insists upon the distinction. Previously in their state of innocence,

> Love unlibidinous reign'd.

Now, with reason overthrown and the will powerless, the many-headed desires hold sway. Ironically, Milton recalls the allegory in *Phaedrus* of the winged soul:

> They swim in mirth, and fancy that they feel
> Divinity within them breeding wings
> Wherewith to scorn the earth. (9. 1009-11.)

But the wings that love might have bred in them are not, Milton would have us know, produced by sin:

> That false Fruit
> Far other operation first display'd,
> Carnal desire inflaming. (9. 1011-3.)

The rule of reason once broken, the reign of lust begins; and now, Milton insists,

> Love was not in thir looks, either to God
> Or to each other. (10. 113-4.)

Their loss of love for each other, a consequence of their loss of love for God, is the lowest point in the degradation of the pair. Happiness has been completely lost.

It remains for Adam to learn from a second angelic teacher how he may regain a measure of happiness by restoring his sense of values. The most important part of the lesson Adam makes clear:

> Henceforth I learn, that to obey is best,
> And love with fear the only God. (12. 561-2.)

Such loving and fearful obedience, by making Adam desire most what is most desirable, the merited possession of God's favor, will win him that favor, and therein he will find lasting happiness.

We now can see why Milton substituted love for knowledge as the mainspring of human joy, and how the theory of love which he learned from Plato led him to go beyond the Platonic scale of values. Since love is the moving impulse without which man rests content in his limited self, it becomes the source of every good, as it is the power which moves man to reach for the good that is not in him. And reason being the faculty that recognizes good, love is rational, beginning in the soul and desiring what will perfect it. Thus much Milton could learn from Diotima and Socrates: knowledge is the effect of love in action. But what precisely does love seek to possess and know? Plato had said that the object of love is an Idea, the perfect Beauty, the whole and complete Good. Christianity said that God alone is wholly good and perfectly beautiful; that is, Christianity identified God with the universals that Plato thought the ultimate object of knowledge. If God, then, becomes the proper goal of Christian philosophy, knowledge cannot be the highest aim of humanity, and this for the good reason that God is unknowable. Milton had declared in *De Doctrina Christiana* (14. 61): 'It follows, finally, that God must be styled by us *wonderful* and *incomprehensible*.' The Perfection by participating in which man becomes happy is then to be won, not by knowledge, but by love. And this love, this perpetual impulse to mount up to God, will of itself bring man to whatever knowledge is possible and valuable to him. In *Colasterion* (4. 264) Milton wrote:

> For seeing love includes faith, what is there that can fulfil every commandment but only love?

Man may call his goal by the name of truth, but God alone is Truth (*Doct. Christ*. 14. 41). And therefore God alone is the right object of man's longing, and love alone the means of its fulfilment.

Much the same tale is retold in *Samson Agonistes*, except that the fall from right to wrong desire, being less fully intended than Adam's, is more easily repaired. Samson, like Adam, forgot at the critical moment where true good really lay; but unlike Adam he never argued himself into believing the false good true. He

> Whose strength, while virtue was her mate,
> Might have subdu'd the Earth, (173-4)

has fallen by 'impotence of mind, in body strong'; for, wisdom and virtue being one,

> What is strength without a double share
> Of wisdom? vast, unwieldy, burdensome,

> Proudly secure, yet liable to fall
> By weakest subtleties, not made to rule,
> But to subserve where wisdom bears command. (54-8.)

He has not sunk low enough to mistake his error, nor so low as those who are willing to come to terms with a fallen state,

> to love Bondage more than Liberty,
> Bondage with ease than strenuous liberty. (270-1.)

Samson is curable, and the cure, like the crime, grows out of a change of aim. The crime has brought its own penalty, the sense of God's favor lost, of evil merited. Nothing, Samson exclaims,

> Nothing of all these evils hath befall'n me
> But justly; I myself have brought them on,
> Sole Author I, sole cause. (374-6.)

And the outer punishment is only the expected reflex of the inner wrong:

> Servile mind
> Rewarded well with servile punishment!
> The base degree to which I now am fall'n,
> These rags, this grinding, is not yet so base
> As was my former servitude, ignoble,
> Unmanly, ignominous, infamous,
> True slavery, and that blindness worse than this,
> That saw not how degenerately I serv'd. (412-9.)

Therefore he will 'expiate, if possible' his crime—a crime which he explicitly calls a species of intemperance (558-62). The cure can be helped from outside; on that score Milton had long before accepted the opinion of Plato:

He that will not let these [admonition and reproof] pass into him, though he be the greatest king, as Plato affirms, must . . . remain impure within. (*Church-Gov.* 3. 264.)

And even if admonition and reproof fail, according to

Plato, a soul not too far gone can be cleansed by the punishment which inevitably springs from crime. Samson is thus cleansed. Taught by his blindness and imprisonment where his true strength lay, steadied by all the trials of his visitants' counsel, reproaches, temptations, and taunts, victorious over his own pride and despair, when the last test comes, he knows what alone will bring him to peace. That is why the death he chooses is, even to his father, a triumph, not a catastrophe; it is Samson's conquest of himself as well as of the Philistines:

> And which is best and happiest yet, all this
> With God not parted from him, as was fear'd,
> But favouring and assisting to the end.
> Nothing is here for tears, nothing to wail
> Or knock the breast, no weakness, no contempt,
> Dispraise, or blame, nothing but well and fair,
> And what may quiet us in a death so noble. (1718-24.)

The purgation is accomplished; Samson has atoned, has made himself at one with the will of God, has regained in death the harmony that a foolish mistake in values had cost him in life. And God, having shown through his career how the lost good can be rewon,

> His servants he with new acquist
> Of true experience from this great event
> With peace and consolation hath dismist,
> And calm of mind all passion spent.

But there is a more direct road to happiness than the one Adam and Samson must take after they have lost their way. In *Paradise Regained* Jesus arrives at the desired end without a fall, by choosing from the first against every temptation the one sure source of joy. Milton has the angelic chorus sing before the trial begins:

> Victory and Triumph to the Son of God
> Now ent'ring his great duel, not of arms,
> But to vanquish by wisdom hellish wiles. (1. 173-5.)

As Agar says, Paradise is 'to be regained by a reassertion of the supremacy of reason over the passions' (p. 9). There is no talk of love as the one thing needful in *Paradise Regained;* there are no explicit statements to compare with the emphatic doctrine of heavenly love in *Paradise Lost.* Satan is no more the person to whom Christ would speak of that high mystery than Comus seemed a fit auditor to the Lady of the Mask. But, clearly enough, when Jesus reasserts the supremacy of reason, he is not asserting the purely Platonic notion that knowledge is the chief good. Far from it! He rejects knowledge as decisively as he had rejected pleasure, wealth, power, and fame, and always on the same ground: each of these is good, as Plato said and Milton repeated in *Samson Agonistes,* only to the good man, that is, only when added to that which can make it useful for human happiness. And for Milton that one irreplaceable source of all human good is loving trust in God. Jesus defeats his antagonist by wisdom, the virtue produced by knowledge, as Adam, Eve, and Samson were defeated through their foolish ignorance of true values. But the origins of that wisdom and that error are made clear at the beginning of *Paradise Regained* when Milton defines the themes of his two companion poems:

> I who erewhile the happy Garden sung,
> By one man's disobedience lost, now sing
> Recover'd Paradise to all mankind,
> By one man's firm obedience fully tried
> Through all temptation.

The Paradise that Adam lost and Jesus regained is the happiness of love, founded in trust, expressing itself in obedience to the moral law, and fulfilled in the perfect harmony of the soul within itself and with the divinely ordered universe which is its home.

A LIST OF REFERENCES TO PUBLICATIONS

EDITIONS AND TRANSLATIONS

Plato. Opera. Ed. by John Burnet. Oxford, 1896-1906.
    The Republic. Trans. by A. D. Lindsay. Everyman's Library, London, 1935.
    The Laws. Trans. by A. E. Taylor. London, 1934.
    On the Trial and Death of Socrates: *Euthyphro, Apology, Crito, Phaedo*. Trans. by Lane Cooper. Ithaca, New York, 1941.
    Phaedrus, Ion, Gorgias, and *Symposium,* with Passages from the *Republic* and *Laws*. Trans. by Lane Cooper. London, 1938.
    Timaeus and *Critias*. Trans. by A. E. Taylor. London, 1929.
    Dialogues. Trans. by Benjamin Jowett. New York, 1892.
    Glenn R. Morrow. Studies in the Platonic Epistles. Illinois Studies in Language and Literature 18, Nos. 3-4. Urbana, Illinois, 1935.
Milton. The Works of John Milton. Ed. by F. A. Patterson and others. Columbia University Press, New York, 1931-8.
    The Poems of John Milton. Ed. by Sir H. J. C. Grierson. London, 1925.
    The Latin Poems of John Milton. Ed. and trans. by Walter Mac Kellar. Cornell Studies in English, No. 15. New Haven, 1930.
    The Sonnets of Milton. Ed. and trans. by John S. Smart. Glasgow, 1921.
    Private Correspondence and Academic Exercises. Trans. by Phyllis B. Tillyard. Cambridge, 1932.
    Milton on Education. Ed. by Oliver Morley Ainsworth. Cornell Studies in English, No. 12. New Haven, 1928.

WORKS CITED

Agar, Herbert. Milton and Plato. Princeton Studies in English, No. 2. Princeton, 1928.
Ast, D. Friedrich. Lexicon Platonicum. Leipzig, 1835.
Aristotle. The Works of Aristotle. Ed. by W. D. Ross. Oxford, 1908-31.
Augustine. De Civitate Dei. Ed. by J. E. C. Welldon. London, 1924.
    The Confessions of Saint Augustine. Trans. by E. B. Pusey, ed. by Arthur Symons. London, 1898.
Baldwin, E. C. 'Milton and Plato's *Timaeus,*' PMLA. 35 (1920). 210-7.
    'A Note on *Il Penseroso,*' MLN. 33 (1918). 184-5.
Barker, Arthur. 'Milton's Schoolmasters,' MLR. 32 (1937). 517-36.

Campagnac, E. T. The Cambridge Platonists. Oxford, 1901.

Cassirer, Ernst. Die platonische Renaissance in England und die Schule von Cambridge. Leipzig, 1932.

Cicero. Three Books of Offices, etc. Trans. by C. R. Edmonds. London, 1916.

Dante. Convivio. Trans. by W. W. Jackson. Oxford, 1909.

Darbishire, Helen, ed. The Early Lives of Milton. London, 1932.

Diogenes Laertius. Lives of Eminent Philosophers. Ed. and trans. by R. D. Hicks. Loeb Classical Library, London, 1925.

Downham, George. Rami Dialecticae Libri Duo cum Commentariis. London, 1669. [The commentary is the same as that published separately in 1631.]

Einstein, Lewis. The Italian Renaissance in England. New York, 1902.

Gill, Alexander. Logonomia Anglica. Ed. by O. L. Jiriczek. Strassburg, 1903.

Graves, Frank P. Peter Ramus and the Educational Reformation of the Sixteenth Century. New York, 1912.

Greenlaw, Edwin. 'A Better Teacher than Aquinas,' SP. 14 (1917). 196-217.

'Spenser's Influence on *Paradise Lost,*' SP. 17 (1920). 320-59.

Grierson, Sir Herbert. Cross Currents in English Literature of the Seventeenth Century. London, 1929.

Hanford, James Holly. A Milton Handbook. New York, 1939.

'The Youth of Milton,' Studies in Shakespeare, Milton, and Donne. Ann Arbor, Michigan, 1925.

Langdon, Ida. Milton's Theory of Poetry and Fine Art. Cornell Studies in English, No. 8. New Haven, 1924.

Lewis, C. S. A Preface to *Paradise Lost.* London, 1942.

Lupton, Joseph H. A Life of John Colet. London, 1887.

Muirhead, John H. The Platonic Tradition in Anglo-Saxon Philosophy. London, 1931.

Nicolson, Marjorie H. 'The Spirit World of Milton and More,' SP. 22 (1925). 433-52.

Philo, with an English translation by F. H. Colson. Loeb Classical Library, London, 1937.

Saurat, Denis. La Pensée de Milton. Paris, 1920.

Schroeder, Kurt. Platonismus in der Englischen Renaissance vor und bei Thomas Eliot. Berlin, 1920.

Skeat, Walter, and E. H. Visiak. Milton's *Lament for Damon* and his Other Latin Poems. London, 1935.

Spaeth, Sigmund G. Milton's Knowledge of Music. Princeton, 1913.

Thompson, E. N. S. 'A Forerunner of Milton,' MLN. 32 (1917). 479-82.

Tulloch, John. Rational Theology and Christian Philosophy in England in the Seventeenth Century. Edinburgh, 1874.

Warren, William F. The Universe as Pictured in Milton's *Paradise Lost*. New York, 1915.

Watson, Foster. The English Grammar Schools to 1660. Cambridge, 1908.

COMMENTS ON THE RELATION OF MILTON AND PLATO, ARRANGED IN CHRONOLOGICAL SEQUENCE

Joseph Addison. The Spectator, No. 16. Works, ed. Richard Hurd. London, 1891. 2. 504.

William Hayley. The Life of Milton. London, 1796. Pp. 56-8, 206.

Samuel Taylor Coleridge. Letter to W. Sotheby, September 10, 1802. Letters, ed. by E. H. Coleridge. Boston, 1895. 1. 406.

Benjamin Jowett. 'The Genius of Plato,' Edinburgh Review 87 (1848). 321-67.

Alfred Stern. Milton und seine Zeit. Leipzig, 1877. 1. 115-7.

David Masson, ed. The Poetical Works of John Milton. London, 1890. 1. 178-9.

Charles Grosvenor Osgood. The Classical Mythology of Milton's English Poems. New York, 1900. Pp. xl-xli, lxx-lxxi.

John Smith Harrison. Platonism in English Poetry of the Sixteenth and Seventeenth Centuries. New York, 1903. Pp. 40-65, 82-3, 180-1.

Marianna Woodhull. The Epic of *Paradise Lost*. New York, 1907. Pp. 127, 312.

Alden Sampson. Studies in Milton. New York, 1913. Pp. 11-2, 243-305.

Sigmund Gottfried Spaeth. Milton's Knowledge of Music. Princeton, 1913. Pp. 15-6, 45, 66-7, 84-5, 97.

Evert Mordecai Clark, ed. *The Ready and Easy Way to Establish a Free Commonwealth* by John Milton. New Haven, 1915. Pp. xxxviii, lvii.

Lane Cooper. A Review of *Milton and Jakob Boehme* by Margaret Lewis Bailey. JEGP. 14 (1915). 290-6.

William Fairfield Warren. The Universe as Pictured in Milton's *Paradise Lost*. New York, 1915. Pp. 11, 14.

Edwin Greenlaw. 'A Better Teacher than Aquinas,' SP. 14 (1917). 196-217.

Robert L. Ramsay. 'Morality Themes in Milton's Poetry,' SP. 15 (1918). 123-58.

Elbert N. S. Thompson. 'Milton's *Of Education*,' SP. 15 (1918). 159-75.

James Holly Hanford. 'The Temptation Motive in Milton,' SP. 15 (1918). 176-94.

'Milton and the Return to Humanism,' SP. 16 (1919). 126-47.

Edwin Greenlaw. 'Spenser's Influence on *Paradise Lost,*' SP. 17 (1920). 320-9.

Denis Saurat. La Pensée de Milton. Paris, 1920. Pp. 85, 274-5.

Edward Chauncey Baldwin. 'Milton and Plato's *Timaeus,*' PMLA. 35 (1920). 210-7.

Elbert N. S. Thompson. 'Mysticism in Seventeenth-Century English Literature,' SP. 18 (1921). 180-1, 191-2.

Herbert Agar. Milton and Plato. Princeton, 1928.

Oliver Morley Ainsworth. Milton on Education. New Haven, 1928. Pp. 43-5.

Ronald B. Levinson. 'Milton and Plato,' MLN. 46 (1931). 85-91.

E. M. W. Tillyard. Milton, Private Correspondence and Academic Exercises. Cambridge, 1932. Pp. xiii, xxvii, xxxiii- xxxiv.

Clara Starrett Gage. Sources of Milton's Concepts of Angels and the Angelic World. Cornell University dissertation, 1936. Pp. 137-9.

Merritt Y. Hughes, ed. John Milton, *Paradise Regained,* the Minor Poems, and *Samson Agonistes.* New York, 1937. Pp. xxxii-xxxiii, xlv, 411-2.

Clarence C. Green. 'The Paradox of the Fall in *Paradise Lost,*' MLN. 53 (1938). 557-71.

Josephine Waters Bennett. 'Milton's Use of the Vision of Er,' MP. 36 (1939). 351-8.

Don M. Wolfe. Milton in the Puritan Revolution. New York, 1941. P. 302.

Joseph Moody McDill. Milton and the Pattern of Calvinism. Vanderbilt University, Nashville, Tennessee, 1942. Pp. 121-3.

Index of Names and Titles

[*The Index includes proper names and titles, save that 'Milton,' 'Plato,' and 'Socrates' are omitted, and also the names and titles of publications found on pages 173-6.*]

Abdiel 142

Academic Exercises of Milton 7, 9, 88, 103, and see *Prolusions.*

Accidence Commenced Grammar of Milton 18-9, 24, 29

Adam viii, 76, 105, 110-23, 126, 140, 144, 150, 160, 162-8, 171

Adeimantus 90

Ad Leonoram of Milton 35

Ad Patrem of Milton 40 49, 80

Advancement of Learning of Bacon 42

Aeschines 5, 29

Agar, Herbert vii, ix, 4, 22-5, 35, 40-3, 69, 132, 137-8, 157, 159, 171

Agathon 151-2

Aglaophamus 35

Ainsworth, Oliver Morley 107

Alcibiades 96

Alcibiades I of Plato 17, 22, 24

Animadversions of Milton 22, 29, 159

Anytus 124

Aphrodite 151, 152

Apology of Plato 5, 15, 17, 22, 23, 24, 25, 30, 47

Apology of Xenophon 15, 22, 29, 30

Apology for Smectymnuus of Milton 5, 9, 11, 14, 16, 17, 18, 20, 23, 30, 46, 53, 61, 80, 96, 97, 106, 145, 149, 154, 162

Aquinas, Thomas 38, 43

Areopagitica of Milton, viii, 15, 18, 23, 31, 58-61, 97, 98, 111, 119-20, 142

Aristophanes 11, 60, 64, 96, 98, 151

Aristotle 6, 13, 14, 21, 25, 31, 32, 33-4, 43, 46, 60, 67, 85, 99, 103, 132, 133, 134, 137, 151

Ascham 42

Ast 86

Athenaeus 14, 15, 23

Athens 19, 69

Augustine viii, ix, 20, 38-9, 43, 69, 103, 125, 126, 139, 143

Bacon 15, 20, 42

Baldwin, Edward Chauncey 8, 69

Banquet of Xenophon 22, 30

Barker, Arthur 5

Belial 75, 77, 92, 110

Bembo 41

Bible 13, 16, 20, 27, 33, 39, 40, 51, 85, 125, 143

Bishop of Winchester, *see* Elegy III.

Blake 114

Bradshaw 141

Bruno, Giordano 42

Bucer, Martin 23

Buommattei, Milton to 12, 22, 41, 97

Bush, Douglas x

Cabala 4

Callicles 72

Cambridge 5, 27, 42, 88

Cambridge Manuscript 162

Cambridge Platonists 36-41

Cambridge Platonists, The 40

Campagnac, E. T. 40

Cassirer, Ernst 37

Castelvetro 66

Castiglione 151

Cebes 5, 28, 29

Ceres 9, 48, 132, 156

Charmides of Plato 101

Cheke, Sir John 42

Christ 54, 80, 150, 157, 158, 171

Christ's College 6, 87

Church-Government, see Reason of Church-Government.

Chrysippus 33

Cicero 20, 25, 28, 31-2, 35, 36, 91

City of God, see De Civitate Dei.

Clarendon Press ix

Clarke, John 6

Clement 38

Clitophon of Plato 17

Colasterion of Milton 135, 168

Coleridge 10, 36

Colet 42

Columbia University Press ix

Commentary on Plato's Timaeus, A 36

Commonplace Book of Milton 29

Comus 11, 73-5, 171

Comus of Milton 10, 11, 21, 35, 40, 43, 75, 89, 104, 138, 153, 158, 161-2

Concordance of Bradshaw 141

Confessions of Augustine 125

Constantine 81

Convivio of Dante ix, 145

Cooper, Lane vii, ix, x

Cratylus of Plato 17, 24, 25

Critias of Plato 15, 17, 23, 61, 97

Crito of Plato 5, 17, 25

Cross Currents in English Literature of the Seventeenth Century 126

Cudworth, Ralph 125-6

Culverwel, Nathanael 40

Cyrene 72

Damon of Milton 39

Dante ix, 39, 145

Darbishare, Helen 29

David 28

De Civitate Dei of Augustine ix, 103, 139

De Daemonibus of Psellus 36

De Diversis Quaestionibus of Augustine 139

De Doctrina Christiana of Milton 33, 117, 135, 157, 158, 168

De Duplici Copia rerum ac verborum Commentarii duo of Erasmus 5

Defense of Knowledge, see *Prolusion* VII.

Defensio of Milton 18, 24, 32, 38, 81, 98

Defensio Secunda of Milton 18, 24, 30, 143

De Finibus of Cicero 31

De Idea Platonica of Milton 7, 22, 34, 35, 45, 99, 132, 146

Deipnosophists of Athenaeus 14, 15, 23

Demetrius of Phalerum 32

Demosthenes 25

De placitis philosophorum of Plutarch 133

De Quincey 65

De Republica of Cicero 31

De Sphaerarum Concentu, see *Prolusion* II.

Dialectica of Ramus 19

Dialogues of Plato vii, 9-15, 18, 20, 21, 23, 30, 36, 39, 43, 45, 60, 69, 70, 79, 94, 96, 97, 102, 103, 107, 109-10, 131, 143, 146, 149, 159, 160

Dialogues of Plato, The ix

Diekhoff, John S. x

Diodati, Milton to 9-10, 11, 12, 22, 48, 49, 98, 99, 114, 154-6

Diogenes Laertius 14, 15, 17, 22, 23, 24, 28, 30, 31, 33

Dionysius 60

Diotima 11, 17, 89, 152-6, 162, 163, 167

Discourse on the Light of Nature of Culverwel 40

Doctrine and Discipline of Divorce of Milton 17, 20, 23, 32, 34, 40, 96, 97, 98, 141, 154, 157, 163

Downham, George 20-1, 22, 24, 25, 30, 33, 91

Dream of Scipio of Cicero 91

Dutton, E. P., and Company ix

Early Lives of Milton 29

Eden 17, 75, 121

Eikonoclastes of Milton 4, 40, 81, 82, 141

Einstein 42

Elegies of Milton 7, 11; *Elegy* III 137, 158; *Elegy* IV 6, 7, 22, 29, 96; *Elegy* V 137; *Elegy* VI 48-9; *Elegy* VII 8, 9, 23, 96

Eliot 42

England 13, 17, 41, 49

English Grammar Schools to 1660, The ix, 5

Enneads 36, 37

Epicurus 72

Epistles of Plato vii, 17, 20 *Epistle* III 13; *Epistle* VIII 17, 18, 24, 98

Erasmus 5, 20, 42

Eros 151, 163

Eryximachus 151, 154

Euthydemus of Plato 102

Eve 76, 117, 118, 120, 162-6, 171

Faerie Queene 41, 43
Fair Infant, A of Milton 137, 150
Ficino 35, 36, 41-3, 103, 151
Florence 41
Florentine Academy 27, 41-2
'Forerunner of Milton, A' 37
Four Hymns of Spenser 151

Galileo 42, 111
Gilbert, Allan H. 24
Gill, Alexander 5, 104
Glaucon 82, 90
God, 9, 28, 37, 38, 39, 48, 52, 53, 54, 55, 61, 73, 75, 76, 77, 85, 88, 94, 95, 102, 104, 108, 109, 112, 113, 114, 115, 116, 117, 118, 119, 120, 121, 123, 126, 129, 133, 139, 140, 142, 143, 150, 154, 156, 160, 163, 164, 165, 166, 167, 168, 169, 170, 171
Gorgias of Plato 17, 18, 23, 24, 39, 40, 72, 98
Grammar, see *Accidence Commenced Grammar.*
Graves, Frank Pierrepont 19
Greece 69, 127
Greenlaw, Edwin 43
Grierson, H. J. C. 8, 126

Hanford, James Holly ix, 10
Hermes Trismegistus 7, 35, 36
Hermetica of Ficino ix, 35
Hermogenes 32
Hipparchus of Plato 17
Hippias 14
Hippias Minor of Plato 23
Hippocrates 6
Holy Scripture, see Bible.
Holy Writ, see Bible.
Homer 11, 25, 73
Horace 66, 67
Horton 49
Hughes, Merritt, Y. ix

Il Penseroso 7, 9, 22, 35, 99
Inge, Dean viii
In obitum Praesulis Wintoniensis, see *Elegy* III.
Ion of Plato 49
Isocrates 31
Italian Renaissance in England, The 42

Jackson, Son and Company ix
Jackson, W. W. ix
Jesus 19, 21, 29, 31, 63-4, 69, 71, 77-9, 83-5, 92-5, 122-8, 142, 170-1
Job 29, 94, 95
Jones, Charles W. x
Jones, Richard 127
Josephus 38
Jove 48, 49, 80
Jowett, Benjamin ix
Judgment of Martin Bucer of Milton 23

King Edward 42
Kipling 11

Labadie, Jean 88
Lady in *Comus* 11, 73-4, 153, 171
Laertius, *see* Diogenes Laertius.
Langdon, Ida 107
Latin Poems of John Milton, The 7, 8
Laws of Plato 12, 13, 14, 17, 18, 20, 22, 23, 24, 25, 47, 50-1, 54-7, 59, 62, 65-7, 72, 76, 79, 80, 84, 86, 91, 94, 97, 102, 108, 109, 112
Lewis, C. S. ix-x, 36, 120
Lexicon Platonicum 86
Liber de Causis 146
Life of Dean Colet 5
Life of Plato of Diogenes Laertius 14, 15, 23, 31
Life of Plato of Olympiodorus 14
Life of Socrates of Diogenes Laertius 22
Linacre, Thomas 42
Lincoln Grammar-School 6
Lindsay, A. D. ix
Lives and Opinions of Eminent Philosophers of Diogenes Laertius 33
'Locrian remnants' 28, 31
Logic of Milton 17, 19, 21, 22, 24, 29, 31, 32, 33, 91, 134-5
Logonomia Anglica of Gill 5
'Longinus' 31, 32, 35
Lucretius 33
Lupton, J. H. 5
Lycidas 35, 89-92, 104
Lycurgus 32, 98

Mac Kellar, Walter 7, 8

Macmillan Company ix

Mammon 82

Manicheism 39

Margaret of Navarre 41

Matthew 23, 24, 85

Mazzoni 66

Means to Remove Hirelings of Milton 14, 81

Memorabilia of Xenophon 15, 22, 29

Menexenus of Plato 17

Meno of Plato 17, 23, 25, 133

Mercurius Trismegistus, *see* Hermes Trismegistus.

Metaphysics of Aristotle 133

Michael 83, 120-2, 145-6, 150

Milton and Plato vii, ix, 22

'Milton and Plato's *Timaeus*' 69

Milton's Knowledge of Music 69

Milton's Lament for Damon and His Other Latin Poems 7

'Milton's References to Plato and Socrates' ix

'Milton's Schoolmasters' 5

Milton's Theory of Poetry and Fine Art 107

Mimus 60, 64

Mirandola, Giovanni Pico della 103, 151

More, Henry 36

More, Thomas 15, 42

Moses 13, 38, 124, 154, 163

Muirhead, John H. 37, 41

Neoplatonism 35-40, 43, 145

New Atlantis of Bacon 15, 61

Nichomachean Ethics of Aristotle 34, 85

Nicolson, Marjorie H. 37

Nimrod 87

'Note on *Il Penseroso*, A' 8

Novum Organum of Bacon 42

Odyssey Press ix

Of Education of Milton 5, 17, 18, 20, 23, 27, 30-4, 66, 96, 98, 99, 107, 115

Of Reformation of Milton 13, 22, 73, 98

Of the Kingdom of Christ of Bucer 23

Olympiodorus 14

On Mrs. Thomason of Milton 150, 158

On the Morning of Christ's Nativity of Milton 137, 158

On the Soul of the World, see 'Locrian remnants.'

On the Sublime of 'Longinus' 32

On Time of Milton 158

On Worthy Master Shakespeare of Milton 25

Origen 38

Orpheus 35

Oxford 42

Oxford University Press ix

Paradise 163, 171

Paradise Lost vii, viii, 21, 24, 35, 39, 40, 41, 43, 49, 59, 65-7, 70, 75-6, 82-3, 87, 88, 110-23, 133, 144-7, 150, 160-1, 162-7, 171

'*Paradise Lost*' in Our Time x

Paradise Regained vii, viii, 19, 21, 25, 29, 30, 31, 34, 40, 43, 49, 59, 63, 69, 70, 71, 76-9, 83-5, 92-5, 96, 97, 110, 122-9, 138, 142, 145, 146, 147, 170-1

Pausanias 151

Pegasus 10, 48, 114

Pensée de Milton, La 29

Περι Παιδων 'Αγογίας [*sic*] 29

Peripatetics 33, 34, 85, 124

Peter Ramus and the Educational Reformation of the Sixteenth Century 19

Phaedo of Plato 5, 10, 15, 17, 22, 25, 39

Phaedrus 151, 155, 165

Phaedrus of Plato 10, 12, 17, 21, 22, 23, 24, 25, 32, 48, 49, 66, 67, 73, 90, 98, 99, 111, 114, 137, 151-3, 159, 166

Phalereus 32

Philebus of Plato 17, 24, 25, 72, 135

Philistines 170

Phillips, Edward 29

Philo Judaeus 37-8

Philolaus 35

Picture of Human Life, see *Pinax*

Pinax of Cebes 5, 29

Placita Philosophorum of Plutarch 29

Platonic Tradition in Anglo-Saxon Philosophy 37

Platonische Renaissance in England, Die 37

Platonism in the Poetry of John Milton vii

Platonismus in der Englischen Renaissance vor und bei Thomas Eliot 42

Plotinus 36, 37, 39, 43

Plutarch 28, 29, 31, 35, 133

Poems of John Milton, The 8

Poetics of Aristotle 33, 66

Polus 124

Pontianus 15, 23

Porphyry 37, 39

Preface to Paradise Lost x, 36

Princeton University Press ix

Private Correspondence and Academic Exercises ix, 6

Proclus 36, 37, 39

Prolusions of Milton 31; *Prolusion II* 6, 22, 31, 34, 99; *Prolusion III* 106, 146, 158; *Prolusion V* 141-2; *Prolusion VI* 6, 22, 30, 97; *Prolusion VII* 7, 22, 30, 96, 103, 140

Pro Se Defensio of Milton 14, 18, 20, 24, 30, 97, 159

Proserpine 9, 48, 132, 156

Protagoras 14, 31, 72

Protagoras of Plato 14, 17, 23, 34, 72, 97, 166

Proverbs 57

Psellus, Michael 36

Psyche 119

Pythagoras 6, 30-1, 33, 35, 99

Pythian Apollo 6

Rami Dialecticae Libri Duo cum Commentariis of Downham 22

Ramus, Peter 19, 20, 30, 33, 42

Raphael 75, 105, 111-6, 120, 144-6, 163-6

Rational Theology . . . in the Seventeenth Century of Tulloch 36

Reason of Church-Government of Milton 13, 14, 23, 30, 50-8, 61, 88, 96, 97, 105, 106, 107, 139, 142, 143, 169

Renaissance 5, 36, 40-6, 150, 151

Republic of Plato 5, 14, 17, 22, 23, 24, 25, 32, 39, 46-7, 54, 59, 62, 71, 72, 79, 80-5, 90-5, 97, 98, 101, 102, 109, 140, 159

Republic of Plato, The ix

Rivals of Plato 17

Ruskin 79

St. John 27

St. Paul 27

St. Paul's 5, 6

Samson 168-71

Samson Agonistes viii, 34, 40, 49, 59, 70, 147, 158, 168-71

Santayana 147

Satan 19, 31, 63, 69, 77-8, 83, 92-5, 110, 112, 113, 118, 119, 122-4, 127-8, 160, 171

Saurat, Denis 29

Schroeder, Kurt 42

Scott, Walter ix, 35

Scotus Erigena 39, 43

Scripture, see Bible.

Seneca 33

Shelley viii, 45, 65

Sidney 42, 45, 64

Skeat, W. 7

Smart, John S. ix, 132, 155

Solomon 28, 57, 92

Solon 32

Sonnet IV of Milton 132

Sonnet XII of Milton 161

Sonnets of Milton, The ix

Sophist of Plato 14, 17, 23

Sophron 14, 60, 64

Spaeth, Sigmund Gottfried 69

Special Laws of Philo 38

Spenser viii, 10, 11, 20, 41, 42-3, 73, 75, 151

'Spenser's Influence on *Paradise Lost*' 43

'Spirit World of Milton and More, The' 37

Statesman of Plato 17, 25

Studies in Philology ix

Studies in Shakespeare, Milton, and Donne ix, 10

Symposium of Plato 5, 15, 17, 22, 23, 32, 90, 96, 104, 151-6, 165

Syracusans 78

Tasso 66

Taylor, A. E. 36

Temporis Partus Masculus of Bacon 42

Tenure of Kings of Milton 141
Tetrachordon of Milton 18, 20, 23-4, 30, 32, 96, 97, 98, 159, 161
Theaetetus of Plato 24
Thomas, *see* Aquinas.
Thompson, Elbert N. S. 37
Thrasymachus 72
Tillyard, Phyllis B. ix, 6, 106
Timaeus of Plato 22, 23, 25, 32, 36, 39, 113, 159
Tractate, see *Of Education*
Tulloch, John 36
Tully, *see* Cicero.
Tusculan Disputations of Cicero 31

Universe as Pictured in Milton's Paradise Lost, The 69
University of Michigan Press ix
Upon the Circumcision of Milton 150
Uriel 112-3
Utopia of More 15, 61

Vacation Exercise of Milton 137
Virgil 25, 91
Visiak, E. H. 7

Warren, William Fairfield 69
Watson, Foster ix, 5, 6
Welldon, J. E. C. ix
Whichcote 36
Whitehead 147
Whitman 114
Wordsworth 64, 114
Works of John Milton, The, Columbia edition ix, 5, 22, 106
Works of Ralph Cudworth, The 126

Xanthippe 22
Xenophon 4, 5, 15, 16, 22, 28-30, 96

Young, Thomas 5, 6, 80
'Youth of Milton, The' ix, 10

Zorobabel 141

CORNELL PAPERBACKS

Advice to the Privileged Orders in the Several States of Europe. *By Joel Barlow.* $1.25.

The American Revolution: A Constitutional Interpretation. *By Charles Howard McIlwain.* $1.75.

The American Way. *By Dexter Perkins.* $1.45.

Are Men Equal? An Inquiry into the Meaning of American Democracy. *By Henry Alonzo Myers.* $1.45.

Aristotle on the Art of Poetry. *By Lane Cooper.* $1.50.

The Art of War in the Middle Ages. *By C. W. C. Oman.* $1.75.

The Atlantic Frontier: Colonial American Civilization (1607-1763). *By Louis B. Wright.* $1.85.

The Autobiography of Giambattista Vico. *Translated by Max Harold Fisch* AND *Thomas Goddard Bergin.* $1.95.

Bees: Their Vision, Chemical Senses, and Language. *By Karl von Frisch.* $1.45.

Beginnings of the American People. *By Carl L. Becker.* $1.95.

Chapters of Erie. *By Charles Francis Adams, Jr.,* AND *Henry Adams.* $1.45.

Conservatism in Early American History. *By Leonard Woods Labaree.* $1.75.

Constitutionalism: Ancient and Modern. *By Charles Howard McIlwain.* $1.75.

Ethical Systems and Legal Ideals. *By Felix S. Cohen.* $1.95.

French Chivalry. *By Sidney Painter.* $1.75.

The Golden Age of Colonial Culture. *By Thomas Jefferson Wertenbaker.* $1.75.

Hawthorne. *By Henry James.* $1.45.

The "Higher Law" Background of American Constitutional Law. *By Edward S. Corwin.* $0.95.

The History of the Five Indian Nations. *By Cadwallader Colden.* $1.95.

Industry and Government in France and England, 1540-1640. *By John U. Nef.* $1.75.

The Intellectual Life of Colonial New England. *By Samuel Eliot Morison.* $1.95.

Latin America and the Enlightenment. *Edited by Arthur P. Whitaker.* $1.75.

Leaves of Grass. Facsimile edition of the 1860 text. *By Walt Whitman.* $2.25.

The Legend of the Founding Fathers. *By Wesley Frank Craven.* $1.95.

Mediaeval Feudalism. *By Carl Stephenson.* $1.50.

Medicine and Society in America: 1660-1860. *By Richard H. Shryock.* $1.75.

Our Earliest Colonial Settlements. *By Charles M. Andrews.* $1.75.

Parties and Politics in America. *By Clinton Rossiter.* $1.45.

Patrick Henry. *By Moses Coit Tyler.* $2.25.

Plato and Milton. *By Irene Samuel.* $1.45.

The Poetic Mind. *By Frederick C. Prescott.* $1.95.

Power, Morals, and the Founding Fathers. *By Adrienne Koch.* $1.95.

The Primitive World and Its Transformations. *By Robert Redfield.* $1.45

Religion and the State. *By Evarts B. Greene.* $1.75.

The Rise of Universities. *By Charles Homer Haskins.* $1.45.

Science and Imagination. *By Marjorie Nicolson.* $1.75.

Travels through the Middle Settlements in North-America. *By Andrew Burnaby.* $1.45.

The United States in 1800. *By Henry Adams.* $1.50.

Visible Saints: The History of a Puritan Idea. *By Edmund Sears Morgan.* $1.45.

CORNELL UNIVERSITY PRESS, 124 ROBERTS PLACE, ITHACA, NEW YORK

LITERATURE

PLATO AND MILTON

By IRENE SAMUEL

Viewing Milton as an avowed student of Plato, Dr. Samuel seeks to explain the poetic and ethical theories that underlie *Paradise Lost, Paradise Regained*, and *Samson Agonistes* by examining the similarities in treatment by Milton and Plato of the same concepts— the good life, pleasure, knowledge, love, the nature of the true poet, and the theory of Ideas.

"Validity and integrity mark Irene Samuel's scholarly treatise. The author knows her Platonism and her point of view is fresh and plausible. A volume to delight all Greek scholars, and to renew faith in the substantial in literature."—*The World in Books*

". . . carefully planned, well integrated and documented, and the difficult subject is set forth attractively and with conviction. Both the lover of Milton and the lover of Plato will be pleased with the result." —*The U. S. Quarterly Booklist*

Cornell Paperbacks ꝯ *Cornell University Press*